ERRATA—OXIDATION POTENTIALS, Second Edition

Page 8, lines 9 and 11: 51,170 should be 57,170

Page 37, line 12: 1014 should be 954

Page 40, line 12: − 1.52 should be − 1.51

Page 47, line 3: 23.3 should be 23163

    line 4: 5.4 should be − 4.54

    line 3 from bottom: − 55.5 should be − 54.49

Page 49, line 3: 34.8 should be 34.69

Page 57, line 24: − 34.3 should be − 36.28

Page 62, line 10 from bottom: − 30,900 should be − 20,150

Page 66, last line: − 123,900 should be − 128,500

Page 74, line 5: $6e^-$ should be $4e^-$

Page 78, line 12: 103e should be 10e

    line 20: − 5 kcal. should be − 7 kcal.

Page 80, line 11: − 51,800 should be − 53,060

Page 84, line 11: − 56 should be − 53

Page 86, line 17: $TeO(OH_2)(c)$ should be $TeO(OH)_2(c)$

Page 92, line 14: − 39.71 should be − 39.67

    line 21: 2.46 should be 2.06

    line 26: − 2.34 should be − 3.22

    last line: − 12.26 should be 12.62

Page 95, line 14 from bottom: − 37.5 should be − 40.5

    line 12 from bottom: − 0.833 should be − 0.86

    line 9 from bottom: − 0.496 should be − 0.387

Page 96, line 21: − 61.7 should be − 62.26

Page 97, line 13: 6.67 should be 6.45

    line 6 from bottom: − 118.7 should be − 115.9

Page 103, line 8: − 202 should be − 220

    line 19: − 37.65 should be − 3.49

Page 104, line 3: − 1.41 should be − 1.42 and − 0.79 should be − 0.80

    line 7: − 0.496 should be − 0.387

Page 108, line 12: $HP_2O_7^{---}$ should be $HP_2O_7^{-3}$

    line 13: HP_2O^{---} should be HP_2O^{-3}

Page 111, line 15 from bottom: 1.82 should be 2.05

Page 115, line 6 from bottom: − 45.5 should be − 46.1

    line 5 from bottom: $As_2S_3^{--}$ should be As_2S_3

Page 116, line 2: AsS_2^{--} should be AsS_2^{-}

Page 119, line 3: − 0.692 should be − 0.671

Page 130, line 5 from bottom: 0.01 should be − 0.056

Page 132, line 2: -3398 should be -4398

Page 142, line 19: -30.0 should be -40.0

Page 151, last line: "iodine" should be "iodide"

Page 153, line 2: "iodine" should be "iodide"

Page 154, line 8 from bottom: $2H_2O$ should be $3H_2O$

        line 3 from bottom: $Pb(BrO_3)$ should be $Pb(BrO_3)_2$

Page 166, line 5: $Tl(OH)$ should be $Tl(OH)_3$

Page 171, line 8 from bottom: ZnI^- should be ZnI^+

Page 186, line 8 from bottom: I should be I^-

Page 187, line 7: CuO_2^- should be $CuO_2^{--} + H_2O$

        line 16: $Cu(IO_3)$ should be $Cu(IO_3)_2$

        last line of footnote: 1530 (1950) should be 1550 (1951)

Page 189, line 9: $Ag(NH_3)+$ should be $Ag(NH_3)^+$

Page 206, line 6 from bottom: PtI_4^{--} should be $2PtI_4^{--}$

Page 208, line 8 from bottom: -1.78 should be -1.68

Page 215, line 13: $Rh + 3H_2O =$ etc. should be $2Rh + 3H_2O =$

Page 218, line 16: $2IrO_2 + Ir$ should be $3IrO_2 + Ir$

Page 219, line 1 following Basic Solution: 0.72 should be 0.73 and -0.14 should be -0.17

Page 226, line 11: CNS^- should be $3CNS^-$

Page 233, line 3: $HOsO_6^-$ should be $HOsO_5^-$

Page 237, line 5: ca 1.5 should be ca -1.5

        line 13: H_2O should be $2H_2O$

        line 6 from bottom: $Mn(C_2O_4)_3$ should be $Mn(C_2O_4)_3^{---}$

Page 243, line 9: $2H^+$ should be H^+

        line 10: H_2O should be $2H_2O$

Page 252, line 21: MoO_4 should be MoO_3

Page 257, line 2 from bottom: (1.25) should be (1.05)

Page 265, line 5 from bottom: -0.26 should be -0.274

Page 269, line 4 from bottom: (0.86) should be (0.89)

Page 274, line 7: 1.56 should be 1.53

Page 279, line 9 from bottom: $2H_2O$ should be H_2O

Page 307, line 6: 2.03 should be 2.07

Page 308, line 8: 2.03 should be 2.07

Page 326, line 16: iodide should be iodate

        line 17: $2BrO_3^-$ should be $2IO_3^-$

Page 327, line 4 from bottom: $Cu - Cu^{++}$ should be $Ca - Ca^{++}$

Page 333, line 6 from bottom: K_2CO should be K_2CO_3

Page 334, line 5 from bottom: 58.9 should be − 58.9

Page 336, line 5 from bottom of table: $CsCO_3$ should be Cs_2CO_3

    last line of table: $CsAl(SO_4)$ should be $CsAl(SO_4)_2$

Page 337, line 1 of table 83: − 1,720 should be − 1,920

                             − 4,000 should be 4,000

    line 2 of table 83: − 10,087 should be − 10,084

    line 4 of table 83: − 17,150 should be − 17,950

    line 5 of table 83: − 2,150 should be 7840

Page 340, line 5 of table 84: $As = As^+ + e^-$ should be $Cs = Cs^+ + e^-$

Page 341, line 22 of table 84: $H_3PO_3 = H_3PO_4 + 2H^+ + 2e^-$ should be

                           $H_2O + H_2PO_3 = H_3PO_4 + 2H^+ + 2e^-$

Page 389, right column, line 7 from bottom: Phosphorous should be

                           Phosphorus

PRENTICE-HALL CHEMISTRY SERIES

WENDELL M. LATIMER, *Editor*

GENERAL CHEMISTRY (Third Edition), *by* Leona E. Young *and* C. W. Porter.

GENERAL CHEMISTRY, Laboratory Manual, *by* Leona E. Young *and* C. W. Porter.

A SYSTEM OF CHEMICAL ANALYSIS, *by* Ernest H. Swift.

INTRODUCTORY QUANTITATIVE ANALYSIS, *by* Ernest H. Swift.

QUANTITATIVE ANALYSIS, *by* Eugene W. Kanning.

QUALITATIVE ANALYSIS (Third Edition), *by* H. V. Anderson *and* T. H. Hazelhurst.

INTRODUCTION TO SEMIMICRO QUALITATIVE ANALYSIS, *by* C. H. Sorum.

SEMIMICRO QUALITATIVE ANALYSIS, *by* Arthur R. Middleton.

SEMIMICRO QUALITATIVE ANALYSIS (Brief Edition), *by* Arthur R. Middleton *and* John W. Willard.

SEMIMICRO EXPERIMENTS IN GENERAL CHEMISTRY, *by* W. Bernard King.

ORGANIC CHEMISTRY, *by* Ray Q. Brewster.

ORGANIC CHEMISTRY (Brief Course), *by* Ray Q. Brewster.

THEORY OF ORGANIC CHEMISTRY, *by* Gerald E. K. Branch *and* Melvin Calvin.

LABORATORY TEXT IN ORGANIC CHEMISTRY, *by* James Cason *and* Henry Rapoport.

STRUCTURAL CARBOHYDRATE CHEMISTRY, *by* E. G. V. Percival.

SYSTEMATIC INORGANIC CHEMISTRY, *by* Don M. Yost *and* Horace Russell, Jr.

INORGANIC PREPARATIONS, *by* Harold F. Walton.

PHYSICAL CHEMISTRY, *by* Walter J. Moore.

PROBLEMS IN PHYSICAL CHEMISTRY, *by* L. G. Sillén, Paul W. Lange, *and* C. Olof Gabrielson.

CHEMICAL THERMODYNAMICS, *by* Irving M. Klotz.

EXPERIMENTAL ELECTRONICS, *by* Ralph H. Muller, R. L. Garman *and* M. E. Droz.

TECHNIQUE OF GLASS MANIPULATION IN SCIENTIFIC RESEARCH, *by* Julius D. Heldman.

GERMAN FOR CHEMISTS, *by* John H. Yoe *and* Alfred Burger.

CHEMISTRY OF THE METAL CHELATE COMPOUNDS, *by* Arthur Martell *and* Melvin Calvin.

THE OXIDATION STATES OF THE ELEMENTS AND THEIR POTENTIALS IN AQUEOUS SOLUTIONS (Second Edition), *by* Wendell M. Latimer.

THE OXIDATION STATES

OF THE ELEMENTS AND

THEIR POTENTIALS IN

AQUEOUS SOLUTIONS

Second Edition

BY

WENDELL M. LATIMER

PRENTICE-HALL, INC.
Englewood Cliffs, N. J.

QD
561
.L35
1952

Current printing (last digit):
16 15 14 13 12 11 10 9

64756–C

Preface to Second Edition

In the *Second Edition* the author has sought to extend the summarization of those thermodynamic data which are of special significance in the interpretation of inorganic chemistry. For each element the heats of formation, free energies of formation and entropies have been tabulated for all important compounds. Many of the free energies are based upon estimated entropy values and a discussion has been given in the Appendix of the methods by which accurate estimations of entropy values may be made.

The author has been gratified by the extensive use of the potential diagrams, which were introduced in the *First Edition*, and such diagrams are now given for all the elements which have more than one oxidation state. A discussion of the use of these diagrams in the interpretation of the chemistry of an element is given in Chapter I. Several hundred new potential values and equilibrium constants also have been added.

The treatment of reaction rates and reaction mechanisms has been extended, but the author has not been able to expand these topics as fully as he would like. The chemistry of uranium, neptunium, plutonium and americium has been greatly amplified and the actinide elements are treated in a new chapter.

For the great majority of substances, the U. S. Bureau of Standards values for reaction heats have been employed. In many cases the Bureau of Standards values for the free energies differ by only a few small calories from the author's previous values. In all such cases, the Bureau of Standards values are adapted for the sake of conformity and to avoid unnecessary complications in secondary calculations employing these free energies. In all tables the Bureau of Standards values are indicated by italics.

Since the book has been employed as a text for courses in Advanced Inorganic Chemistry, a set of study questions has been included in the Appendix.

v

The author is indebted to the many chemists who have written suggestions and corrections and to his colleagues at the University of California, especially to Dr. R. E. Connick and Dr. Z. Z. Hugus.

WENDELL M. LATIMER

Preface to the First Edition

The most convenient method of ascertaining the relative heights of two mountains is generally by reference to a table of measured altitudes. In order to use the table, it is not necessary to understand the principles of triangulation by which the altitudes have been determined. So, also, a table of the energies of the elements in their various oxidation states may be used by one with a very elementary knowledge of thermodynamics to answer many of the qualitative questions involved in the interpretation of inorganic chemistry.

In making this summary of existing data, the author has adopted the point of view of one interested in the chemistry of the various elements, rather than the point of view of one whose interest is largely in thermodynamics as a science. The author hopes that readers of the latter class, who are disappointed at the frequent inclusion of approximate data, will find in these obvious shortcomings an incentive for careful investigations in the near future. Much of the older work should have been recalculated by modern methods, but the labor involved is beyond the capacity of a single author.

The free energies of the oxidation-reduction couples, taken with reference to the hydrogen couple, have been expressed as volts per equivalent, since this affords the simplest comparison of the relative driving power of the various couples. However, for completed oxidation-reduction reactions, the free energies have been given in calories, as the number of equivalents of electricity is sometimes ambiguous. Solubility products and the dissociation constants of weak acids, bases, and complex ions have been included whenever the data were available.

The author, in calculating many new free energies from reaction heats, has drawn largely upon his own experimental work on the entropies of solids and aqueous ions. Our present knowledge of the entropy values permits the estimation of many entropies from the values of similar substances, and these estimates have frequently been employed in third-law calculations to obtain approximate reaction potentials.

Potentials have been given for many couples which are not thermodynamically reversible. These values, of course, cannot be used in equilibrium reasoning. However, these potentials are of value in indicating the minimum energy which must be employed to accomplish the oxidation or reduction, and they often give considerable information regarding the possible reaction mechanisms and the cause of the slowness of the reactions.

In some cases it would be valuable to list potentials for couples at 1 M concentration, rather than list the $E°$ values. However, these molal potentials are not so useful as one might at first think. They can be used accurately only at 1 M concentration; and, if an approximate value is desired, the $E°$ without corrections for the activity might as well be used.

References have been given for all values employed. These references may usually be consulted for additional references to older works. The author has endeavored to include in his references all works published up to 1938.

Some mention should be made of the author's attempt to avoid the confusion existing with regard to the use of the term *valence*. This term has been restricted to mean, in the organic chemistry sense, the number of bonds (electron pairs) which an atom shares with other atoms. Such a usage renders the terms *covalence* and *coördination number* unnecessary but requires additional nomenclature to designate the charge upon an atom. In many cases this charge is a readily determinable number as, for example, the charge of -1 on chloride ion. This charge will be called the *polar number*. In a large number of compounds the polar number of each atom cannot be readily determined experimentally, but a fair approximation is obtained by assuming that the two electrons of a bond are shared equally between the two atoms. On this basis the charge upon the sulfur atom in sulfate is $+2$ and that upon each oxygen is -1. The term *formal polar number* has been suggested for the charge estimated in this manner.

However, for the purpose of classification, a still more arbitrary method of assigning values to the charges upon the atoms of a compound has proved extremely useful. As an example, we may again use the sulfate ion. This method assumes that each oxygen has a charge of -2, which then gives a charge of $+6$ to the sulfur. These assumptions not only simplify the classification of compounds but are also valuable in the interpretation of oxidation-reduction reactions. Thus, the $+6$ charge on the sulfur may be correlated with the six electrons involved in the half-reaction for the oxidation of sulfur to sulfate,

$$S + 4H_2O = 8H^+ + SO_4^{--} + 6e^-.$$

Similar half-reactions may be written for the oxidation (or reduction) of any free element to any of its compounds, and the number of electrons involved in the reaction may be used to define the oxidation number or oxidation state of the element.

To summarize the illustration of nomenclature for the sulfate example, we may state: the valence of the sulfur is four; the polar number is unknown, but the formal polar number is $+2$; and the oxidation state is $+6$.

The author owes much to the spirit of coöperation which has been so carefully fostered in this department by Professor Gilbert N. Lewis. In the author's opinion there is no man who has such a complete understanding of the mechanism of inorganic reactions as does Professor William C. Bray, and he is especially indebted to Professor Bray for the advice so willingly given on many problems. The author wishes to thank both the many graduate students who have read and criticized the manuscript and Dr. George G. Manov for his recalculation of many of the free energies.

WENDELL M. LATIMER

Contents

Bismuth: Oxidation states. Bismuth hydrogen compounds. The bismuth-bismuthyl couple. Bismuth trichloride and oxychloride. Bismuth monoxide. Bismuth tetroxide and pentoxide. Trends in the Group V potentials.

and other cuprous couples. The copper-cupric ion couple. The copper-cupric oxide or hyroxide couple. The copper-cupric sulfide couple. Other copper-cupric couples. Various cuprous-cupric couples. Copper in the $+3$ state. Silver: Oxidation states. The silver-silver ion couple. The silver-silver oxide couple. The silver halide and cyanide couples. The complex silver, ammonia, sulfite, and thiosulfate ions. The silver-silver sulfide couple. Additional silver-silver salt potentials. Silver in the $+2$ and $+3$ oxidation states. Gold: Oxidation states. Gold-auric couples. The gold-aurous couples. Gold in the $+2$ oxidation state. Summary of Subgroup I potentials.

chloride. Molybdenum: Oxidation states. The free energy of molybdate and molybdic acid. The reduction of molybdic acid to the $+5$ and $+3$ states. Molybdenum cyanides. Molybdenum dioxide. Molybdenum peroxide. Tungsten: Oxidation states. Free energies of the oxides. The free energy of tungstate. The reduction of tungstate in hydrochloric acid.

APPENDICES

OXIDATION POTENTIALS

CHAPTER 1

Units, Conventions, and General Methods Employed in the Determination of Oxidation-Reduction Potentials

As stated in the Preface, the primary object of this work is to gather together the large, scattered mass of free-energy data and present it in a simple form as an aid in the interpretation of inorganic chemistry. Although the author does not wish to stress in detail the methods by which these data have been obtained, it seems desirable, for the sake of clarity, to discuss general methods in a preliminary chapter and to give references to more detailed treatments.

The potentials have been derived from four sources: (1) the direct measurement of cells, (2) equilibrium data, (3) thermal data, and (4) approximate limiting values based upon the chemical behavior of a couple with respect to known oxidizing and reducing agents. Before outlining these methods, a statement of the energy units employed and the general conventions in nomenclature will be given.

Energy units. The units of energy and potential employed are those adopted by the U. S. Bureau of Standards[1] as of January 1, 1948, consistent with international agreement. The absolute joule, instead of the international joule, is now the unit of energy. The thermal calorie, previously defined as 4.1833 international joules, is now defined as

$$1 \text{ calorie} = 4.1840 \text{ absolute joules.}$$

Other units and conversion factors which enter into various calculations are:

---

[1] U.S. Bureau of Standards, *Selected Values of Chemical Thermodynamic Properties*, 1949.

0° Centigrade = 273.16° Absolute or Kelvin,

1 Faraday = 96,484 absolute coulombs,

1 volt equivalent = 23,060.3 cal./abs. volt gram equivalent,

1 absolute volt = 0.999670 international volt,

1 absolute ampere = 1.000165 international amperes,

R (gas constant) = 8.31439 abs. joules/deg. mole

$\qquad\qquad\quad$ = 1.98719 cal./deg. mole,

$RT_{298.16} \ln x$ = 1364.282 log x, cal./deg. mole,

$$\frac{RT_{298.16}}{\text{volt equivalent}} \ln x = 0.05916 \log X, \text{ volts/equivalent.}$$

E° values. A potential is referred to as an $E°$ value if all gases involved in the reaction are at a fugacity (thermodynamic pressure) of 1 atmosphere and all dissolved substances at an activity (thermodynamic concentration) of 1 molal, i.e., 1 mole per 1000 grams of water.

The potential, E, at other concentrations and pressures at 25° C. is given by the expression

$$E = E° - \frac{0.05916}{n} \log_{10} Q, \tag{1}$$

where Q is the product of the activities (or fugacities) of the resulting substances divided by the product of the activities of the reacting substances, each activity raised to that power whose exponent is the coefficient of the substance in the chemical equation; and n is the number of Faradays of electricity involved in the reaction as written. Thus Q has the same general form as the equilibrium constant, but it differs in that the activities refer not to the equilibrium state but to the actual activities of the reacting substances and their products. Activities of pure solids and liquids are taken as unity. For the equilibrium state, Q becomes the equilibrium constant, K, and since E for a reaction at equilibrium is zero,

$$E° = \frac{0.05916}{n} \log K. \tag{2}$$

Hydrogen reference couple. Any oxidation-reduction reaction may be broken up into two "half-reactions," or "couples," that indicate the mechanism by which the electrons are transferred from the reducing agent to the oxidizing agent. For example, in the reaction

$$2Ag^+ + H_2 = 2Ag + 2H^+,$$

the two half-reactions, or couples, are:

$$Ag = Ag^+ + e^-, \quad \text{and} \quad H_2 = 2H^+ + 2e^-.$$

The experimental determination of the absolute potential of any couple is a difficult problem (see p. 22), but since any chemical reaction involves only the difference in potential between two couples, the absolute values are unnecessary. For this reason the procedure has come into general use of choosing the potential of some one couple as an arbitrary zero and using this as a reference couple for potentials of all other couples. The reference couple so chosen is the hydrogen gas-hydrogen ion couple:

$$H_2 = 2H^+ + 2e^-, \quad E° = 0.$$

Reactions which involve hydroxide ion will also be referred to the hydrogen couple, but in such solutions this couple has the form (see p. 32)

$$H_2 + 2OH^- = 2H_2O + 2e^-, \quad E° = 0.828.$$

The $E°$ values of half-reactions in alkaline solution will be designated as $E_B°$ to indicate that this basic potential of the hydrogen couple must be used to obtain the completed reaction potential against hydrogen.

EXAMPLE

$$Cl^- + 2OH^- = ClO^- + H_2O + 2e^-, \quad E_B° = -0.88.$$
$$ClO^- + H_2 = Cl^- + H_2O, \quad E° = 0.83 + 0.88$$
$$= 1.71.$$

Conventions regarding sign. All couples will be written with the electrons on the right-hand side of the equation. A positive value for $E°$ will mean that the reduced form of the couple is a better reducing agent than H_2. For example,

$$Zn = Zn^{++} + 2e^-, \quad E° = 0.763$$

will mean that the reaction

$$Zn + 2H^+ = Zn^{++} + H_2$$

goes as written with a potential of 0.763 volt. And, similarly, a negative $E°$ will mean that the oxidized form of the couple is a better oxidizing agent than H^+. For example,

$$Cu = Cu^{++} + 2e^-, \qquad E° = -0.337$$

will mean that the reaction

$$Cu^{++} + H_2 = Cu + 2H^+$$

goes as written with a potential of 0.337 volt.

The convention, illustrated in these examples, of giving a positive sign to the potential of any complete reaction which goes spontaneously in the direction as written, will be followed.

Addition or subtraction of half-reaction potentials. When one half-reaction is subtracted from another to give a complete reaction, the potential of the complete reaction is the algebraic difference in the potentials of the two half-reactions.

EXAMPLE

$$Zn = Zn^{++} + 2e^-, \qquad E° = \quad 0.763.$$
$$2Ag = 2Ag^+ + 2e^-, \qquad E° = -0.799.$$
$$\overline{Zn + 2Ag^+ = Zn^{++} + 2Ag,} \qquad E° = \quad 1.562.$$

However, in the addition or subtraction of two half-reactions to give a third half-reaction, the free energies, i.e., volt equivalents of the two half-reactions, must be added or subtracted to give the free energies of the third half-reaction.

EXAMPLE

	$E°$	volt equivalents
$Cl^- + 3H_2O = ClO_3^- + 6H^+ + 6e^-$	-1.45	-8.70
$Cl^- = \frac{1}{2}Cl_2 + e^-$	-1.36	-1.36
$\frac{1}{2}Cl_2 + 3H_2O = ClO_3^- + 6H^+ + 5e^-$	-1.47	-7.34

Thus the volt equivalents for the new half-reaction are -7.34, and since there are 5 electrons for this reaction, E° is $-7.34/5$, or -1.47.

POTENTIALS FROM GALVANIC CELLS

Cells without liquid junctions. The potential of a fairly large number of reactions may be measured directly in cells having a single electrolyte. Thus, for the reaction

$$2AgCl + H_2 = 2Ag + 2H^+ + 2Cl^-,$$

having as half-reactions

$$H_2 = 2H^+ + 2e^-, \quad \text{and} \quad AgCl + e^- = Ag + Cl^-,$$

a cell may be constructed, using as one electrode metallic silver in contact with silver chloride, and as the other electrode hydrogen gas in contact with hydrogen ion on a platinum surface. The electrolyte throughout the cell may then be hydrochloric acid and is uniform except for the slight solubility of silver chloride. The two electrode reactions must be reversible and reasonably rapid. On many surfaces the hydrogen couple does not meet this requirement, but the reaction is sufficiently catalyzed by a platinized platinum surface. In the construction of any cell, the reducing and oxidizing agents must not come into direct contact with each other. Moreover, the reducing agent must be the strongest reducing agent present at the anode and the oxidizing agent must be the strongest oxidizing agent present at the cathode. These requirements are met by the above cell with the exception that, if air is not excluded, the oxygen is a stronger oxidizing agent than silver chloride.

From the electromotive force of this cell, at any given concentration of hydrochloric acid and pressure of hydrogen, the E° value may be calculated from equation (1) if the activities of the hydrogen and chloride ions are known. Strictly speaking, it is not possible to measure the activity of an ion of one sign independently of the ion of opposite sign, so the information required is the *mean activity*, $a\pm$, of the two ions. By definition, the *activity coefficient*, γ, is the ratio of the mean activity to the mean molality, $m\pm$. That is,

$$\gamma = \frac{a\pm}{m\pm}. \tag{3}$$

At infinite dilution, the activity equals the molality and γ equals 1; and for each type of salt, the mean molality is defined in such a way that the ratio approaches unity at infinite dilution (see Appendix II). If the potential measurements are carried out in dilute solutions, one may assume that the concentration equals the activity and calculate approximate $E°$ values. However, for the highest accuracy it is necessary to determine the γ values, and Appendix II should be consulted for general references dealing with these experimental procedures. Fairly complete values of γ for various types of salts are also given in this appendix, and the following example illustrates their use in calculating $E°$ values.

The measured potential of a silver, silver chloride–hydrogen ion, hydrogen cell at a hydrogen pressure of 0.962 atmosphere and a molality of 0.100 for the hydrochloric acid is 0.3516 volt. The γ for the molality of this acid is 0.796. Assuming the hydrogen to be a sufficiently perfect gas so that no correction need be made for deviations from the gas laws, one may then write the reactions,

$$AgCl + \tfrac{1}{2}H_2 = Ag + Cl^- + H^+,$$

$$0.3516 = E° - \frac{0.05916}{n} \log \frac{a_{H^+} a_{Cl^-}}{(P_{H_2})^{\frac{1}{2}}}$$

$$= E° - 0.05916 \log \frac{(0.796 \times 0.1)^2}{(0.962)^{\frac{1}{2}}},$$

$$E° = 0.222 \text{ for the reaction, and}$$

$$Cl^- + Ag = AgCl + e^-, \qquad E° = -0.222.$$

The activity coefficient may be thought of as the thermodynamic ionization constant, but the modern theory of strong electrolytes assumes that they are completely ionized, in the sense that the ions are capable of independent motion and that the apparent nonionization results from the forces acting between an ion and its neighbors in general rather than from its attraction to any particular ion. The Debye and Huckel[1] theory has been very successful in calculating activity coefficients from the electrostatic forces in very dilute solutions. At high concentrations other factors enter, such as the force of repulsion between the large hydrated ions or the change in the

---

[1] P. Debye and E. Huckel, *Z. Physik.*, **24**, 185, 305 (1923). See also the review by V. K. LaMer, *Trans. Am. Electrochem. Soc.*, **51**, 507 (1927).

hydration of the ions, and the activity coefficient often becomes greater than unity, or the apparent ionization greater than 100 per cent. The theoretical treatment of the concentrated solutions is still incomplete. Appendix II should also be consulted for a discussion of the principle of ionic strength.

Cells with liquid junctions. Many cells may be constructed which have one electrolyte around the cathode and another around the anode. The familiar zinc-copper gravity cell is an example, the anode consisting of zinc in a solution of zinc sulfate and the cathode of copper in a copper sulfate solution. The accurate evaluation of the $E°$ potentials for such cells involves the same general problem of the activity coefficients discussed in the previous section, together with the added difficulty of determining the potential which exists at the junction of the two electrolytes. For the simple case of salts of monovalent positive and negative ions, good theoretical evaluations of the liquid junction potential may be made,[1] but with many electrolytes the problem is a difficult one.[2] A bridge of concentrated potassium chloride often reduces the liquid potential to a few millivolts.

POTENTIAL VALUES FROM FREE ENERGIES AND EQUILIBRIUM CONSTANTS

The free energy ΔF of a chemical reaction is the maximum available work which can be obtained in going from the initial to the final state; it is related to the reaction potential by the equations

$$\Delta F \text{ (joule)} = -E \cdot n \cdot 96{,}484, \qquad (4a)$$

$$\Delta F \text{ (cal.)} = -E \cdot n \cdot 23{,}060. \qquad (4b)$$

The symbol $\Delta F°$ is used when all the reacting substances are at unit activity. The free energy of formation of a substance (often called simply the free energy of the substance) refers to its formation from its elements, and the free energies of all elements and H^+ are taken as zero in their standard states of unit activity.

EXAMPLE

$$\tfrac{1}{2}H_2 + \tfrac{1}{2}N_2 + \tfrac{3}{2}O_2 = H^+ + NO_3^-, \qquad \Delta F° = -26.43 \text{ kcal.}$$

$$\Delta F° \text{ of formation of } NO_3^- = F°_{NO_3^-} = -26.43 \text{ kcal.}$$

---

[1] D. A. MacInnes, *International Critical Tables*, **VI**, 338 (1926).

[2] G. N. Lewis and M. Randall, *Thermodynamics and the Free Energy of Chemical Substances*, New York: McGraw-Hill Book Company, Inc., 1923, p. 333.

The free energy of a reaction is the sum of the free energies of formation of the products of the reaction, less the sum of the free energies of formation of the reacting substances.

EXAMPLE

$$3I^- + H_2O_2 + 2H^+ = I_3^- + 2H_2O,$$
$$\Delta F^\circ = F^\circ_{I_3^-} + 2F^\circ_{H_2O} - 3F^\circ_{I^-} - F^\circ_{H_2O_2} - 2F^\circ_{H^+}$$
$$= (-12,310) + 2(-56,690) - 3(-12,350)$$
$$- (-31,470) - 2(0)$$
$$= -51,170 \text{ cal.}$$

The E° for the reaction may then be calculated from equation (4b):

$$E^\circ = \frac{51,170}{2 \times 23,060} = 1.239 \text{ volts.}$$

The relation between the free energy of a chemical reaction and the equilibrium constant is

$$\Delta F = -RT \ln \frac{K}{Q}, \tag{5}$$

where R is the gas constant, T the absolute reaction temperature, K the equilibrium constant, and Q a constant which has the same form as K but in which the concentrations refer to the actual values for the substances in the reaction. When all substances are at unit concentration, $Q = 1$ and $\Delta F = \Delta F^\circ$.

$$\Delta F^\circ = -RT \ln K. \tag{6a}$$

$$\Delta F^\circ_{298.16} \text{ (cal.)} = -1364.3 \log K. \tag{6b}$$

A knowledge of the equilibrium constant thus permits the calculation of ΔF° and E°.

EXAMPLE

For the reaction

$$2Cl_2 + 2H_2O = O_2 + 4Cl^- + 4H^+,$$

the equilibrium constant has been determined at $25°$ C. as 1.122×10^9.

Hence,

$$\Delta F^\circ = -1364.3 \log K = -12,345 \text{ cal.}$$

$$E^\circ = \frac{12,345}{4 \times 23,060} = 0.134 \text{ volt.}$$

POTENTIAL VALUES FROM THERMAL DATA

When zinc dissolves in hydrochloric acid or—to make the conditions more exact—in hydrochloric acid containing some definite concentration of zinc ion, the chemical energy, with the exception of the small amount of work which is done against the atmospheric pressure, is converted into heat. This heat is called the heat of the reaction or the change in heat content, ΔH, and differs from the free energy or the reversible energy by a quantity called the "irreversible energy," which is equal to the absolute temperature times the entropy of the reaction, ΔS.

$$\Delta F = \Delta H - T\Delta S. \tag{7}$$

ΔF° and E° may then be calculated if the corresponding ΔH° and ΔS° values are known.

Reference should be made to standard works on thermal chemistry[1] for the general calorimetric methods employed in the experimental determination of ΔH°. For the calculations in this book the author has used the ΔH° values of the Bureau of Standards tabulation unless otherwise designated. *In all tables of thermodynamic data, the Bureau of Standards values are in italics.*

The entropy, S°, of a pure solid at 298.16° K. is given by the equation

$$S^\circ = \int_0^{298.16} C_p d \ln T + R \ln g, \tag{8}$$

where C_p is the specific heat at constant pressure and g the number of detailed states or the multiplicity of the solid when cooled to absolute zero. For all substances, C_p becomes zero at very low temperatures and if the substance in its lowest energy level has but a single configuration, g then equals unity and *the entropy of the substance at the absolute zero is zero.*

---

[1] J. Thomsen, *Thermochemische Untersuchungen*, Leipzig: J. A. Barth, 1886; F. D. Rossini, U. S. Bureau of Standards, Research Paper 686 (1934).

The italicized clause is a statement of the third law of thermodynamics. The validity of this law, which has been the subject of much controversy during the past two decades, can no longer be doubted. Its application has made possible the experimental evaluation of absolute entropies from specific-heat measurements and thus the calculation of $\Delta F°$ and $E°$ from thermal data by equation (7). At least half of the free energies which we shall employ have been computed by this method.

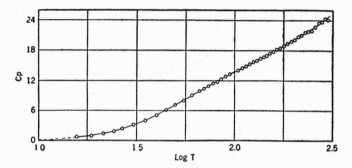

Fig. 1.   Molal heat capacity of BaSO₄ against log of absolute temperature.

Figure 1 gives a typical plot of C_p against log T. The area under the curve is a graphical integration of the integral in equation (8), and hence the entropy of barium sulfate at 298.16° K. It is obvious from equation (8) that caution must be observed in applying the third law to substances which may have multiplicity in this lowest energy state. Investigations of large numbers of substances have now indicated fairly well the types of compounds in which this may be true.

To obtain the entropy of a substance which is liquid at 25° C., it is necessary to determine the entropy of the solid at the melting point, the entropy of fusion (heat of fusion divided by the absolute temperature) and the C_p vs. log T curve for the liquid. Similarly, for a gas, the additional information needed is the entropy of vaporization and the C_p vs. log T curve for the gas.

For a number of comparatively simple gas molecules, spectroscopy has supplied complete information in regard to the number of quantum states and their energies. By purely statistical methods the entropy of such gases may be calculated from these data.[1] Thus, for a monatomic gas with only translational energy, the entropy is given by the Sackur equation,

$$S_t = \tfrac{3}{2}R \ln M + \tfrac{3}{2}R \ln T + R \ln V + \tfrac{5}{2}R + S_0,$$

and for 1 atmosphere and 25° C.

$$S_{t(298.16)} = \tfrac{3}{2}R \ln M + 25.996.$$

If the gas has rotation, vibration, and electronic contributions, the additional entropy from molecules in the various excited states may be calculated from a knowledge of the energies of the various states.[2] The spectroscopic entropies have been a very valuable check on the corresponding values calculated from specific-heat data[3] and have served to show the types of molecules which have multiplicity at absolute zero, or rather the molecules in which transitions to the lowest state do not occur in the temperature range used for specific-heat measurements.

Extensive use has been made of the entropies of the aqueous ions which have been determined by the author and his co-workers.[4] These entropies have been obtained from the entropies of compounds at 25° C. and their entropies of solution as calculated from the heats and free energies of solution by equation (7). The heats of formation are known for many substances in solution for which it has been impossible to determine the free energies by electromotive force or equilibrium methods because of the slowness or irreversibility of the reactions. A knowledge of the entropy values has thus made available these thermal data for the calculation of reaction potentials. For the most reliable data, the accuracy obtained is of the order of 0.001 to 0.01 volt. In some cases, however, the errors in the heats of reaction may run as high as 2000 cal. per equivalent, which would give errors of 0.1 in the potentials. The various experimental entropy values are given in the tables for each element. The entropy of a substance which has not been determined experimentally may be closely estimated

[1] W. F. Giauque, *J. Am. Chem. Soc.*, **52**, 4808 (1930).

[2] K. K. Kelley, *Bureau of Mines Bul. 477* (1950).

[3] E. D. Eastman, *Chem. Rev.*, **18**, 257 (1936).

[4] W. M. Latimer, P. W. Schutz and J. F. G. Hicks, Jr., *J. Chem. Phys.*, **2**, 82 (1934); W. M. Latimer, *Chem. Rev.*, **18**, 349 (1936); W. M. Latimer, W. V. Smith and K. S. Pitzer, *J. Am. Chem. Soc.*, **60**, 1829 (1938).

from the values of a similar substance, and in many cases such values have been used (see Appendix III).

The following example will serve to illustrate the use of thermal data in potential calculations.

EXAMPLE

$$\tfrac{1}{2}H_2 + AgCl(s) = H^+ + Cl^- + Ag(s)$$
$$\Delta H^\circ = -9661 \text{ cal.}$$
$$\Delta S^\circ = S^\circ_{H^+} + S^\circ_{Cl^-} + S^\circ_{Ag} - \tfrac{1}{2}S^\circ_{H_2} - S^\circ_{AgCl}$$
$$= 0 + 13.2 + 10.2 - \tfrac{1}{2} \times 31.2 - 23.0 = -15.2$$
$$\Delta F^\circ = -9661 - 298.16 \times (-15.2) = -5120 \text{ cal.}$$
$$E^\circ = \frac{-5120}{23,060} = 0.222.$$

Hence,

$$Ag(s) + Cl^- = AgCl + e^-, \qquad E^\circ = -0.222.$$

Estimation of potential values from chemical evidence. For the interpretation of inorganic chemistry, the knowledge of the approximate value, say within 0.2 volt, of an oxidation-reduction couple is often as valuable as a potential given to a thousandth of a volt. There are many reactions for which every type of thermodynamic data is lacking but for which there are sufficient chemical data, in the form of reactions with oxidation-reduction couples of known potentials, to fix the value within narrow limits.

A single example will serve to illustrate the method. The potential of the Re^-—Re couple is not known. The Re^- ion is formed by passing an acid perrhenate solution through a Jones reductor (Zn). The Re^- ion is unstable at 25° C. with respect to the evolution of hydrogen from water. Since the overvoltage for hydrogen evolution is normally around 0.5 volt, we estimate, taking into consideration the fairly slow decomposition of the water,

$$Re^- = Re + e^-, \qquad E^\circ = 0.4 \text{ volt.}$$

Potential diagrams. Diagrams showing the potentials between the various oxidation states of an element are very useful in summarizing and correlating the chemistry of the element. The following diagram is given as an illustration.

$1M$ H^+

$$\begin{array}{cccccc}
0.2 & 0.6 & -0.2 & -1.2 & -0.8 & -1.8 \\
\end{array}$$

$\mathrm{M}\text{——}\mathrm{M}^+\text{——}\mathrm{M}^{++}\text{——}\ \mathrm{M}^{+++}\text{——}\ \mathrm{MO}^{++}\text{——}\ \mathrm{MO}_3^-\text{——}\ \mathrm{MO}_4^{--}$

$\mid \quad 0.4 \qquad\qquad \mid \qquad\quad \mid \qquad\quad -1.0 \qquad\qquad \mid$

The numerical values are for the $E°$ potentials relating the oxidation states, for example,

$$\mathrm{M} = \mathrm{M}^{++} + 2e^-, \qquad\qquad E° = 0.4.$$

$$\mathrm{MO}_3^- + \mathrm{H_2O} = \mathrm{MO}_4^{--} + 2\mathrm{H}^+ + e^-, \qquad E° = -1.8.$$

The $+1$ ion is unstable with respect to disproportionation and to the evolution of H_2 (see Chap. 3):

$$2\mathrm{M}^+ = \mathrm{M} + \mathrm{M}^{++},$$

$$\mathrm{M}^+ + \mathrm{H}^+ = \mathrm{M}^{++} + \tfrac{1}{2}\mathrm{H_2}.$$

The ion MO^{++} is unstable with respect to disproportionation:

$$2\mathrm{MO}^{++} + \mathrm{H_2O} = \mathrm{M}^{+++} + \mathrm{MO}_3^- + 2\mathrm{H}^+.$$

The ion of the $+6$ state, MO_4^{--}, is an extremely powerful oxidizing agent and will evolve oxygen (see Chap. 4) in $1M$ H^+:

$$2\mathrm{MO}_4^{--} + 2\mathrm{H}^+ = 2\mathrm{MO}_3^- + \tfrac{1}{2}\mathrm{O_2} + \mathrm{H_2O}.$$

Dilute acid will oxidize the metal to the $+2$ ion:

$$\mathrm{M} + 2\mathrm{H}^+ = \mathrm{M}^{++} + \mathrm{H_2}.$$

The reaction will stop at this state, since the potential of the M^{++}—M^{+++} couple is negative. Excess chlorine (Cl^-—$\mathrm{Cl_2}$, $E°$ -1.35 volt) will oxidize the metal, or M^{++}, or M^{+++} to MO_3^- but cannot oxidize the latter to MO_4^{--}.

CHAPTER 2

Ionization Potentials, Electron Affinities, Lattice Energies, and their Relation to Standard Oxidation-Reduction Potentials

The values for the ionization potentials and the electron affinities of the elements have contributed much to the interpretation of many types of chemical reactions, and it is important to consider the relation of these quantities, obtained for the monatomic gas atoms, to the oxidation-reduction potentials of the elements and their compounds in their standard states at 25° C. It is also interesting to see to what extent the atomic energies can be used to answer such questions as why silver is a noble metal and sodium basic or why fluorine is more electronegative than iodine.

Ionization potentials. The analysis of atomic line spectra has provided highly accurate values for the ionization potentials. For most atoms the potential required to remove one or all of the valence electrons is known, and it is known in some cases for electrons from the closed shell lying below the valence electrons. A summary of these potentials is given in Table 1 (see p. 15).

Some interesting relations may be observed in the first ionization potential of the various atoms. The value depends upon the type of electron, s, p, d, or f; upon the total quantum number; and upon the number of electrons already in the uncompleted shell. It will be seen that maximum potentials are attained for the noble gases, with the completion of the $1s$ shell for helium and of the eight electrons of the s and p groups for the other gases; and the minimum potentials occur in the alkali metals which have but a single s electron in the valence shell. The first p electron has a slightly lower value than the preceding s electron, and the potentials for succeeding p electrons rise rapidly, with the exception of a slightly lower value for the fourth p electron.

14

TABLE 1

IONIZATION POTENTIALS OF THE ELEMENTS

(Values, expressed in volts, are from Atomic Energy Levels,
Bureau of Standards *Circular 467*, and Bureau of Standards Selected Values
of Chemical Thermodynamic Properties.)

Element	I	II	III	IV	V
1H[1]	13.595				
2He[4]	24.58	54.4			
3Li[7]	5.39	75.62	122.42		
4Be	9.32	18.21	153.5	217.66	
5B	8.296	15.15	37.75	259.30	340.1
6C	11.264	24.376	47.26	67.48	391.99
7N	14.54	29.60	47.43	77.45	97.86
8O	13.64	35.146	54.93	77.39	113.87
9F	17.42	34.98	62.65	86.23	114.21
10Ne	21.559	41.07	64.	97.16	126.4
11Na	5.38	47.29	71.65	98.88	138.6
12Mg	7.644	15.03	80.12	109.29	141.23
13Al	5.984	18.82	28.44	119.96	153.77
14Si	8.49	16.34	33.46	45.13	166.73
15P	11.0	19.65	30.156	51.34	65.00
16S	10.357	23.4	34.55	47.29	72.5
17Cl	13.01	23.80	39.90	53.5	64.80
18A	15.755	27.62	40.90	57.79	75.0
19K	4.339	31.8	46.	60.9	
20Ca	6.111	11.87	51.21	66.7	84.39
21Sc	6.56	12.89	24.75	73.9	92.
22Ti	6.83	13.62	28.14	43.34	99.8
23V	6.71	14.1	26.4	48.4	64.4
24Cr	6.76	16.6	29.8	50.2	73.9
25Mn	7.43	15.64			
26Fe	7.80	16.11	43.43		
27Co	7.84	17.31			
28Ni	7.633	18.22			
29Cu	7.736	20.287			
30Zn	9.40	17.960	39.66		
31Ga	6.00	20.510	30.66	64.2	
32Ge	8.13	15.95	34.22	45.70	93.45
33As	10.500	20.178	27.30	50.13	62.62
34Se	9.751	21.514	30.079	42.902	73.109
35Br	11.844	21.584	35.890		119.70
36Kr	13.99	24.57	36.94		
37Rb	4.177	27.501	39.68		
38Sr	5.70	11.03			
39Y	6.6	12.40	20.49		
40Zr	6.96	14.032	24.2	34.0	

TABLE I (*Continued*)

IONIZATION POTENTIALS OF THE ELEMENTS

(Values, expressed in volts, are from Atomic Energy Levels,
Bureau of Standards *Circular 467*, and Bureau of Standards Selected Values
of Chemical Thermodynamic Properties.)

Element	I	II	III	IV	V
41Nb			24.2		(49.3)
42Mo	7.40				(60.8)
45Rh	7.3				
46Pd	7.9	19.9			
47Ag	7.575	21.48	36.10		
48Cd	8.992	16.9052	35.0		
49In	5.80	18.87	28.04	58.0	
50Sn	7.4	14.63	30.66	40.8	80.8
51Sb	8.64	18.01	24.7	43.91	55.5
52Te	9.01	21.55	30.613	37.82	60.30
53I	10.4412	19.010			
54Xe	12.127	21.206	32.13	46.62	(76.)
55Cs	3.90	23.46	35.	(51)	(58)
56Ba	5.21	10.022			
57La	5.7	11.434	19.17		
58Ce	7.0	12.31	20.1	36.7	
62Sm	5.7	11.5		(36.5)	
63Eu	5.7	11.3			
76Os	8.8				
78Pt	9.0				
80Hg	10.43	18.752	34.3	(72)	(82)
81Tl	6.11	20.41	29.83	50.54	
82Pb	7.42	15.03	32.08	42.25	69.7
83Bi	7.29	16.7	25.56	45.4	56.1
86Rn	10.75				
88Ru	5.3	10.15			
90Th			(29.4)		

For the process of filling up the *d* and *f* groups, the potentials are fairly constant, with just a slight but often irregular rise as the number of electrons in the group increases. The relations are shown graphically in Figure 2, which is taken from Herzberg.[1]

Electron affinities. The evaluation of the electron affinities of the electronegative elements, namely, the potentials for the capture of one or more electrons by the monatomic gas atoms, has been

[1] G. Herzberg, *Atomic Spectra and Atomic Structure*, New York: Prentice-Hall, Inc., 1937, pp. 200–201.

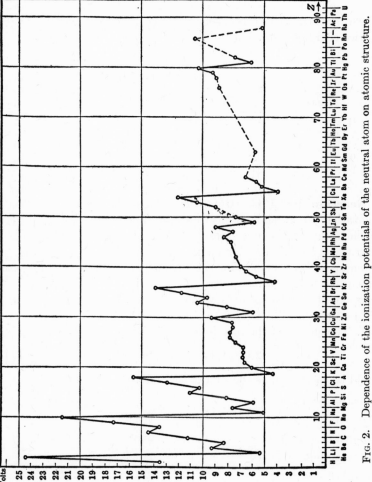

FIG. 2. Dependence of the ionization potentials of the neutral atom on atomic structure.

difficult inasmuch as the methods of line spectra have not been applicable. In a few cases direct determinations have been made as, for example, iodine—by Sutton and Mayer,[1] but most of the values given in Table 2 have been obtained by indirect calculations.[2] (See lattice energies below.)

TABLE 2

ELECTRON AFFINITIES

Element	Volts	Element	Volts
$H + e^- = H^-$	0.78	$O + e^- = O^-$	3.4
$F + e^- = F^-$	4.24	$S + e^- = S^-$	2.8
$Cl + e^- = Cl^-$	3.78	$O^- + e^- = O^{--}$	−5.0
$Br + e^- = Br^-$	3.56	$S^- + e^- = S^{--}$	−5.9
$I + e^- = I^-$	3.28		

Reactions at 25° C. Unfortunately for the direct application of ionization potentials and electron affinities to the general problem of chemical-free energies, most elements and their ions do not exist at room temperatures as monatomic gases. Moreover when one attempts to use the data for the gaseous atoms to calculate reaction potentials under ordinary reaction conditions, there is usually at least one step in the process which is difficult to evaluate accurately. Two examples will be given to illustrate this difficulty.

1. The energy of the reaction between silver and iodine,

$$2Ag(s) + I_2(s) = 2AgI(s), \tag{1}$$

could be calculated as the sum of the following steps:

SUBLIMATION ENERGY: $I_2(s) = I_2(g)$

DISSOCIATION ENERGY: $I_2(g) = 2I(g)$

ELECTRON AFFINITY: $2I(g) + 2e^-(g) = 2I^-(g)$

SUBLIMATION ENERGY: $2Ag(s) = 2Ag(g)$

IONIZATION ENERGY: $2Ag(g) = 2Ag^+(g) + 2e^-(g)$

LATTICE ENERGY: $Ag^+(g) + I^-(g) = AgI(s)$

But the energy of the last reaction, the lattice energy (i.e., the

[1] P. P. Sutton and J. E. Mayer, *J. Chem. Phys.*, **3**, 20 (1935).

[2] J. E. Mayer and L. Helmholz, *Z. Physik*, **75**, 19 (1932); J. Sherman, *Chem. Rev.*, **11**, 94 (1932); L. Pauling, *Phys. Rev.*, **29**, 285 (1927). See also value for hydrogen by E. A. Hylleraas, *Z. Physik*, **65**, 209 (1930).

energy required to separate the ions of solid silver iodide to infinity) cannot be directly determined. However, in a few cases the lattice energies (vide infra) can be theoretically estimated and used, with a series of reactions such as the above, to calculate reaction potentials.

2. The energy of the reaction between hydrogen and chlorine to form hydrochloric acid in solution,

$$H_2(g) + Cl_2(g) = 2H^+(aq) + 2Cl^-(aq), \qquad (2)$$

could be calculated as the sum of the following steps:

IONIZATION ENERGY: $2H(g) = 2H^+(g) + 2e^-(g)$
DISSOCIATION ENERGY: $H_2(g) = 2H(g)$
HYDRATION ENERGY: $2H^+(g) = 2H^+(aq)$
ELECTRON AFFINITY: $2Cl(g) + 2e^-(g) = 2Cl^-(g)$
DISSOCIATION ENERGY: $Cl_2(g) = 2Cl(g)$
HYDRATION ENERGY: $2Cl^-(g) = 2Cl^-(aq)$

The two hydration energies cannot be obtained experimentally; hence the process is not a feasible method of determining the potential of the chlorine-hydrogen reaction.

However, it is obvious that, if the energies of the two reactions, (1) and (2), are known, they may be used to calculate, in the first case, the lattice energy of the silver iodide, and in the second, the sum of the hydration energies of hydrogen and chloride ions. In this way the so-called experimental values for these quantities have been obtained.

Lattice energies. When the values for these energies were first tabulated, it was evident that they were largely coulombic in nature, that is, they were roughly directly proportional to the product of the charges of the ions and inversely to the distance between the ions in the solid. Born and Landé[1] first attacked the problem of their theoretical evaluation as a purely electrostatic calculation, assuming that the ions are held in equilibrium in the lattice by attractive forces which are coulombic and repulsive forces which change rapidly with the distance. Later workers have so refined the methods that, for the alkali halides at least, the theoretical values are probably better than the experimental, since the latter depend upon somewhat question-

---

[1] M. Born and A. Landé, *Sitzber. königl. preuss. Akad. Wiss. Berlin*, **45**, 1048 (1918).

able data for the electron affinities. In fact, the best values for the electron affinities are obtained by solving for them in series of equations such as those in example 1 and using the theoretical values for the alkali halide lattice energies. The data for Table 3 are those given by Mayer and Helmholz[1] for the alkali halides and by Sherman[2] for the other compounds. The latter reference may be consulted for additional data.

TABLE 3

LATTICE ENERGIES
(In kcal. at 0° K)

Ion	F^-	Cl^-	Br^-	I^-	O^{--}
Li^+	240.1	199.2	188.3	174.1	693
Na^+	213.4	183.1	174.6	163.9	
K^+	189.7	165.4	159.3	150.8	
Rb^+	181.6	160.7	153.5	145.3	
Cs^+	173.7	152.2	146.3	139.1	
Ag^+	223.0	207.0	204.0	202.0	715
Cd^{++}	662.0			563.0	911

Hydration energies. Since the energies of solution of solid salts are small in comparison to the large lattice energies, it follows that the lattice energy must be approximately the same as the sum of the energies of hydration of the two ions. In other words the water dipoles neutralize the electrical fields of the ions to about the same extent that the ions neutralize each other in the crystal, unless, as is sometimes the case, the negative ion is highly polarized in the solid. Any evaluation from experimental data always gives the sum of the hydration of the negative and positive ions. A summary of the data for the ions of a number of common salts is given in Table 4.

Born[3] has pointed out that, if the ions be considered as spheres of radius, r, and of charge, e, the energy of solution should be given by the expression

$$\Delta E = \left(\frac{e^2}{2r}\right)\left(1 - \frac{1}{D}\right),$$

where D is the dielectric constant of the solvent. This expression is

[1] J. E. Mayer and L. Helmholz, *Z. Physik*, **75**, 19 (1932).

[2] J. Sherman, *Chem. Rev.*, **11**, 94 (1932).

[3] M. Born, *Z. Physik*, **1**, 45 (1920).

Table 4

ENERGIES OF SOLUTION OF GASEOUS IONS
(In kcal. at 18° C)

(The values are for the sum of the positive and negative ions per mole at infinite dilution.)

Ion	F^-	Cl^-	Br^-	I^-
Li^+	246.6	208.8	199.9	189.1
Na^+	213.9	182.4	174.9	165.5
K^+	194.6	161.5	154.5	145.9
Rb^+	187.9	156.4	147.2	138.8
Cs^+	182.4	147.4	139.7	131.1
Ag^+	227.0	192.0		186.0
Cd^{++}				563.0

derived by taking the difference in the energy of the electric field of the ion in a vacuum and in the solvent. From it one could obtain the absolute values for the energies of hydration of the individual ions but its application is difficult because of the uncertainty in the magnitude of the radii of the ions in aqueous solution. These radii differ from the crystal lattice values since they refer to the distance from the center of the ion to the center of the water dipole. This distance is further complicated by the fact that for positive ions the oxygen of the water is directed in, while for negative ions it is the hydrogen end of the dipole which is attracted. Another obvious difficulty is the inconstancy of the dielectric constant in the high electrical field of the ion.

However, it is a matter of considerable interest to obtain the individual ionic hydration energies, instead of the sums given in Table 4. A similar problem exists with respect to the ionic entropies in aqueous solution, where the experimental values are obtained as sums of the entropies of a plus and a negative ion (or the differences between ions of like charge). However, in this case, fairly reliable absolute values for the individual ionic entropies are known,[1] so that a division of the sum of the entropies of a plus and a negative ion can be made. In general, the entropies of hydration may be expected to be proportional to the energies of hydration. Latimer, Pitzer, and Slansky[2] employed this principle to calculate the absolute values for

[1] J. C. Goodrich, F. M. Gowan, E. E. Morse, R. G. Preston, and M. B. Young, *J. Am. Chem. Soc.*, **2**, 4411 (1950).

[2] W. M. Latimer, K. S. Pitzer, and C. M. Slansky, *J. Chem. Phys.*, **7**, 108 (1939).

the hydration energies of the individual ions. The values in Table 5 are in agreement with their calculations.

TABLE 5

APPROXIMATE VALUES FOR THE HYDRATION HEATS, $-\Delta H°$, OF THE INDIVIDUAL IONS

(In kcal. per mole)

Cs^+	62	Na^+	95
I^-	72	Ag^+	111
Rb^+	69	F^-	123
K^+	76	Li^+	121
Br^-	81	H^+	256
Cl^-	89	Cd^{++}	420

Absolute electrode potentials. Fortunately for all ordinary chemical calculations, it is not necessary to know absolute potentials since one is always concerned with potential differences. However, absolute potentials are of some theoretical interest and, from the historical point of view, it is desirable to discuss the determination of absolute potentials as given by the Lippmann capillary electrometer.[1] This makes use of the ingenious assumption that the surface tension of a mercury surface, in contact with an electrolyte, is a maximum when no potential difference exists between the metal and the electrolyte, i.e., when there is no charge upon the mercury. The electrometer consists of two mercury electrodes with a common electrolyte—for example, potassium chloride containing a small amount of calomel. For one of the electrodes the contact between the electrolyte and the mercury is made through a capillary tube. If a potential is applied across this cell, the mercury in the capillary falls if that electrode is made positive, but if it is made negative, the column rises to a maximum of about 0.56 volt and then falls again at higher negative potentials. The interpretation given is that the mercury is normally positive to the solution and a potential of 0.56 volt is required to reduce it to the potential of the solution. If the height of the mercury in the capillary is plotted against the applied potential, one obtains a parabolic curve which is not quite symmetrical, indicating that the nature of the ion-absorption layer is different, depending upon whether it is positive or negative. A controversy has continued for many years as to the validity of the results. Grahame[2] has given a

---

[1] F. Kruger and H. Krumreich, Z. *Elektrochem.*, **29**, 617 (1913).
[2] D. C. Grahame, *Chem. Rev.*, **41**, 441 (1947).

careful analysis of the assumptions involved. Guggenheim[1] has taken the point of view that absolute or true potential differences between dissimilar phases are unmeasurable because they are not defined. However, it appears to the author that the free energy of the calomel half-cell reaction is a definite quantity which may be calculated if the values of the hydration energies are known. The following calculations were given by Latimer, Pitzer, and Slansky.[2]

$$\Delta F°$$

$$Na^+(g) = Na^+(aq) \qquad -89.7$$
$$Na(g) = Na^+(g) + e^-(g) \qquad 118.1$$
$$Na(c) = Na(g) \qquad 18.7$$
$$Hg + Na^+(aq) + Cl^-(aq) = HgCl(c) + Na(c) \qquad 68.76$$
$$\underline{e^-(g) = e^- \text{ (in Hg)} \qquad -104.5}$$
$$Hg + Cl^-(aq) = HgCl(c) + e^- \text{ (in Hg)}, \qquad 11.4 \text{ kcal.}$$

$$E° = -0.495.$$

This calculated value is only 0.065 volt lower than the capillary electrometer value.

Factors which determine the magnitude of oxidation-reduction potentials. An analysis may now be made of the factors which determine whether a couple is electropositive or electronegative. Consider, for example, the question as to why sodium is a base metal and silver a noble metal.

	$\Delta H°$		$\Delta H°$
$Na(s) = Na(g)$	26	$Ag(s) = Ag(g)$	67
$Na(g) = Na^+(g)$		$Ag(g) = Ag^+(g)$	
$\quad + e^-(g)$	118	$\quad + e^-(g)$	174
$Na^+(g) = Na^+(aq)$	-95	$Ag^+(g) = Ag^+(aq)$	-111
$Na(s) = Na^+(aq)$	49 kcal.	$Ag(s) = Ag^+(aq)$	130 kcal.
$\quad + e^-(g)$		$\quad + e^-(g)$	

These half-reactions as written contain the electrons as a gas, but that is unimportant for the comparisons. Since ΔH is positive, the larger positive value for the silver means a smaller tendency for the reaction to go, and this larger positive value is the result not

[1] E. A. Guggenheim, *J. Phys. Chem.*, **33**, 842 (1929).
[2] W. M. Latimer, K. S. Pitzer, and C. M. Slansky, *J. Chem. Phys.*, **7**, 108 (1939).

only of the higher ionization potential but also the higher sublimation energy and is only slightly offset by the greater hydration energy.

Factors, then, which tend to make a metal noble are: (1) high ionization potential; (2) high sublimation energy, which is associated with high boiling point; and (3) low energy of hydration. In the case of silver, its noble character arises as much from the high value of factor (2) as from factor (1).

$$Na + Ag^+ = Na^+ + Ag, \qquad \Delta H° = -81 \text{ kcal.}$$

Because the entropy change for the reaction is very small, the free energy is approximately equal to the heat of the reaction, $E° = 3.5$ volts, in agreement with the measured reaction potential.

As another example, consider the relative oxidizing power of fluorine and iodine.

$$
\begin{array}{rl}
 & \Delta H° \\
\tfrac{1}{2}F_2(g) = F(g) & 32 \\
F(g) + e^-(g) = F^-(g) & -92 \\
\underline{F^-(g) = F^-(aq)} & \underline{-123} \\
\tfrac{1}{2}F_2(g) + e^-(g) = F^-(aq) & -183 \text{ kcal.}
\end{array}
$$

$$
\begin{array}{rl}
\tfrac{1}{2}I_2(s) = I(g) & 26 \\
I(g) + e^-(g) = I^-(g) & -75 \\
\underline{I^-(g) = I^-(aq)} & \underline{-72} \\
\tfrac{1}{2}I_2(s) + e^-(g) = I^-(aq) & -121 \text{ kcal.}
\end{array}
$$

These equations show that fluorine is the better oxidizing agent, in part because of the higher electron affinity, but principally because of the greater energy of hydration of the smaller fluoride ion. In general, a large electron affinity, large energy of hydration, and small energy of formation of the monatomic gas atom from the standard state will favor a high oxidizing potential for elements forming negative ions.

An analysis of the factors which determine the oxidizing power of the oxygen acids and their compounds is more difficult. A half reaction, such as that for permanganate,

$$MnO_4^- + 8H^+ + 5e^- = Mn^{++} + 4H_2O,$$

can be broken up into a number of hypothetical steps:

1. Energy of dehydration of MnO_4^-.
2. Dissociation of MnO_4^- into Mn^{+7} and $4O^{--}$.
3. Energy of hydration of Mn^{++}.
4. Energy of union of H^+ and O^{--} to form water.
5. Ionization of Mn^{++} to Mn^{+7}.

It is obvious that low values for 1 and 2 and high values for the others will favor high oxidizing power but at present it is impossible to evaluate several of these steps accurately.

Proton affinities. The energy of the addition of a proton (hydrogen ion) to a negative ion or neutral molecule is called the proton affinity. Juza[1] has given the values summarized in Table 6. If one

TABLE 6

PROTON AFFINITIES

(All substances are gases)

Reaction	kcal.
$N^{---} + H^+ = NH^{---}$	ca 820
$NH^{---} + H^+ = NH_2^-$	ca 650
$NH_2^- + H^+ = NH_3$	380
$NH_3 + H^+ = NH_4^+$	200
$O^{--} + H^+ = OH^-$	ca 640
$OH^- + H^+ = H_2O$	385
$H_2O + H^+ = H_3O^+$	170
$F^- + H^+ = HF$	366
$Cl^- + H^+ = HCl$	331
$Br^- + H^+ = HBr$	320
$I^- + H^+ = HI$	311

attempts to calculate these quantities as the coulombic energy of bringing two point charges, positive and negative, up to the known interatomic distances, the calculated energies are too small. Thus for HCl the calculated coulombic energy is about 250 kcal., and the experimental, 330 kcal. The difference represents the energy arising from the polarization of the negative ion or the energy of the bond (electron pair) formation. However, the coulombic picture is a very useful one in correlating the strength of the hydrogen compounds as

[1] R. Juza, *Z. anorg. allgem. Chem.*, **231**, 121 (1937). NOTE: Certain of the values have been corrected to conform to the Bureau of Standards data.

acids. In general it may be stated: the ionization of the hydrogen acids increases (1) with increasing size of the negative ion, and (2) with decreasing charge on the negative ion. Thus HI is a stronger acid than HF and H_2S is stronger than H_2O because of the effect of the size. HF is stronger than H_2O because of the effect of the charge. It also follows that if the negative element forms hydrogen compounds of different oxidation states, the smaller the negative number of the oxidation state, the stronger will be the acid. Thus H_2O_2 is a stronger acid than H_2O and N_2H_4 is less basic than NH_3.

Acidic and basic oxides. The coulombic picture of the structure of oxides is also very useful in interpreting their acidic or basic properties. If the energy of attraction of a positive ion for oxide ion is small, the compound will ionize in water and since the oxide ion is completely hydrolyzed, hydroxide is formed. Thus, for barium oxide,

$$\overset{(+2)}{BaO} + H_2O = Ba^{++} + 2OH^-.$$

On the other hand, if the attraction of the positive ion for oxide is very great it tends to take on additional oxides. For example, in the case of sulfur trioxide,

$$\overset{(+6)}{SO_3} + H_2O = SO_4^{--} + 2H^+.$$

In the oxygen acids the ionization constants appear to depend upon the charge on the central atom. Although the exact charge is not known, the formal charge, which is calculated by assuming that the electrons in the bonds are equally divided between the two atoms, may be used as a good approximation. The correlation between formal charge and ionization constants is indicated in Table 7.

It may be observed that if the formal charge on the negative central atom is zero, K_1 is ca 10^{-9} and K_2, ca 10^{-13}; with the formal charge $+1$, K_1 is ca 10^{-3}, K_2, ca 10^{-8} and K_3, ca 10^{-13}; with the formal charge $+2$, K_1 is large and K_2, ca 10^{-2}; if the formal charge is $+3$ the acid is very strong. In general K_2 for a given acid is similar to K_1 for an acid with formal charge one less. Kossiakoff and Harker[1] were reasonably successful in calculating the free energy of dissociation

---

[1] A. Kossiakoff and D. Harker, *J. Am. Chem. Soc.*, **60**, 2047 (1938).

TABLE 7

CORRELATION OF DISSOCIATION CONSTANT WITH FORMAL CHARGE ON THE CENTRAL ATOM

Formal Charge 0			Formal Charge +1				Formal Charge +2			Formal Charge +3	
	K_1	K_2		K_1	K_2	K_3		K_1	K_2		K_1
H_3AsO_3	6×10^{-10}		H_3PO_4	7.5×10^{-3}	6×10^{-8}	10^{-12}	H_2SO_4	lg^1	1.2×10^{-2}	$HClO_4$	v. lg^1
H_4GeO_4	2.6×10^{-9}		H_3PO_3	1.6×10^{-3}			H_2SeO_4	lg	9×10^{-3}	$HMnO_4$	v. lg
H_6TeO_6	1.6×10^{-9}	10^{-13}	H_3PO_3	10^{-2}							
$HClO$	3.2×10^{-8}		H_3AsO_4	3×10^{-4}	6×10^{-8}	3×10^{-13}					
$HBrO$	2.1×10^{-9}		H_5IO_6	10^{-4}							
			H_2SeO_3	3×10^{-3}							
			$HClO_2$	1.1×10^{-2}							
			H_2SO_3	1.2×10^{-2}							
			H_2CO_3	2×10^{-4}							
			HNO_2	5×10^{-4}							

[1] Lg, large; v. lg, very large.

in terms of the electrostatic energy of transfer of the proton to the water, and Ricci[1] gave the following empirical equation:

$$pK = 8.0 - m(9.0) + n(4.0),$$

where m is the formal charge and n the number of non-hydroxyl oxygen atoms.

[1] J. E. Ricci, *J. Am. Chem. Soc.*, **70**, 109 (1948).

CHAPTER 3

Hydrogen

Hydrogen has but a single valence electron, and in the monatomic gas the electronic state is $s^1(^2S_{1/2})$. In addition to the isotope of mass one, molecular hydrogen and its compounds ordinarily contain appreciable quantities of the isotope of mass two, deuterium, H^2 or D, and traces of the isotope of mass three, tritium, H^3 or T. Thus, ordinary water contains approximately one part in seven thousand of deuterium.[1] Because of the much greater percentage differences in the masses, these isotopes show a larger variation in their physical and chemical properties than do the isotopes of any other element. In fact, this is the only case where we shall consider differences in the thermodynamics of chemical reactions for two isotopes.

The standard state of the element is the diatomic molecule in the equilibrium mixture of the two molecular species, ortho- and para-. These molecules differ in the orientation of the spins of the two hydrogen nuclei; in the latter the spins are opposed and in the former, additive. At the temperature of liquid hydrogen the equilibrium mixture is almost completely parahydrogen, and at room temperatures the equilibrium mixture is an approximately 3 to 1 mixture of ortho- and para-. Giauque[2] has calculated -337.17 cal. for the $\Delta H°$ of transition of ortho- to parahydrogen.

The energy of the deuterium molecule differs from that of hydrogen of mass one largely in the energy of the zero vibrational state. For H_2 the zero point energy is 6195 cal. and for D_2 it is 4394. The dissociation energy of D_2 is therefore 1.8 kcal. higher than that for H_2.[3]

---

[1] J. L. Gabbard and M. Dole, *J. Am. Chem. Soc.*, **59**, 181 (1937); G. N. Lewis and R. T. Macdonald, *J. Chem. Phys.*, **1**, 341 (1933).

[2] W. F. Giauque, *J. Am. Chem. Soc.*, **52**, 4828 (1930).

[3] A. Farkas, *Orthohydrogen, Parahydrogen and Heavy Hydrogen*, London: Cambridge University Press, 1935, p. 155.

Tritium (H^3) is unstable with respect to β-emission and the formation of He^3, and its half-life is about 12 years. It is most readily prepared by the action of neutrons on Li^6:

$$Li^6 + n^1 = He^4 + H^3.$$

The half-life of the neutron with respect to β-emission and the formation of hydrogen mass one is about 20 minutes.

TABLE 8

THERMODYNAMIC DATA ON HYDROGEN[1]

Heat and free energy of formation, in kcal. Entropy of substance in cal./deg.

Formula	Description	State	$\Delta H°$	$\Delta F°$	$S°$
H	($^2S_{1/2}$)	g	*52.089*	*48.575*	*27.393*
H^+		g	*367.083*		
H^+		aq	0.0	0.0	0.0
D^+		aq		−0.08	
H_2		g	0.0	0.0	*31.211*
H^-		g	*34.05*		
H^-		aq		51.9	
H_2^+		g	*357.15*		
D	($^2S_{1/2}$)	g	*52.982*	*49.358*	*29.456*
D_2		g	0.0	0.0	*34.602*
D_2^+		g	*368.06*		
D^-		g	*34.94*		
HD		g	*0.037*	*−0.391*	*34.34*

[1] Bureau of Standards values appear in *italics*.

Oxidation states. The oxidation states of hydrogen are +1 and −1. Acids and hydrogen ion are examples of the former. The compounds of hydrogen with highly electropositive elements, such as sodium and calcium, are true hydrides; and the oxidation state of the hydrogen is −1. In molten solution they give the hydride ion, H^-. This ion is oxidized at the anode upon electrolysis to molecular hydrogen.[1] The hydride ion has the electronic structure of helium and thus resembles the halides, all of which add one electron to form the noble gas type of ion. Between these two classes are many compounds, especially with carbon, in which two electrons are shared between the hydrogen and the other atom (covalence) and in which it is therefore ambiguous to talk of the oxidation state of the hydro-

---

[1] D. C. Bardwell, *J. Am. Chem. Soc.*, **44**, 2499 (1922).

gen. However, it is customary to refer to the oxidation state of
hydrogen in all compounds except the true hydrides as $+1$ without
raising the question of the distribution of the electrons in the bond.

The formula of hydrogen ion. In ice each oxygen atom is
linked to four other oxygen atoms through hydrogen bonds, and liquid
water certainly possesses very large molecular structures with similar
hydrogen bonding. Hydrogen ion in water becomes a part of these
hydrogen-bonded complexes, and for that reason it is difficult to
write a simple formula. Some authors write hydrogen ion as H_3O^+,
but in our opinion the following formulas for H^+ and OH^- in water
solutions are to be preferred.

$$
\begin{array}{cc}
\text{H} & \text{H}^+ \\
\text{O} \quad \text{H} \quad \text{O} & \text{H} \quad \text{O} \quad \text{H} \quad \text{O} \quad \text{H}^- \\
\text{H} & \text{H}
\end{array}
$$

hydrogen ion   hydroxide ion

These formulas are, of course, oversimplified since there will be hydrogen bonding to additional water molecules. In view of the complex
nature of the problem, we shall write for hydrogen ion the simple
formula, H^+, and for hydroxide, OH^-.

The H_2—H^+ couple. As stated in Chap. 1, the hydrogen couple
is taken as the standard reference electrode, and its potential at unit
fugacity of H_2 and activity of H^+ is arbitrarily set at zero.

$$H_2 = 2H^+ + 2e^-, \qquad E^\circ = 0.00.$$

By Equation (1) (Chap. 1) the potential in volts of the couple at any
pressure, P, in atmospheres of H_2 and at any concentration, C, of
H^+ in moles per 1000 g of water at 25° C. is

$$E = -0.05916 \log \frac{C_{H^+}}{P_{H_2}^{\frac{1}{2}}}.$$

This equation is a good approximation in dilute solutions and at low
hydrogen pressures, but for exact calculations the thermodynamic
concentration or activity and the thermodynamic pressure or fugacity
must be used (see Chap. 1).

For the interpretation of reactions in aqueous solutions, it is important to know the potential of the hydrogen couple in pure water
and in $1M$ OH^-. These values may be calculated from the ionization
constant of water at 25° C. For this constant Lewis and Randall

give 1.005×10^{-14}, and Harned and Hamer[1] give 1.008×10^{-14}. We shall use the latter.

$$H_2O = H^+ + OH^-, \qquad\qquad K = 1.008 \times 10^{-14};$$
$$H_2 = 2H^+(10^{-7}M) + 2e^-, \qquad E = 0.414;$$
$$H_2 + 2OH^- = 2H_2O + 2e^-, \qquad E_B^\circ = 0.828.$$

From these values it follows that the reducing agent of a couple more positive than 0.414 should liberate hydrogen from water and of a couple more positive than 0.828 should liberate hydrogen from molal hydroxide solutions. In general then, it may be stated that the potential of the hydrogen couple may be correlated with the stability of reducing agents in water solutions. For example, of the two couples,

$$Sn^{++} = Sn^{++++} + 2e^-, \qquad E^\circ = -0.15;$$
$$Cr^{++} = Cr^{+++} + e^-, \qquad E^\circ = 0.41;$$

it is obvious that Sn^{++} should not be oxidized by concentrated acid solution and that Cr^{++} is unstable in respect to the evolution of hydrogen even in low acid solutions. These conclusions follow from our conventions with respect to the sign of the potentials: the negative sign is employed for couples in which the oxidizing agent is more powerful than H^+, and conversely, the positive sign if the oxidizing agent is less powerful than H^+.

The hydrogen couple is reversible, but the rate at which equilibrium is reached is generally slow. The reaction of acids with metallic zinc may be cited as an example of the slowness of hydrogen ion as an oxidizing agent. In this case, although there is a potential of 0.8 volt in favor of the oxidation of the zinc to zinc ion, there is no appreciable evolution of hydrogen with pure zinc in cold dilute acids. However if the zinc be touched with a piece of platinum, the reaction proceeds rapidly, with the evolution of the gas taking place on the surface of the platinum In the electrolytic reduction of hydrogen at a cathode, it is possible to measure the excess voltage, over the reversible potential, which is required to liberate hydrogen. This excess voltage is termed overvoltage. Values for various experimental conditions are summarized in Table 9.[2]

It will be observed that the overvoltage depends upon the element

---

[1] H. S. Harned and W. J. Hamer, *J. Am. Chem. Soc.*, **55**, 2198 (1935).

[2] Table 9 is compiled from *International Critical Tables*, **VI**, 339; and from *Handbuch der Physik*, **XIII**, 564.

TABLE 9

OVERVOLTAGES OF HYDROGEN IN $1M$ H_2SO_4 IN VOLTS

(Current density in amperes per square centimeter)

Cathode	10^{-4}	10^{-3}	10^{-2}	10^{-1}	1
Pt (black)	.003	.01	0.03	0.04	0.05
Pt		.02	0.07	0.29	0.68
Au	.12	.24	0.39	0.59	0.80
Fe	.22	.40	0.56	0.82	1.29
Cu	.35	.48	0.58	0.80	1.25
Pb	.45	.52	1.09	1.18	1.26
Zn	.55	.72	0.75	1.06	1.23
Ni	.20	.56	0.74	1.05	1.24
Cd	.65	.98	1.13	1.22	1.25
Hg	.60	.78	0.93	1.03	1.07
C	.29	.55	0.70	0.89	1.17
Ag	.30	.48	0.76	0.98	1.10
Al	.50	.57	0.83	1.00	1.29

used as cathode, its physical condition, and the current density. The lowest overvoltage is observed with platinized platinum surfaces. This substance is therefore used as electrodes to obtain reversible hydrogen potentials. At higher temperatures the magnitude of the overvoltage decreases, the change being 0.02 to 0.03 volt per each 10°. The net effect of the overvoltage phenomenon is to cause the hydrogen ion to act as though it were a much less powerful oxidizing agent, and hydrogen gas as though it were a much less powerful reducing agent, than the reversible potential would indicate.

The explanation of the slowness of hydrogen reactions is to be found in the reaction mechanism. Thus the first step in the reduction of the hydrogen ion would appear to be the formation of atomic hydrogen. The potential of the hydrogen atom-hydrogen ion couples may be calculated from the free energy of formation of atomic hydrogen, 48.57 kcal.,

$$H = H^+ + e^-, \qquad E^\circ = 2.10;$$
$$H + OH^- = H_2O + e^-, \qquad E_B^\circ = 2.93.$$

The union of two hydrogen atoms, of course, supplies energy for the net reaction but the very high positive value for this atomic hydrogen-hydrogen ion couple acts as a potential barrier which the electron must cross before the reaction can proceed. Gurney[1] has given a

[1] R. W. Gurney, *Proc. Roy. Soc.*, A **134**, 137 (1931).

quantum mechanical treatment of the probability of the leakage of an electron across the barrier and has obtained an expression which shows the dependence of overvoltage on current density and temperature.

However the problem has another important chemical factor, namely, the reaction of the atomic hydrogen with the electrode metal to form a surface layer. The greater the stability of such a compound the lower will be the potential of this couple and the lower the potential barrier.

$$2M + 2H^+ + 2e^- = 2HM \qquad\qquad M + H^+ + e^- = HM$$
$$\underline{\qquad 2HM = H_2 + 2M \qquad} \quad \text{or} \quad \underline{HM + H^+ + e^- = M + H_2}$$
$$2H^+ + 2e^- = H_2 \qquad\qquad\qquad 2H^+ + 2e^- = H_2$$

The variation of hydrogen overvoltages with different metals will then depend upon the energy of formation of the surface hydrides. There is ample evidence for the formation of such hydrogen compounds, and the very high solubility of hydrogen in nickel, palladium, and platinum is associated with the catalysis of hydrogen (H_2) reactions by these metals and the low overvoltage for the cathodic reduction of hydrogen ion on their surfaces.

The decrease of the hydrogen-ion concentration has but slight effect upon the overvoltage until it becomes so low that the formation of a hydroxide coating upon the metal surface changes markedly the nature of the electrode.

The second ionization constant of water. The hydrolysis of oxide ion in water is so complete that no measurement of the concentration of the unhydrolyzed oxide ion can be made. A very rough estimate of the hydrolysis can be obtained from the $\Delta H°$ of solution of sodium oxide in water, -55 kcal. This heat is the sum of the true heat of solution of the oxide and the heat of hydrolysis. The corrected $\Delta H°$ of solution of sodium sulfide is -15.5 kcal. and we estimate that the true heat of solution of sodium oxide is not over -25 kcal. This would make the heat of hydrolysis greater than -30 kcal. The entropy of the hydrolysis is not large, so we may write

$$O^{--} + H_2O = 2OH^-, \qquad K > 10^{22};$$
$$OH^- = O^{--} + H^+, \qquad K < 10^{-36}.$$

The hydride-hydrogen ion couple. Hydride ion rapidly reduces water and is therefore unknown in aqueous solution. However, there are a number of calculations pertaining to the energy of the ion which are of interest. First, the free energies of the solid hydrides may be calculated, and from these the oxidation potentials of the solid hydrides determined. These calculations are summarized in Table 10.

TABLE 10

FREE ENERGIES AND POTENTIALS OF SOLID HYDRIDES

Hydride	$\Delta F°$ (kcal.)	Free energy of metal ion	$MH_n = M^{n+} + \dfrac{n}{2} H_2 + ne^-$
			$E°$
CaH_2	−35.8	−132.2	2.09
SrH_2	−33.1	−133.2	2.19
BaH_2	−31.6	−134.0	2.22
LiH	−16.7	−70.2	2.32
NaH	−9.0	−62.6	2.32
KH	−8.9	−67.5	2.54
RbH	−7.3	−67.5	2.61
CsH	−7.3	−67.4	2.61

Only the entropy of calcium hydride has been accurately obtained experimentally, and in this case the entropy of the hydride is almost identical with that of the metal. In calculating the $\Delta S°$ of formation for the other hydrides, the assumption has been made that the same relation holds true as a close approximation.

The $E°$ values, summarized in the last column of Table 10, are of the same order of magnitude and the differences may be interpreted as arising from the different solubilities of the various hydrides. Before discussing these, we shall calculate an approximate value of the H^-—H_2 couple from the electron affinity, ionization potentials, and related data, in the following manner:

$$\Delta H\,(\text{kcal.})$$

$$\tfrac{1}{2}H_2 = H^+_{(g)} + e^-_{(g)} \qquad 367.08$$
$$\tfrac{1}{2}H_2 + e^-_{(g)} = H^-_{(g)} \qquad 34.05$$
$$H^+_{(g)} = H^+_{(aq)} \qquad -256.0$$
$$H^-_{(g)} = H^-_{(aq)} \qquad -103.6$$
$$\overline{H_2 = H^+_{(aq)} + H^-_{(aq)} \qquad 41.5}$$

The heats of formation of $H^+_{(g)}$ and $H^-_{(g)}$ are from Table 8 and the heats of hydration are from Table 5, with the value of the radius of H^-

taken as 1.50 Å from crystal data. In line with this radius of H^-, we estimate the entropy of H^- as -5 cal./deg. Hence $\Delta F°$ of formation of $H^-_{(aq)}$ is 51.9 kcal. and

$$H^- = \tfrac{1}{2}H_2 + e^-, \qquad E° = 2.25.$$

From the nature of the calculation, the $E°$ may be in error by several tenths of a volt. If it is correct, it would mean, by reference to Table 10, that the alkali hydrides are fairly soluble and those of the alkaline earth metals less so. In these solubility relations, the hydrides appear to resemble the fluorides of these elements more than the chlorides. Because of the high positive value of the couple, true hydrides are formed only by metals whose potentials are greater than 2 volts.

The work of Sollers and Crenshaw[1] on the dissociation pressures of sodium and potassium deuteride may be used as a basis for similar calculations on the potential of the deuteride ion.

The D_2—D^+ couple. A direct measurement of the deuterium gas-deuterium ion couple cannot be made in water solution because of the rapid interchange of the deuterium atoms with the hydrogen. However, Abel, Bratu, and Redlich[2] were able to compare the deuterium couple in pure deuterium oxide with the hydrogen couple in water, through a common reference electrode. These authors reported

$$D_2 = 2D^+ + 2e^-, \qquad E° = 0.0034,$$

and for the ionization constant of the "heavy" water,

$$D_2O = OD^- + D^+, \qquad K = 0.3 \times 10^{-14}.$$

The smaller energy of the lowest vibrational state in D_2, as compared to H_2, has been mentioned above, and in general the bond between deuterium and another atom is slightly stronger than the corresponding bond with hydrogen. The lower ionization constant of D_2O is in line with this statement.

When an alkaline solution of water containing deuterium is electrolyzed, an enrichment of the deuterium occurs. The enrichment factor, that is, the percentage loss of hydrogen to the percentage loss of deuterium, is around 5 to 8 in general practice, using nickel and iron cathodes. This preferential reduction of H^+ obviously involves

[1] E. F. Sollers and J. L. Crenshaw, *J. Am. Chem. Soc.* **59**, 2015 and 2724 (1937)

[2] E. Abel, E. Bratu and O. Redlich, *Z. physik. Chem.*, **A 170**, 153 (1934); **A 173**, 353 (1935).

both the equilibrium and overvoltage potentials and the rate of inter-change of the intermediate monatomic hydrogen and deuterium on the metal surface with the atoms of the solution. The greater ionization of the hydrogen is doubtless a most important factor. Novak[1] reported the D_2 overvoltage in 99.6 per cent D_2O with a mercury cathode to be 0.087 volt greater than that for H_2 with similar current density. Heyrovsky[2] and Halpern and Gross[3] have discussed the theory of the enrichment factor.

Johnston and Long[4] have given thermodynamic data for D_2. From the free energies in Tables 8 and 11 we calculate

$$H_2 + D_2 = 2HD_{(g)}, \qquad \Delta F° = -391 \text{ cal.}$$
$$H_2O_{(liq)} + D_2O_{(liq)} = 2HDO_{(liq)}, \qquad \Delta F° = -1014 \text{ cal.}$$
$$H_2O_{(liq)} + HD = HDO_{(liq)} + H_2, \qquad \Delta F° = -844 \text{ cal.}$$

For the equilibrium involving hydrogen ion and deuterium ion, Hamill[5] calculates

$$H^+ + HDO = D^+ + H_2O, \qquad K = 0.141.$$

From this equilibrium, the free energy of $D_{(aq)}^+$ is -80 cal.

Jones[6] has given the following data for tritium: $S_{298.1}^°$ T_2, 39.394 cal./deg. and HT, 38.202 cal./deg. These values include the $R \ln 4$ resulting from nuclear spin.

$$H_2 + T_2 = 2HT, \qquad K = 2.57;$$
$$T_2 = 2T, \qquad K_{1000° K.} = 3.01 \times 10^{-18}.$$

This latter value may be compared with $K = 6.45 \times 10^{-18}$ for H_2 at the same temperature. Jones also reported for the zero point energies T_2 3603.4 cal. and HT 5072.7 cal. as compared to 6193.8 for H_2.

Summary of hydrogen potentials. The following diagrams summarize the hydrogen potentials.

Acid Solution.		Base Solution.	
2.23　　　0.00		2.23　　　　　　0.828	
H⁻————H₂————H⁺,		H⁻————H₂ + OH⁻————H₂O	

[1] J. Novak, *Coll. Czechoslov. Chem. Commun.*, **9**, 207 (1937).
[2] J. Heyrovsky, *Coll. Czechoslov. Chem. Commun.*, **9**, 273 (1937).
[3] O. Halpern and P. Gross, *J. Chem. Phys.*, **3**. 452 (1935).
[4] H .L. Johnston and E. A. Long, *J. Chem. Phys.*, **2**, 389, 710 (1934).
[5] W. H. Hamill, *J. Am. Chem. Soc.*, **59**, 1494 (1937).
[6] W. M. Jones, *J. Chem. Phys.*, **16**, 1077 (1948).

CHAPTER 4

Oxygen

Oxygen has six valence electrons, and in the monatomic gas atoms the lowest electronic state is $s^2p^4(^3P_2)$. Because of the importance of oxygen in the chemistry of water solutions, its potentials and free energies will be considered in advance of the other members of the group.

The standard thermodynamic state of the element is the gas O_2. The element also exists as the gaseous molecule, O_3, ozone. At low temperatures the modification O_4 appears to be formed.[1]

The isotopes 17 and 18 are present in small amounts in all oxygen; however, these differ from oxygen 16 by such small energies that for all ordinary thermodynamics their presence may be ignored.

Oxidation states. In water, and all true oxides and their compounds, oxygen has the oxidation number of -2. The oxidation state in hydrogen peroxide and its salts and the peroxide oxygen of the peroxyacids is -1. This same state should be assigned to the oxygen in free hydroxyl, OH, which does not exist in appreciable concentrations but which does appear to be formed as an intermediate step in a number of reactions. In the compound HO_2 and its derivatives, as KO_2, the oxygen has an average oxidation number of $-\frac{1}{2}$, which might be interpreted as one oxide oxygen and one $+1$ oxygen. Because of the highly electronegative character of fluorine, the oxygen fluoride, OF_2, may logically be considered as having oxygen in the $+2$ state, and there is some evidence of the existence of the corresponding acid H_2O_3.

The water-oxygen couple. Probably the best value for the free energy of formation of liquid water is that calculated from the third law, using heat of formation, -68.317 kcal., and the entropy of

---

[1] G. N. Lewis, *J. Am. Chem. Soc.*, **46**, 2027 (1924).

Table 11

THERMODYNAMIC DATA ON OXYGEN[1]

(Heat and free energy of formation in kcal. Entropy of substance in cal./deg.)

Formula	Description	State	$\Delta H°$	$\Delta F°$	$S°$
O	$(^3P_2)$	g	59.159	54.994	38.469
O	$(^3P_1)$	g	59.612		
O	$(^3P_0)$	g	59.806		
O$^+$	$(^4S_{3/2})$	g	374.608		
O^{++}	$(^3P_0)$	g	1186.619		
O$^-$		g	−13.12		
O$_2$		g	0.0	0.0	49.003
O$_2$		aq	−3.8		
O$_3$		g	34.0	39.06	56.8
O$_3$		aq	32.2		
O$_4$		g	−0.16		
OH		g	10.06	8.93	43.888
OH		aq		8.53	
OH$^-$		g	−76.4		
OH$^-$		aq	−54.957	−37.595	−2.52
H$_2$O		g	−57.798	−54.635	45.106
H$_2$O		liq	−68.317	−56.690	16.716
H$_2$O$_2$		g	−31.83		
H$_2$O$_2$		liq	−44.84	−27.240	(22)
H$_2$O$_2$		aq	−45.68	−31.470	
HO$_2^-$		aq		−15.610	
HO$_2$		aq		+3.0	
O$_2^-$		aq		+13.0	
D$_2$O		g	−59.563	−56.067	47.379
D$_2$O		liq	−70.413	−58.206	18.162
HDO		g	−58.735	−55.828	47.66
HDO		liq	−69.393	−57.925	18.95

[1] Bureau of Standards values in *italics;* estimated values in parentheses.

formation, −39.0 cal./degree. This gives

$$\tfrac{1}{2}O_2 + H_2 = H_2O, \qquad \Delta F° = -56{,}690 \text{ cal.}$$

From the free energy of vaporization 2055 cal., the free energy of $H_2O(g)$ at 25° C. is −54.635 kcal. One then calculates for the oxygen couple in acid solution,

$$2H_2O = O_2 + 4H^+ + 4e^-, \qquad E° = -1.229;$$

in alkaline solution,

$$4OH^- = O_2 + 2H_2O + 4e^-, \qquad E°_B = -0.401;$$

and in pure water,

$$2H_2O = O_2 + 4H^+ (10^{-7}M) + 4e^-, \qquad E = -0.815.$$

From the free energy of ionization of water, the free energy of formation of OH^- is -37.595 kcal.

These potentials have the same importance in reference to the stability of oxidizing agents in water solution that those for hydrogen have to the stability of reducing agents (see Chap. 3). Thus, the oxidized form of any couple with a higher negative potential than oxygen, at a given concentration of hydrogen ion, should liberate oxygen from the solution. For example, this is true for the manganous-permanganate couple:

$$4H_2O + Mn^{++} = MnO_4^- + 8H^+ + 5e^-, \qquad E^\circ = -1.52,$$

and hence permanganate is unstable in acid solution with respect to oxidation of the water to oxygen. However, the oxygen couple is

TABLE 12

OXYGEN OVERVOLTAGES IN VOLTS FOR VARIOUS ANODES
IN $1M$ KOH

(Current density in amperes per square centimeter)

Anode	0.01	0.1	1.0
Graphite	0.52	1.09	1.24
Au	0.67	1.24	1.68
Cu	0.42	0.66	0.84
Ag	0.58	0.98	1.14
Pt (smooth)	0.72	1.28	1.38
Pt (black)	0.40	0.64	0.79
Ni	0.35	0.73	0.87

highly irreversible and in general it is impossible to obtain experimental equilibrium involving the couple. For the discussion of the so-called "oxygen electrode" see the hydrogen peroxide-oxygen couple. As a result of this irreversibility high overvoltages are required for the liberation of oxygen from water. In Table 12 there are given values of the overvoltages required for the anodic oxidation of water on various electrode surfaces.

These potentials are not very reproducible, and for the more electropositive metals in the list they are attainable only because the metal surface becomes coated with an oxide layer which renders it passive; otherwise the metals would be oxidized instead of the water, since their oxidation potentials are smaller. In acid solutions it is impossible, because of the high potential required, to measure oxygen overvoltage except for the very noble metals. For smooth platinum the acid values are about the same as in the alkaline, being 0.45 volt for the formation of the first oxygen bubbles.

A number of theories have been advanced in explanation of the oxygen overvoltage and the mechanism of the oxidation of water or hydroxide, but definite experimental proof is lacking for the support of any one view.

The assumption is frequently made that the first and rate-determining step is

$$OH^- = OH + e^-,$$

or in acid solution,

$$H_2O = OH + H^+ + e^-.$$

However, the potentials of these reactions are so large (see hydroxyl) that, even with the high overvoltage, the concentration of OH must be very small. Glasstone and Hickling[1] believe that the second reaction,

$$2OH = H_2O_2,$$

occurs and O_2 is formed by the catalytic decomposition of the hydrogen peroxide. However, there is but little experimental proof of the formation of the peroxide at an electrode. Walker and Weiss[2] supposed that the second reaction is

$$2OH = H_2O + O,$$

followed by the formation of molecular oxygen.

The author believes that an equally plausible mechanism is the preliminary oxidation of the anode metal to some surface oxide or hydroxide, which then reacts as indicated by the following hypothetical equation:

$$XO_2 + OH^- = XOH + O_2 + e^-;$$

---

[1] S. Glasstone and A. Hickling, *Trans. Faraday Soc.*, **31**, 1656 (1935).
[2] O. J. Walker and J. Weiss, *Trans. Faraday Soc.*, **31**, 1011 (1935).

or if peroxide is an intermediate product, a reaction such as

$$X(OH)_2 + OH^- = XOH + H_2O_2 + e^-$$

follows.

Probably no one mechanism can be given to include all types of electrodes and electrolytes. The latter is certainly important, as the oxidation of the negative ion doubtless enters into the mechanism in a number of cases (see also mechanism of hydrogen overvoltage).

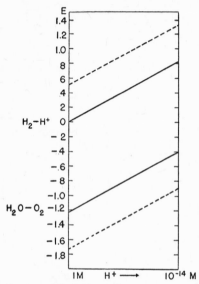

FIG. 3. Region of Stability of Oxidizing and Reducing
Agents in Aqueous Solutions.

Noyes and his co-workers[1] give support to the peroxide theory. They found in their study of the oxidation of water by $+2$ silver in acid solutions that their rate law was best explained by the assumption that the formation of peroxide was the rate-determining process.

Since any oxidizing agent, in a couple more negative than -1.229 in $1M$ acid solution, or -0.401 in $1M$ hydroxide solution, should liberate oxygen, and since any reducing agent in a couple whose potential is more positive than 0.0 in $1M$ acid or more positive than 0.828 in $1M$ hydroxide should liberate hydrogen, we can define the

[1] A. A. Noyes, C. D. Coryell, F. Stitt and A. Kossiakoff, *J. Am. Chem. Soc.,* **59**, 1316 (1937).

region of stability of oxidizing and reducing agents in water solutions as the area between the full lines in Figure 3. Because of the overvoltages for the evolution of H_2 and O_2 this area is extended in general to that bounded by the dotted lines.

The water-oxygen atom couple. From the free energy of atomic oxygen (54.994 kcal.) and the free energy of water, one calculates for the reduction of the atom to water in acid and alkaline solutions

$$H_2O = O(g) + 2H^+ + 2e^-, \qquad E° = -2.42;$$
$$2OH^- = O(g) + H_2O + 2e^-, \qquad E_B° = -1.59.$$

The high negative value for the potential indicates the difficulty in the oxidation of water with the formation of atomic oxygen as an intermediate step.

The peroxide-oxygen couple. However meager the evidence may be for the oxidation of water to peroxide, there is abundant proof that oxygen in the presence of hydrogen ion is generally, if not always, reduced to hydrogen peroxide. With one-electron reducing agents, HO_2 is an intermediate. The one-electron steps in the reduction of O_2 to $2H_2O$ in acid solution are indicated in the following structures:

$$
\begin{array}{ccccc}
& & & \overset{..}{H:O:H} & \overset{..}{H:O:H} \\
\overset{..\,..}{:O:O:} & \overset{..\,..}{:O:O:} & \overset{..\,..}{H:O:O:H} & & \\
\cdot\quad\cdot & \overset{..}{H}\;\cdot & \overset{..\,..}{} & \overset{..}{:O:H} & \overset{..}{H:O:H} \\
\text{(oxygen)} & \text{(perhydroxyl)} & \text{(hydrogen} & \text{(water and} & \text{(two} \\
& & \text{peroxide)} & \text{hydroxyl)} & \text{waters)}
\end{array}
$$

Lewis and Randall[1] give for the free energy of $H_2O_2(aq)$, $-31,470$ cal., and for HO_2^-, $-15,610$ cal.

$$H_2O_2 = H^+ + HO_2^-, \qquad K = 2.4 \times 10^{-12}.$$

From these values one calculates for the reduction of oxygen to peroxide in acid and alkali,

$$H_2O_2 = O_2 + 2H^+ + 2e^-, \qquad E° = -0.682;$$
$$OH^- + HO_2^- = O_2 + H_2O + 2e^-, \qquad E_B° = 0.076.$$

---

[1] G. N. Lewis and M. Randall, *Thermodynamics*, New York: McGraw-Hill Book Company, Inc., 1923, p. 487.

Although many of the experimental attempts to determine the reversible potential of the oxygen electrode appear to have measured merely the potential of the platinum-platinum oxide couple, which is in the neighborhood of one volt, Bornemann[1] has shown that it is possible to obtain a value for the reversible potential of the H_2O_2—O_2 couple by cell measurements. He reported -0.66 ± 0.03 volt for $E°$ in acid solution, which is in agreement with the value given above. The ability to determine this couple in the presence of the H_2O—H_2O_2 couple, with its much higher potential, $E° = -1.77$, shows that the activation energy of the oxygen molecule must be quite low.

The above potentials account for the slowness of many direct oxidations by O_2. If the reaction must go through peroxide, the low potential of this reaction makes it the rate-determining step. Thus, for example, in the oxidation of ferrous ion in acid solution,

$$Fe^{++} = Fe^{+++} + e^-, \qquad E° = -0.77,$$

the couple O_2—H_2O with a voltage of 1.23 has sufficient energy to effect the oxidation of the ferrous ion; but if the initial step is O_2—H_2O_2 with a voltage of 0.68, the oxidation can proceed only slowly.

It is also apparent from these potentials that strong oxidizing agents will oxidize hydrogen peroxide to oxygen. However, the potential of the H_2O_2—H_2O couple is itself so high (see below) that it can generally oxidize the reduced form of the other oxidizing agent, so that the net result is simply the catalytic decomposition of the hydrogen peroxide.[2]

EXAMPLE

$$Br_2 + H_2O_2 = 2H^+ + 2Br^- + O_2$$
$$\frac{H_2O_2 + 2Br^- + 2H^+ = Br_2 + 2H_2O}{2H_2O_2 = O_2 + 2H_2O}$$

In a few cases, however, the peroxide can be oxidized quantitatively, as, for example, by permanganate.

The water-peroxide couple. From free energy data for peroxide given above, one calculates for the water-hydrogen peroxide couple

---

[1] K. Bornemann, *Nernst Festschrift*, Halle: Knapp, 1912, p. 118.

[2] W. C. Bray and R. S. Livingston, *J. Am. Chem. Soc.*, *58*, 1244 (1926).

in acid solution:

$$2H_2O = H_2O_2 + 2H^+ + 2e^-, \qquad E^\circ = -1.77.$$

In alkaline solution this becomes

$$3OH^- = HO_2^- + H_2O + 2e^-, \qquad E_B^\circ = -0.88.$$

These high negative values place peroxide in the group of the most powerful oxidizing agents in both acid and alkaline solution. It is, of course, unstable in respect to the oxidation of water, but more important is its instability in respect to its own oxidation and reduction. In acid solution,

$$2H_2O_2(aq) = 2H_2O + O_2, \qquad \Delta F^\circ = -50.44 \text{ kcal.},$$

and in alkaline solution,

$$2HO_2^- = 2OH^- + O_2, \qquad \Delta F^\circ = -43.97 \text{ kcal.}$$

The reaction rates are slow but are catalyzed by many substances which are constituents of couples with potentials lying between the oxidation and reduction potentials of peroxide as indicated in the bromide–bromine example given above. Catalysis is also effected by many solids and enzymes.

The free energy of solid peroxides. Most of the more electropositive metals form true peroxides. The third law may be employed to calculate their free energies. The following values for ΔF° (kcal.) are given in the tabulations in the various chapters: CaO_2, -143; SrO_2, -139.0; BaO_2, -135.8; Li_2O_2, -135; Na_2O_2, -102.8: K_2O_2, -100.1.

These free energies determine the potentials of the oxides as oxidizing and reducing agents. Although these couples are not thermodynamically reversible since the unhydrated oxides do not exist in equilibrium with water, they are of interest for the purpose of comparing the energies of the oxides. The hydroxide-peroxide potentials in alkaline solution are summarized below:

$$4OH^- + nM^{2+/n} = M_nO_2 + 2H_2O + 2e^-.$$

$E_B^\circ:$ Ca, -0.60;   Sr, -0.67;   Ba, -0.71;

         Li, -0.85;   Na, -1.23.

These potentials differ from the -0.88 value for the OH^-—HO_2^-

couple by the free energy of the hydrolysis of the O_2^{--} ion and by the free energy of solution of the peroxide. The first of these is quite large since the second dissociation constant of H_2O_2 must be around 10^{-25}, and it is a constant factor. The increasing oxidizing power in the series CaO_2 to Na_2O is due then to the increasing solubility of the peroxides, which is obviously in the same order as the basicity of the hydroxides.

The water, oxygen-ozone couple. The action of ozone as an oxidizing agent is unusual in that ordinarily only one of the oxygens is reduced, the other two atoms forming molecular oxygen. From the free energy of ozone and water given above,

$$O_2 + H_2O = O_3 + 2H^+ + 2e^-, \qquad E° = -2.07.$$

In alkaline solution this becomes

$$O_2 + 2OH^- = O_3 + H_2O + 2e^-, \qquad E_B^o = -1.24.$$

These high values place ozone next to fluorine in the list of powerful oxidizing agents, with the exception, of course, of a few substances, like atomic oxygen, which do not exist in appreciable concentrations at room temperature. It is unstable with respect to the decomposition into oxygen, and the catalysis of this reaction in water is a subject of considerable controversy. Many of the points involved are discussed in the following paragraphs.

Couples involving perhydroxyl.[1] It is logically assumed in the kinetics of oxygen reactions that the addition of atomic hydrogen to the oxygen molecule or the removal of one electron from the molecule in acid solution results in the formation of perhydroxyl, HO_2. The compound KO_2 (formerly considered K_2O_4)[2] is, of course, the potassium salt of perhydroxyl, and there is considerable evidence of the formation of the ion O_2^- when ozone is passed into concentrated alkali solution;[3] but the comparative stability of ozone in acid solution indicates that the free energy is unfavorable for the reaction in the presence of hydrogen ion. On this basis the free energies of formation of HO_2 and O_2^- have been estimated as 3000 and 13,000 cals., respec-

---

[1] No name has been adopted by general usage for the compound HO_2. The author proposes to call it *perhydroxyl*, that is, two oxygens in place of the one in hydroxyl.

[2] E. W. Neuman, *J. Chem. Phys.*, **2**, 31 (1934).

[3] J. Weiss, *Trans. Faraday Soc.*, **31**, 668 (1935).

tively; the difference of 10,000 cal. is an estimated free energy of ionization of HO_2. These values then give

$$O_3 + H_2O = 2HO_2, \qquad \Delta F^\circ = 23.3 \text{ kcal.};$$

$$O_3 + 2OH^- = 2O_2^- + H_2O, \qquad \Delta F^\circ = 5.1 \text{ kcal.}$$

Using these free energies of formation with that of hydrogen peroxide, the perhydroxyl-hydrogen peroxide couples then are

$$H_2O_2 = HO_2 + H^+ + e^-, \qquad E^\circ = -1.5;$$

$$OH^- + HO_2^- = O_2^- + H_2O + e^-, \qquad E_B^\circ = -0.4.$$

These potentials lie between the values calculated from the energies of the reactions by Weiss[1] and the earlier work by Haber and Weiss.[2] They can hardly be more negative and still have the $F_{O_2}^\circ$ small enough to give an appreciable concentration of O_2^- by the action of ozone on concentrated hydroxide, but they might be as high as -1.3 and -0.2.

Perhydroxyl is unstable in acid with respect to the decomposition into ozone and water, $\Delta F^\circ = -23.3$ kcal., as given above, but it is also unstable with respect to the decomposition into hydrogen peroxide and oxygen:

$$2HO_2 = H_2O_2 + O_2, \qquad \Delta F^\circ = -37.5 \text{ kcal.}$$

This is the more probable of the two decompositions, and experimentally KO_2 rapidly gives a practically quantitative yield of these products when treated with acid, although a trace of ozone may be formed. Since hydrogen peroxide is a rapid catalyst for the decomposition of ozone into oxygen, these facts rule out the possibility of the formation of any appreciable concentration of HO_2 by the action of ozone on water in acid, although the reaction may be one of the steps in the decomposition of ozone.

The free energy is favorable for the oxidation of water to perhydroxyl by ozone through the reaction

$$3O_3 + H_2O = 2HO_2 + 3O_2, \qquad \Delta F^\circ = -55.5 \text{ kcal.}$$

However, the reaction mechanism involving three ozone molecules might easily lead to a very slow reaction rate. The free energy is also

[1] Ibid.
[2] F. Haber and J. Weiss, Proc. Roy. Soc., A147, 332 (1934).

favorable for the oxidation of hydrogen peroxide to perhydroxyl by ozone:

$$O_3 + 2H_2O_2 = 2HO_2 + H_2O + O_2, \qquad \Delta F° = -27.1 \text{ kcal.}$$

The half-reactions for the reduction of perhydroxyl to water and hydroxide are

$$2H_2O = HO_2 + 3H^+ + 3e^-, \qquad E° = -1.7;$$

$$4OH^- = O_2^- + 2H_2O + 3e^-, \qquad E_B° = -0.7;$$

and for the perhydroxyl–oxygen couples

$$HO_2 = O_2 + H^+ + e^-, \qquad E° = 0.13;$$

$$O_2^- = O_2 + e^-, \qquad E_B° = 0.56.$$

Although hydrogen peroxide ordinarily decomposes into water and oxygen, the free energy is favorable for the reaction to water and perhydroxyl, and there is evidence for the formation of $Ca(O_2)_2$ by the action of H_2O_2 on CaO_2.

Couples involving hydroxyl. There is evidence of the existence of free hydroxyl, OH, in gaseous reactions involving hydrogen and oxygen and their compounds, and it is frequently assumed as an intermediate step in the oxidation of water. Using the value of Hickling and Hill[1] for the free energy of OH(g), 8.53 kcal., and assuming that the free energy of solution is small, we write

$$H_2O = OH + H^+ + e^-, \qquad E° = -2.8;$$

$$OH^- = OH + e^-, \qquad E_B° = -2.0;$$

$$OH + H_2O = H_2O_2 + H^+ + e^-, \qquad E° = -0.72;$$

$$OH + 2OH^- = HO_2^- + H_2O + e^-, \qquad E_B° = 0.24.$$

Two hydroxyls might react to form either hydrogen peroxide or water and atomic oxygen:

$$2OH = H_2O_2, \qquad \Delta F° = -48.7 \text{ kcal.};$$

$$2OH = H_2O + O, \qquad \Delta F° = -18.8 \text{ kcal.}$$

There is no evidence with respect to the rates of either of these reactions.

---

[1] A. Hickling and S. Hill, *Trans. Faraday Soc.*, **46**, 557 (1950).

The free energy of the oxidation of water to hydroxyl by ozone is unfavorable:

$$O_3 + H_2O = 2OH + O_2, \qquad \Delta F° = 34.8 \text{ kcal.}$$

However, the following reaction is possible:

$$2O_3 + H_2O = OH + HO_2 + 2O_2, \qquad \Delta F° = -10 \text{ kcal.}$$

and Alder and Hill[1] in their study of the kinetics of the decomposition of ozone catalyzed by hydroxide suggested a mechanism which included this reaction. They postulated

$$O_3 + H_2O \rightarrow HO_3^+ + OH^-, \tag{1}$$

$$HO_3^+ + OH^- \rightleftarrows 2HO_2, \tag{2}$$

$$O_3 + HO_2 \rightarrow HO + 2O_2, \tag{3}$$

$$HO + HO_2 \rightarrow H_2O + O_2. \tag{4}$$

They assumed that the rate of disappearance of ozone is determined by (1) and (3); that (2) represents an equilibrium which is maintained as long as there is any ozone in the system; and that reaction (4) is the chain-breaking step.

Taube and Bray[2] in their work on the reaction between ozone and hydrogen peroxide found two net reactions,

$$H_2O_2 + O_3 = H_2O + 2O_2 \tag{A}$$

$$2O_3 = 3O_2, \tag{B}$$

and suggested, to account for their observed reaction rates, the following mechanism:

$$H_2O_2 + O_3 \rightarrow HO + HO_2 + O_2, \tag{1}$$

$$HO_2 + O_3 \rightarrow HO + 2O_2, \tag{2}$$

$$HO + O_3 \rightarrow HO_2 + O_2, \tag{3}$$

$$HO + H_2O_2 \rightarrow HO_2 + H_2O. \tag{4}$$

Reaction (1) is the chain-initiating step. Its actual free-energy decrease will be large since the steady state concentrations of HO and HO_2 will be very small. The net result of (2) and (3) is reaction (B). Similarly (2) and (4) constitute a chain process for reaction (A).

[1] M. G. Alder and G. R. Hill, *J. Am. Chem. Soc.*, **72**, 1884 (1950).
[2] H. Taube and W. C. Bray, *J. Am. Chem. Soc.*, **62**, 3357 (1940).

It is possible that HO and HO$_2$ can form H$_2$O$_3$.[1]

As additional proof of the existence of H$_2$O$_3$ reference should be made to the preparation of K$_2$O$_3$ by Kraus and Whyte.[2]

Oxygen potential diagrams.   As a summary of the oxygen potentials the following diagrams are given.

Acid Solution.

-1.229

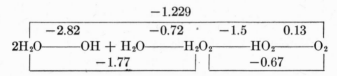

Basic Solution.

$$\begin{array}{ccccc} & -2.0 & & 0.24 & -0.41 & 0.56 \\ 2\text{OH}^- & \!\!\!\!\text{---}\!\!\!\! & \text{OH} + \text{OH}^- & \!\!\!\!\text{---}\!\!\!\! & \text{HO}_2^- \!\!\!\text{---}\!\!\!\text{O}_2^- \!\!\!\text{---}\!\!\!\text{O}_2 \end{array}$$

$$\underline{\quad\quad -0.87 \quad\quad} \quad \underline{\quad 0.08 \quad}$$

Acid Solution.

$$\begin{array}{ccc} & -2.8 & -1.34 \\ \text{H}_2\text{O} + \text{O}_2 & \!\!\!\text{---}\!\!\! \text{HO} + \text{O}_2 \!\!\!\text{---}\!\!\! \text{O}_3 \end{array}$$

$$\underline{\quad\quad\quad -2.07 \quad\quad\quad}$$

$$\begin{array}{cc} -0.89 & 0.13 \\ \text{O}_3 + \text{H}_2\text{O} \!\!\!\text{---}\!\!\! \text{HO}_2 + \text{O}_2 \!\!\!\text{---}\!\!\! 2\text{O}_2 \end{array}$$

$$\underline{\quad\quad\quad -0.38 \quad\quad\quad}$$

[1] W. C. Bray, *J. Am. Chem. Soc.*, **60**, 82 (1938).

[2] C. A. Kraus and E. F. Whyte, *J. Am. Chem. Soc.*, **48**, 1788 (1926).

CHAPTER 5

The Halogens

The members of the halogen family have seven valence electrons, and in the monatomic gas atoms the electronic state is $s^2p^5(^2P_{3/2})$. The outer shell of the kernel contains the following electrons: fluorine, $1s^2$, chlorine, $2s^2$, $2p^6$; bromine, $3s^2$, $3p^6$, $3d^{10}$; and iodine, $4s^2$, $4p^6$, $4d^{10}$. The principal oxidation states are -1, $+1$, $+3$, $+5$, and $+7$, the lowest energy being that of the -1 state. In this sense the halogens as a group are the most electronegative of all the elements. Not only the free elements but the oxygen acids and their salts are powerful oxidizing agents with respect to their reduction to the halide (-1 state). The -1 ion has the same electron structure as the following noble gas, and the tendency to form this ion may be correlated with the stability of this electronic structure.

FLUORINE

Oxidation states. The only oxidation state stable in water solutions is the -1. The oxides, F_2O and F_2O_2, have been prepared, but because of the highly electronegative character of both fluorine and oxygen it is meaningless to attempt to assign a polar number to fluorine in these compounds. However, the oxides are powerful oxidizing agents and the potential for the reduction of the monoxide may be calculated.

The fluoride-fluorine couple. From the free energies given by the Bureau of Standards, we write

$$2F^- = F_2 + 2e^-, \qquad E° = -2.87.$$

This is in approximate agreement with the value given by Latimer.[1]

Broene and DeVries[2] have found for the equilibria in hydrogen

---

[1] W. M. Latimer, *J. Am. Chem. Soc.*, **48**, 2868 (1926).
[2] H. H. Broene and T. DeVries, *J. Am. Chem. Soc.*, **69**, 1644 (1947).

fluoride solution,

$$HF = H^+ + F^-, \qquad K = 6.71 \times 10^{-4};$$
$$F^- + HF = HF_2^-, \qquad K = 3.86.$$

From these constants we calculate for the free energy of HF, −70.41 kcal., and for HF_2^-, −137.3 kcal., and

$$2HF(aq) = F_2 + 2H^+ + 2e^-, \qquad E^\circ = -3.06.$$

It should be noted that the free energy of HF is given for the undissociated molecule and, in an actual solution, the total free energy of

TABLE 13

THERMODYNAMIC DATA ON FLUORINE[1]

(Heat and free energy of formation in kcal. Entropy of substance in cal./deg.)

Formula	Description	State	ΔH°	ΔF°	S°
F	$(^2P_{3/2})$	g	*32.25*	*28.19*	*37.917*
F	$(^2P_{1/2})$	g	*33.41*		
F$^+$	$(^3P_2)$	g	*435.50*		
F^{++}	$(^4S_{3/2})$	g	*1243.62*		
F$^-$		g	*−65.5*		
F$^-$		aq	*−78.66*	*−66.08*	*−2.3*
F$_2$		g	0.0	0.0	*48.6*
F$_2$O		g	5.5	9.7	*58.95*
HF		g	*−64.2*	*−64.7*	*41.47*
HF		aq	*−78.66*	−70.41	26.
HF$_2^-$		aq	*−153.6*	−137.5	0.5
H$_6$F$_6$		g	*−426.0*		

[1] Bureau of Standards values in *italics*.

the HF solution is the sum of the free energies of the undissociated molecules and the fluoride ions. The potential in acid solution is the highest for any oxidizing agent which can be prepared in appreciable concentrations and is so high that fluorine decomposes water with the evolution of oxygen.

The fluorine-oxide potential. From the free energy of the oxide F$_2$O, we may write

$$H_2O + 2F^- = F_2O + 2H^+ + 4e^-, \qquad E^\circ = -2.1.$$

A potential may also be calculated for the reduction to fluoride ion and free oxygen:

$$2F^- + \tfrac{1}{2}O_2 = F_2O + 2e^-, \qquad E^\circ = -3.1.$$

The potential of this reaction is even higher than that for fluorine but it doubtless is impossible of experimental realization, since the first step is the formation of atomic oxygen while much of the energy comes from the union of oxygen atoms to form the O_2 molecule. This would give a potential barrier which would render the reaction rate very slow.

CHLORINE

Oxidation states. Chlorine has an oxidation number of -1 in hydrochloric acid and its salts; $+1$ in the oxide, Cl_2O, in its acid, hypochlorous acid, HClO, and its salts; $+3$ in chlorous acid, $HClO_2$, and its salts; $+4$ in the dioxide, ClO_2; $+5$ in chloric acid, $HClO_3$, and derivatives; and $+7$ in the oxide, Cl_2O_7, in perchloric acid, $HClO_4$, and the perchlorates. The oxide, ClO, is described, but its chemistry is so uncertain that it has not been included in the calculation of potential values.

The chloride-chlorine couple. The best value for the potential for the Cl^-—Cl_2 couple is probably that obtained from the cell measurements of this electrode against the AgCl—Ag electrode. Randall and Young[1] give -1.3583 for the Cl—Cl_2 couple. From the Bureau of Standards free energy, we write

$$2Cl^- = Cl_2 + 2e^-, \qquad E^\circ = -1.3595.$$

Because of the "hydrolysis" of chlorine and the formation of hypochlorite, the potential becomes meaningless in alkaline solutions. The couple is reversible and chlorine is a fairly rapid oxidizing agent, very much faster than oxygen, for example. Because of the mechanism of formation of the Cl_2 molecule by oxidation of the Cl^-, overvoltages must exist (cf. overvoltage of hydrogen and oxygen), and Knobel[2] gives the values at 100 milliamperes per square centimeter of 0.026 volt for platinized platinum and 0.054 for smooth platinum. The problem is complicated by the fact that the oxidation potential of water is lower than that of chloride; hence, were it not for the high oxygen overvoltage, no chlorine would be evolved by the electrolysis of chloride solutions at low current densities. In other words, the chlorine overvoltages must always be measured on an electrode which is polarized with respect to oxygen. The mechanism is doubtless

[1] M. Randall and L. E. Young, *J. Am. Chem. Soc.*, **50**, 989 (1928).
[2] M. Knobel, *International Critical Tables*, **VI**, 340.

TABLE 14

THERMODYNAMIC DATA ON CHLORINE[1]

(Heat and free energy of formation in kcal. Entropy of substance in cal./deg.)

Formula	Description	State	$\Delta H°$	$\Delta F°$	$S°$
Cl		g	*29.012*	*25.192*	*39.457*
Cl$^+$		g	*329.349*		
Cl^{++}		g	*879.66*		
Cl$^-$		g	*−58.3*		
Cl$^-$		aq	*−40.023*	*−31.350*	*13.2*
Cl$_2$		g	*00.0*	0.0	*53.286*
Cl$_2$	sat. sol.	aq	*−6.0*		
Cl$_2$		aq		1.65	
ClO		g	*33*		
ClO$^-$		aq		−8.9	10.0
ClO$_2$		g	*24.7*	*29.5*	*59.6*
ClO$_2$		aq	*19.7*		
ClO$_2^-$		aq	−17.18	2.74	24.1
ClO$_3$		g	*37.0*		
ClO$_3^-$		aq	*−23.50*	−0.62	*39*
ClO$_4^-$		aq	*−31.41*	*−2.47*	*43.2*
Cl$_2$O		g	*18.20*	*22.40*	*63.70*
Cl$_2$O	400 H$_2$O	aq	*11.97*		
Cl$_2$O$_7$		g	*63.4*		
HCl		g	*−22.063*	*−22.769*	*44.617*
HCl		aq	*−40.023*	*−31.350*	*13.2*
HClO		aq	*−27.83*	*−19.110*	31
HClO$_2$		aq	−13.68	0.07	42
HClO$_3$		aq	*−23.50*	*−0.62*	*39.0*
HClO$_4$		aq	*−31.41*	*−2.47*	*43.2*
H$_3$OClO$_4$		c	*−92.1*		(41)
ClF		g	*−25.7*		

[1] Bureau of Standards values in *italics;* estimated values in parentheses.

complex and may involve the formation of hypochlorite surface compounds which react with chloride to give chlorine. The ratio of oxygen to chlorine evolution is also influenced by the presence of positive ions, for example, Mn^{++}, which catalyze one or another of the oxidations.

The chloride-hypochlorite couple. From the hydrolysis of chlorine[1] (disproportionation)

$$Cl_2(aq) + H_2O = H^+ + Cl^- + HClO, \qquad K = 4.66 \times 10^{-4},$$

one calculates the free energy of hypochlorous acid to be −19.11 kcal.

[1] *International Critical Tables,* **VII,** 234.

Skrabal[1] gave 3.6×10^{-8} for the dissociation constant, and Hagisawa[2] reported 2.98×10^{-8}.

We shall write

$$HClO = H^+ + ClO^-, \qquad K = 3.2 \times 10^{-8},$$
$$\Delta F^\circ = 10.2 \, kcal.;$$
$$Cl^- + 2OH^- = ClO^- + H_2O + 2e^-, \qquad E_B^\circ = -0.89;$$
$$\tfrac{1}{2}Cl_2 + H_2O = HClO + H^+ + e^-, \qquad E^\circ = -1.63;$$
$$Cl^- + H_2O = HClO + H^+ + 2e^-, \qquad E^\circ = -1.49.$$

The last couple in acid solution has little chemical significance, since chloride and hypochlorous acid react to give chlorine

$$HClO + Cl^- + H^+ = Cl_2(g) + H_2O, \qquad \Delta F^\circ = -6.2 \, kcal.$$

The oxide, Cl_2O, is the anhydride of hypochlorous acid and the reaction with water is reversible. Yost and Felt[3] report that

$$2HClO = Cl_2O(g) + H_2O, \qquad K = 3.54 \times 10^{-3}.$$

From our free energies the value of the constant is 7.4×10^{-3}.

The hypochlorite-chlorite couple. The free energies of $HClO_2$ and ClO^- given in Table 14 are a recalculation of the values of Fontana and Latimer.[4] These values give

$$HClO_2 = H^+ + ClO_2^-, \qquad K = 1.1 \times 10^{-2};$$
$$HClO + H_2O = HClO_2 + 2H^+ + 2e^-, \qquad E^\circ = -1.64;$$
$$ClO^- + 2OH^- = ClO_2^- + H_2O + 2e^-, \qquad E_B^\circ = -0.66.$$

Chlorine dioxide, chlorate, and perchlorate. The free energy of chlorine dioxide is obtained from the heat of formation and the entropy of the gas as calculated by statistical spectroscopic methods. The free energies of chlorate and perchlorate are calculated from the heats of formation and the ionic entropies. The latter are in approximate agreement with the values given by Latimer, Pitzer, and Smith.[5] The free energy of chlorate, as determined by Olson[6] from equilibrium

---

[1] A. Skrabal, *Z. Electrochem.*, **48**, 448 (1942).

[2] H. Hagisawa, *Bull. Inst. Phys. Chem. Research Japan*, **19**, 1220 (1940).

[3] D. M. Yost and R. C. Felt, *J. Am. Chem. Soc.*, **56**, 68 (1934).

[4] B. J. Fontana and W. M. Latimer, *J. Am. Chem. Soc.*, **69**, 2598 (1947).

[5] W. M. Latimer, K. S. Pitzer and W. V. Smith, *J. Am. Chem. Soc.*, **60**, 1829 (1938).

[6] A. R. Olson, *J. Am. Chem. Soc.*, **42**, 896 (1920).

data, is -0.25 kcal. The potentials of the following important couples may be calculated from these free energies.

$$HClO_2 = ClO_2 + H^+ + e^-, \qquad E^\circ = -1.275;$$
$$ClO_2^- = ClO_2 + e^-, \qquad E_B^\circ = -1.16;$$
$$ClO_2 + H_2O = ClO_3^- + 2H^+ + e^-, \qquad E^\circ = -1.15;$$
$$ClO_2 + 2OH^- = ClO_3^- + H_2O + e^-, \qquad E_B^\circ = +0.50;$$
$$HClO_2 + H_2O = ClO_3^- + 3H^+ + 2e^-, \qquad E^\circ = -1.21;$$
$$ClO_2^- + 2OH^- = ClO_3^- + H_2O + 2e^-, \qquad E_B^\circ = -0.33;$$
$$ClO_{3]} + H_2O = ClO_4^- + 2H^+ + 2e^-, \qquad E^\circ = -1.19;$$
$$ClO_3^- + 2OH^- = ClO_4^- + H_2O + 2e^-, \qquad E_B^\circ = -0.36.$$

Perchlorate radical. From the work of Gomberg[1] silver perchlorate treated with bromine yields free perchlorate, ClO_4, in which one of the oxygens has doubtless lost an electron.

The bromide couple (see p. 60) in the presence of silver ion would have a potential of about -2 volts, i.e., it would be about 0.9 volt more negative than the E° bromine value because of the slight solubility of silver bromide. Hence, the potential of the perchlorate radical must be more positive than -2 volts.

The chlorine potentials diagrams. The following diagrams are given to summarize the chlorine potentials.

Acid Solution.

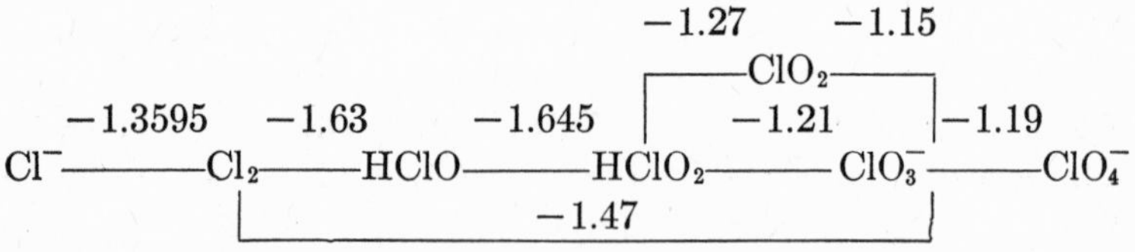

Basic Solution.

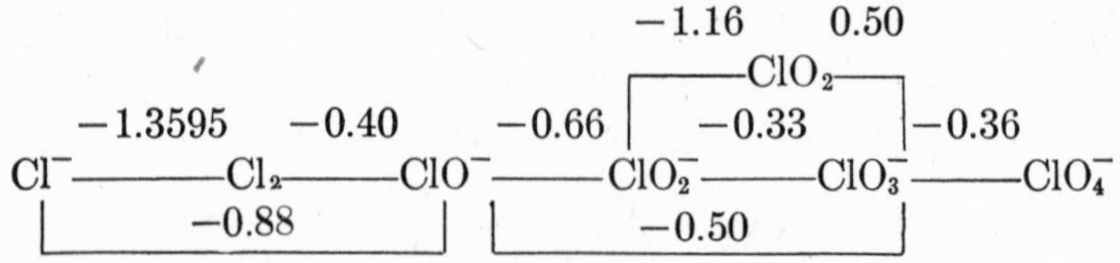

[1] M. Gomberg, *J. Am. Chem. Soc.*, **45**, 398 (1923).

Notes on the chlorine potentials. It will be observed that Cl_2 is stable in acid solution with respect to disproportionation, but the reaction does go to a measurable equilibrium. It is also unstable with respect to the evolution of oxygen, and chlorine solutions do slowly oxidize the water. Hypochlorous acid and chlorous acid are highly unstable with respect to both disproportionation and to oxygen evolution. Chloric acid has similar instabilities, but its reactions in dilute solution are very slow; even boiling a solution of chlorate in excess hydrochloric acid requires some time for the complete reduction. A hot solution is reduced fairly rapidly by ferrous ion. Chlorate is not readily reduced at a cathode upon electrolysis of chlorate solutions. It may also be noted that there is a decrease in potential of each step in going from $HClO$ to ClO_4^-. This fact is doubtless significant in the interpretation of the slowness of chlorate and perchlorate as oxidizing agents, as the lower potentials for the first step of the reduction act as a barrier to the net reaction. However, once the reaction starts, the evolution of heat may cause the reaction to go with explosive violence, and both chlorate and perchlorate reactions must be handled with extreme caution.

The following disproportionation reactions in alkaline solution are of importance.

$$Cl_2 + 2OH^- = Cl^- + ClO^- + H_2O, \qquad \Delta F^\circ = -22.0 \text{ kcal.};$$
$$3ClO^- = ClO_3^- + 2Cl^-, \qquad \Delta F^\circ = -36. \text{ kcal.};$$
$$4ClO_3^- = 3ClO_4^- + Cl^-, \qquad \Delta F^\circ = -34.3 \text{ kcal.};$$
$$2ClO_2 + 2OH^- = ClO^- + ClO_2^- + H_2O, \qquad \Delta F^\circ = -38.3 \text{ kcal.}$$

The first of these is the hydrolysis of chlorine, which is practically complete in alkaline solution but is reversed to a measurable equilibrium in acid solution. The preparation of chloride of lime and the release of chlorine by it when acidified is an example of this equilibrium.

The second reaction is important in the commercial preparation of chlorates. If hypochlorite is heated in the presence of a catalyst, such as cobalt hydroxide, oxygen is evolved. In the absence of a catalyst, chlorate is formed and the rate of the reaction is favored by the presence of both $HClO$ and ClO^-, that is, the reaction is slow in high concentrations of both acid and base. The reaction is not reversible.

The third reaction, the decomposition of chlorate to chloride and perchlorate, occurs if solid alkali chlorate is heated carefully in the absence of a catalyst for the decomposition into oxygen and chloride.

The last reaction goes readily in alkaline solution and the free energy would indicate that it should be reversed to give appreciable concentrations of chlorine dioxide in acid, but experimentally chlorine dioxide is not formed under these conditions.

The oxidation of chlorate to perchlorate requires a potential of only about one volt, but experimentally the most powerful oxidizing agents are required to bring it about. It may, however, be accomplished by anodic oxidation of alkali chlorates. The most favorable conditions are low temperature, neutral or slightly acid solution, and a smooth platinum electrode. In alkaline solution and on platinized platinum, oxygen is evolved, and the efficiency of the process is low. The oxidation is thus favored by the conditions for high oxygen overvoltage, but the influence of hydroxide upon the rate cannot be explained by reasoning based upon equilibrium data, as the potentials of oxygen and perchlorate are equally dependent upon hydrogen ion. It seems likely then that the rate-determining step is the oxidation of chlorate to free ClO_4, which would be independent of hydrogen ion and cannot occur in alkaline solution where the potential is more favorable for the oxidation of water. (See oxygen potential in alkali.)

Taube and Dodgen[1] have studied the mechanism of oxidation and reduction of the chlorine acids by using Cl^{38} as a tracer. They state: (a) In the reaction of chlorite with chlorine or hypochlorous acid to form chlorine dioxide or chlorate and chloride ion, most of the chlorine atoms in the chlorine dioxide or chlorate are derived from the chlorite. (b) In the reaction of chloride ion with chlorate in acid to produce chlorine or chlorine dioxide, the chlorine atoms in the chlorine dioxide are for the most part derived from the chlorate. (c) In the disproportionation of chlorite in acid catalyzed by chloride ion, the chlorine atoms in the chlorine dioxide are for the most part derived from the chlorite. In order to account for these facts they

---

[1] H. Taube and H. Dodgen, *J. Am. Chem. Soc.*, **71**, 3330 (1949).

postulated an unsymmetrical intermediate,

$$\text{Cl—Cl}\diagup^{\textstyle O}_{\diagdown\,\text{O}} \qquad \text{or} \qquad \text{Cl—O—Cl—O,}$$

common to all of the systems (a), (b), and (c).

BROMINE

Oxidation states. Bromine has compounds with the following oxidation numbers: -1, hydrobromic acid and its salts; $+1$, hypobromous acid; and $+5$, bromic acid and the bromates. Bromous acid,

TABLE 15

THERMODYNAMIC DATA ON BROMINE[1]

(Heat and free energy of formation in kcal. Entropy of substance in cal./deg.)

Formula	Description	State	$\Delta H°$	$\Delta F°$	$S°$
Br	$(^2P_{3/2})$	g	*26.71*	*19.69*	*41.8052*
Br$^+$		g	*301.32*		
Br^{++}		g	*800.52*		
Br$^-$		g	*−55.3*		
Br$^-$		aq	*−28.90*	*−24.574*	*19.29*
Br$_2$		g	*7.34*	*0.751*	*58.639*
Br$_2$		liq	*0.0*	*0.0*	*36.4*
Br$_2$		aq	*−1.1*	*0.977*	
Br$_3^-$		aq	*−32.0*	−25.27	*40.* (?)
BrO$^-$		aq		−8.0	
BrO$_3^-$		aq		(5.0)	38.5
HBr		g	*−8.66*	*−12.72*	*47.437*
HBrO		aq		−19.9	
HBrO$_2$		aq	*−11.63* (?)	(5.0)	
BrCl		g	*3.51*	*−0.210*	*57.34*

[1] Bureau of Standards values in *italics;* estimated values in parentheses.

$+3$, is doubtless formed as an intermediate step in various reactions, but it is too unstable to exist in appreciable concentrations. Perbromic acid or its salts, $+7$, are unknown. Evidence has been presented for the existence of the oxides Br_2O and BrO_2.[1]

[1] W. Brenschede and H. J. Schumacher, *Z. anorg. allgem. Chem.*, **226**, 370 (1936); R. Schwarz and M. Schmeisser, *Ber.*, **70B**, 1163 (1937).

The bromide-bromine couple. From cell measurements by Jones and Baeckstrom,[1]

$$2Br^- = Br_2(l) + 2e^-, \qquad E^\circ = -1.0652;$$

$$2Br^- = Br_2(aq) + 2e^-, \qquad E^\circ = -1.087.$$

The corresponding free energy of bromide ion, Br^-, is $-24,578$ cal., and this value is in agreement with the thermal data.

The couple is reversible and bromine is a comparatively rapid oxidizing agent. The overvoltage for the anodic oxidation of bromide is given by Knobel[2] as somewhat less than the values for chlorine.

At a concentration of $10^{-7}M$ H^+, bromine has a potential of 0.2 volt in favor of the oxidation of water, but the reaction is reversed in one molal acid. However, in low acid the reaction is not rapid, and bromine solutions in water are comparatively stable.

Bromine reacts with bromide to form the tribromide Br_3^-. From the work of Griffith, McKeown, and Winn,[3]

$$Br_2(aq) + Br^- = Br_3^-, \qquad K = 17.$$

Hence the free energy of formation of Br_3^- is $-25,270$ cal. and

$$3Br^- = Br_3^- + 2e^-, \qquad E^\circ = -1.05.$$

At high concentration the pentabromide appears to form, and Liebhafsky[4] calculates the constant for the dissociation of Br_5^- to be 0.055.

The bromide-hypobromite couple. Liebhafsky[5] has reviewed the data on the hydrolysis of bromine and gives

$$Br_2 + H_2O = HBrO + H^+ + Br^-, \qquad K = 5.8 \times 10^{-9}.$$

This leads to $-19,900$ cal. as the free energy of formation of HBrO.

---

[1] G. Jones and S. Baeckstrom, *J. Am. Chem. Soc.*, **56**, 1524 (1934); cf. also M. Randall, *International Critical Tables*, **VII**, 234.

[2] Knobel, *loc. cit.*, **VI**, 340.

[3] R. O. Griffith, A. McKeown and A. G. Winn, *Trans. Faraday Soc.*, **28**, 101 (1932).

[4] H. A. Liebhafsky, *J. Am. Chem. Soc.*, **56**, 1500 (1934).

[5] *Ibid.*

Shilov[1] reported that

$$HBrO = H^+ + BrO^-, \qquad K = 2.06 \times 10^{-9}.$$

This corresponds to -8000 cal. as the free energy of BrO^-. These values appear to be consistent with the heat of formation of hypobromous acid, $\Delta H^\circ = -25,200$ cal., given by Bichowsky and Rossini. The following potentials are calculated from the free energies:

$$H_2O + \tfrac{1}{2}Br_2 = HBrO + H^+ + e^-, \qquad E^\circ = -1.59;$$
$$2OH^- + Br^- = BrO^- + H_2O + 2e^-, \qquad E^\circ_B = -0.76.$$

Hypobromous acid cannot be prepared except at the very low concentrations given by the hydrolysis of bromine; and when alkali is added, the hypobromite ion decomposes almost instantly into bromide and bromate in the light but is more stable in the dark.

The bromide-bromate couple. Lewis and Randall calculate from the measurements of Sammet on[2] the bromine-bromate electrode that the free energy of formation of BrO_3^- is 2300 cal. The third-law value, calculated from the heat of formation, is -11.63 kcal., and the entropy of formation (69.1 cal./deg.), is 9.1 kcal. High accuracy cannot be claimed for either the heat of formation or the cell measurements. The value $\Delta F^\circ = 5000$ cal. will be chosen, and also the same value will be used for $HBrO_3$ since it is at least a moderately strong acid. Then,

$$3H_2O + \tfrac{1}{2}Br_2 = BrO_3^- + 6H^+ + 5e^-, \qquad E^\circ = -1.52;$$
$$6OH^- + Br^- = BrO_3^- + 3H_2O + 5e^-, \qquad E^\circ = -0.61.$$

Bromic acid is a faster oxidizing agent than chloric acid, and in high acid it will oxidize water to oxygen.

Bromine chloride as an oxidizing agent. The spectroscopic data for the entropy and heat of formation of bromine chloride lead to a value of -0.210 kcal. for the free energy.

$$Br^- + Cl^- = BrCl(g) + 2e^-, \qquad E^\circ = -1.2.$$

Potential diagrams for bromine oxidation states. The following diagrams are given as a summary of the potentials of the various bromine couples.

[1] E. A. Shilov, *J. Am. Chem. Soc.*, **60**, 490 (1938).
[2] V. Sammet, *Z. physik. Chem.*, **53**, 678 (1905).

Acid Solution.

$$\begin{array}{c}
-1.52 \\
-1.07 \; \overline{\begin{array}{ccc} -1.59 & & -1.49 \end{array}} \\
\text{Br}^- \!\!-\!\!-\!\!-\!\!-\text{Br}_2\!\!-\!\!-\!\!-\!\!-\text{HBrO}\!\!-\!\!-\!\!-\!\!-\text{BrO}_3^- \\
\quad -1.087 \\
\qquad \quad \text{Br}_2(\text{aq})
\end{array}$$

Basic Solution.

$$\begin{array}{c}
-0.61 \\
\overline{\begin{array}{ccc} -1.07 & -0.45 & -0.54 \end{array}} \\
\text{Br}^- \!\!-\!\!-\!\!-\!\!-\text{Br}_2\!\!-\!\!-\!\!-\!\!-\text{BrO}^-\!\!-\!\!-\!\!-\!\!-\text{BrO}_3^- \\
\quad -0.76
\end{array}$$

Notes on the bromine potentials. The free energy of the simultaneous oxidation-reduction of bromine in alkaline solutions may be calculated from the potentials above.

$$3\text{Br}_2 + 6\text{OH}^- = 5\text{Br}^- + \text{BrO}_3^- + 3\text{H}_2\text{O}, \qquad \Delta F^\circ = -62{,}400 \text{ cal.}$$

This reaction goes readily in alkali, but in acid solution it is reversed, as indicated by the free energy.

$$5\text{Br}^- + \text{BrO}_3^- + 6\text{H}^+ = 3\text{Br}_2 + 3\text{H}_2\text{O}, \qquad \Delta F^\circ = -52{,}200 \text{ cal.}$$

The first step of the bromine in alkali reaction is doubtless the hydrolysis reaction

$$\text{Br}_2 + 2\text{OH}^- = \text{BrO}^- + \text{Br}^- + \text{H}_2\text{O}, \qquad \Delta F^\circ = -14{,}100 \text{ cal.},$$

followed by the rapid oxidation-reduction of the hypobromite,

$$3\text{BrO}^- = 2\text{Br}^- + \text{BrO}_3^-, \qquad \Delta F^\circ = -30{,}900 \text{ cal.}$$

IODINE

Oxidation states. Iodine has an oxidation number of -1 in hydroiodic acid and its salts, $+1$ in the unstable hypoiodous acid and iodine monochloride, $+5$ in iodic acid and its salts, and $+7$ in periodic acid and its derivatives. The $+4$ oxide, IO_2 or I_2O_4, has been prepared. There is also some evidence for I_2O_3. It seems probable that HIO_2 (oxidation number $+3$) is formed momentarily in the oxidation of iodine or the reduction of iodate, and the trichloride ICl_3, in which the iodine may be considered as $+3$, is well known.

The iodide-iodine couple. From the iodide-iodine electrode and accurate measurements of the activity of iodide solutions[1] the free energy of iodide, I^-, is -12.35 kcal., and the half-reaction is

$$2I^- = I_2 + 2e^-, \qquad E^\circ = -0.5355.$$

Although, as the potential value indicates, iodine is not a powerful oxidizing agent, its action is in general rapid, that is, the heat of

TABLE 16

THERMODYNAMIC DATA ON IODINE[1]

(Heat and free energy of formation in kcal. Entropy of substance in cal./deg.)

Formula	Description	State	ΔH°	ΔF°	S°
I	($^2P_{3/2}$)	g	*25.482*	*16.766*	*43.184*
I+		g	*267.737*		
I++		g	*707.60*		
I−		g	*−50.2*		
I−		aq	*−13.37*	*−12.35*	*26.14*
I₂		g	*14.876*	*4.63*	*62.280*
I₂		c	0.0	0.0	*27.9*
I₂		aq	*5.0*	3.926	
I₃−		aq	*−12.4*	*−12.31*	*57.1*
HI		g	*6.2*	*0.31*	*49.314*
IO−		aq	*−34.* (?)	−8.5	
HIO		aq	*−38.* (?)	−23.5	
IO₃−		aq		−32.250	28.0
H₄IO₆−		aq	−178.8		
H₅IO₆		aq		(−128.5)	
ICl		g	*4.2*	*−1.32*	*59.12*
ICl		c	−8.03	−3.24	24.5
ICl		aq		−4.0	
ICl₂−		aq		−38.35	
ICl₃		c	−21.1	*−5.40*	*41.1*
IBr		g	*9.75*	*0.91*	*61.8*
IBr		aq		−0.90	
IBr₂−		aq		−28.97	

[1] Bureau of Standards values in *italics;* estimated values in parentheses.

activation is small. However, Knobel[2] gives the overvoltage for the liberation of iodine on platinum as higher than the corresponding values for bromine or chlorine. This is difficult to understand in view of the lower energy of dissociation of the I_2 molecule.

[1] Randall, *op. cit.* See also R. G. Bates and W. C. Vosburgh, *J. Am. Chem. Soc.*, **59**, 1190 (1937).
[2] Knobel, *op. cit.*

The iodide–tri-iodide couple. Lewis and Randall[1] have reviewed the data on the free energy of the reaction, iodine and iodide to give tri-iodide, I_3^-. Using their value and the iodide free energy above, one obtains for the free energy of tri-iodide, -12.31 kcal.

$$I_2(aq) + I^- = I_3^-, \qquad K = 7.14 \times 10^2;$$
$$3I^- = I_3^- + 2e^-, \qquad E^\circ = -0.536.$$

The iodide–hypoiodite couple. From the work of Bray and Connolly[2] on the hydrolysis of iodine,

$$I_2(aq) + H_2O = HIO + H^+ + I^-, \qquad K = 3 \times 10^{-13}.$$

Horiguchi and Hagisawa[3] report 4.6×10^{-13} for this constant. The free energy of HIO is calculated to be -23.5 kcal. Then, for the couple,

$$H_2O + I^- = HIO + H^+ + 2e^-, \qquad E_B^\circ = -0.99.$$

Furth[4] gave as a rough value for the dissociation constant of hypoiodous acid, $K = 10^{-11}$. This would make the free energy of the hypoiodite ion -8.5 kcal.

$$2OH^- + I^- = IO^- + H_2O + 2e^-, \qquad E_B^\circ = -0.49.$$

The agreement with the thermal data is not good (ΔH° appears to be 10 kcal. too large) but the equilibrium data are probably to be preferred, although no high accuracy can be claimed for them, since these substances are too unstable to permit any direct calorimetric determinations. The energies of these decomposition reactions will be discussed in a later paragraph.

Iodine monochloride. Hypoiodous acid has basic properties and in moderately large concentration of hydrochloric acid it forms ICl and ICl_2^-. Faull[5] has determined the equilibrium constants for the reactions.

$$ICl_2^- = ICl(aq) + Cl^-, \qquad K = 6 \times 10^{-3};$$
$$2ICl(aq) = I_2(aq) + Cl_2(aq), \qquad K = 1.6 \times 10^{-10}.$$

[1] G. N. Lewis and M. Randall, *Thermodynamics*, New York: McGraw-Hill Book Company, Inc., 1923, p. 526. See also G. Jones, and B. B. Kaplan, *J. Am. Chem. Soc.*, **50**, 1845 (1928).

[2] W. C. Bray and E. L. Connolly, *J. Am. Chem. Soc.*, **33**, 1485 (1911).

[3] G. Horiguchi and H. Hagisawa, *Bull. Inst. Phy. Chem. Research Japan*, **22**, 661 (1943).

[4] A. Furth, *Z. Electrochem.*, **28**, 57 (1922).

[5] J. H. Faull, *J. Am. Chem. Soc.*, **56**, 522 (1934).

These constants lead to the values of the free energy of formation of $ICl(aq)$, -4000 cal., and of ICl_2^-, $-38,350$ cal. From thermal data, we calculate for the free energies $ICl(aq)$, -3.55 kcal., and ICl_2^-, -37.93 kcal., but we shall continue to use Faull's values. The work of Philbrick[1] also is in substantial agreement. The most important potentials are the reduction to iodine and chloride.

$$Cl^- + \tfrac{1}{2}I_2 = ICl(aq) + e^-, \qquad E° = -1.19;$$
$$2Cl^- + \tfrac{1}{2}I_2 = ICl_2^- + e^-, \qquad E° = -1.06.$$

Iodine monobromide. Faull has also determined the corresponding constants for IBr_2^- and IBr and finds

$$IBr_2^- = IBr(aq) + Br^-, \qquad K = 2.7 \times 10^{-3};$$
$$2IBr(aq) = I_2(aq) + Br_2(aq), \qquad K = 1.2 \times 10^{-5}.$$

The free energies are $IBr(aq)$, -900 cal., and IBr_2^-, $-28,970$ cal.; and the potentials to iodine and bromide are

$$Br^- + \tfrac{1}{2}I_2 = IBr(aq) + e^-, \qquad E° = -1.02;$$
$$2Br^- + \tfrac{1}{2}I_2 = IBr_2^- + e^-, \qquad E° = -0.87.$$

Iodine trichloride. Nies and Yost[2] give $-21,150$ cal. as the heat of formation of the trichloride ICl_3. From the entropy, the free energy is -5.40 kcal. Hence,

$$2Cl^- + ICl(s) = ICl_3(s) + 2e^-, \qquad E° = -1.31;$$
$$3Cl^- + \tfrac{1}{2}I_2 = ICl_3(s) + 3e^-, \qquad E° = -1.28.$$

The iodide-iodate couple. Lundberg, Vestling, and Ahlberg[3] found $-32,251$ cal. for the free energy of formation of iodate from direct potential measurements. Hence,

$$\tfrac{1}{2}I_2 + 3H_2O = IO_3^- + 6H^+ + 5e^-, \qquad E° = -1.195;$$
$$I^- + 6OH^- = IO_3^- + 3H_2O + 6e^-, \qquad E_B° = -0.26.$$

Iodate in acid solution is a rapid oxidizing agent and oxidizes iodide to iodine. This reaction may be used to determine I^-, IO_3^-, or H^+, quantitatively. With the iodine-iodate couple, reversible equilibria may be attained.

---

[1] F. A. Philbrick, *J. Am. Chem. Soc.*, **56**, 1257 (1934).

[2] N. P. Nies and D. M. Yost, *J. Am. Chem. Soc.*, **57**, 306 (1935).

[3] W. O. Lundberg, C. S. Vestling and J. E. Ahlberg, *J. Am. Chem. Soc.*, **59**, 264 (1937).

Periodic acid. Of the various hypothetical hydrates of iodine heptoxide the following are the more important: paraper-iodic acid, H_5IO_6; metaper-iodic acid, HIO_4; and mesodiper-iodic acid, $H_4I_2O_9$. The paraper-iodic acid is the only solid acid which exists in equilibrium with water. The solubility is quite high. The composition of the solution is probably largely this acid, although slightly soluble meta-salts, for example, KIO_4, may be precipitated upon the addition of the metal ion to the acid solution. This fact is in agreement with the following constants by Crouthamel, Hayes, and Martin.[1]

$$H_5IO_6 = H^+ + H_4IO_6^-, \qquad K = 5.1 \times 10^{-4}$$
$$H_4IO_6^- = IO_4^- + 2H_2O, \qquad K = 40$$
$$H_4IO_6^- = H^+ + H_3IO_6^{--}, \qquad K = 2 \times 10^{-7}$$
$$H_3IO_6^{--} = H^+ + H_2IO_6^{---}, \qquad K = 1 \times 10^{-15}.$$

The second dissociation may also be complicated by the equilibrium

$$2H_3IO_6^- = I_2O_9^{-4} + 3H_2O$$

since both $K_2H_3IO_6$ and $K_4I_2O_9 \cdot 9H_2O$ may be crystallized from the solution. In the case of the very slightly soluble salts, all of the hydrogens appear to be replaceable, for example, Ag_5IO_6. However, the concentration of $H_2IO_6^{---}$ is small, even in $1M$ KOH.

Abel and Smetana[2] studied the potential of the iodate-periodate couple and gave for the $E°$ in acid solution -1.51. However, they considered the periodic acid to be completely dissociated and to have the formula HIO_4. In view of the fact that periodic acid will quantitatively oxidize manganous ion to permanganate, $E° = -1.52$, their value appears to be too low. The heat of formation data are somewhat conflicting and there are no data on the entropy of periodic acid. The thermal data certainly do not take into consideration the equilibrium between $H_4IO_6^-$ and IO_4^-, and we shall not attempt to calculate a free energy for H_5IO_6. From purely chemical evidence, we shall write

$$IO_3^- + 3H_2O = H_5IO_6 + H^+ + 2e^-, \qquad E° = ca -1.6.$$

The corresponding free energy of formation of periodic acid is ca $-123,900$ cal. For the couple in alkaline solution, one computes

---

[1] C. E. Crouthamel, A. M. Hayes, and D. S. Martin, *Am. Chem. Soc. Paper Detroit*, 1950, and *J. Am. Chem. Soc.*, 73, 82 (1951).

[2] E. Abel and O. Smetana, *Monatsh.*, 60, 181 (1932).

from the approximate ionization constants given above,

$$3OH^- + IO_3^- = H_3IO_6^{--} + 2e^-, \qquad E_B^\circ = ca\ -0.7.$$

The iodate-periodate couple, even in neutral or slightly alkaline solution, will oxidize iodide to iodine. This is a distinction from iodate.

Periodates may be made from iodates by anodic oxidation on a smooth platinum anode. The most favorable conditions are low temperature and high concentrations of iodate and hydroxide.

Potential diagram for iodine oxidation states. The following diagrams are given as a summary of the iodine couples.

Acid Solution.

$$
\begin{array}{c}
-1.20 \\
\end{array}
$$

$$
\overset{-0.535}{\underset{}{I^-}} \quad
\begin{array}{cc}
-1.45 & -1.14 \\
\end{array} \quad (-1.7)
$$

I⁻————I₂(c)————HIO————IO₃⁻————H₅IO₆

$$
\begin{array}{cc}
-1.06 & -1.23 \\
\end{array}
$$

————ICl₂⁻————

Basic Solution.

$$
-0.26
$$

$$
\begin{array}{ccc}
-0.535 & -0.45 & -0.14 \\
\end{array} \quad (-0.7)
$$

I⁻————I₂(c)————IO⁻————IO₃⁻————H₃IO₆⁻⁻

$$
-0.49
$$

Notes on the iodine couples. A number of important relations between the iodine oxidation states may be discussed in terms of these potential values.

Unlike chlorate, iodate is stable with respect to decomposition into higher and lower states.

$$9H_2O + 7IO_3^- + 7H^+ = I_2 + 5H_5IO_6, \qquad \Delta F^\circ = 116\ \text{kcal.}$$
$$3H_2O + 3OH^- + 4IO_3^- = I^- + 3H_3IO_6^{--}, \qquad \Delta F^\circ = \ 60\ \text{kcal.}$$

As these positive free energies indicate, the reverse reactions, in both acid and base, go readily.

Hypoiodous acid and hypoiodite in alkali are unstable with respect to their own oxidation and reduction.

$$5HIO = 2I_2 + IO_3^- + H^+ + 2H_2O, \qquad \Delta F^\circ = -29.0\ \text{kcal.}$$
$$3IO^- = 2I^- + IO_3^-, \qquad \Delta F^\circ = -32\ \text{kcal.}$$

Since the iodous acid, HIO_2, which is postulated as an intermediate step in many reactions, does not exist in appreciable concentrations, it is unstable with respect to the reaction

$$5HIO_2 = I_2 + 3IO_3^- + 3H^+ + H_2O.$$

From the free energies of the other substances involved, ΔF° for HIO_2 must be larger than $-30,000$ cal. and

$$2H_2O + \tfrac{1}{2}I_2 = HIO_2 + 3H^+ + 3e^-, \qquad E^\circ < -1.2.$$

The oxidation of iodine to ICl_2^- by iodate in hydrochloric acid is a well-known analytical procedure. From the potentials we may calculate

$$IO_3^- + 6H^+ + 10Cl^- + 2I_2 = 5ICl_2^- + 3H_2O, \qquad \Delta F^\circ = -16.3 \text{ kcal.}$$

The small value for the free energy is in agreement with the fact that a moderately high concentration of hydrochloric acid is required to make the reaction quantitative.

ASTATINE

Although 10 isotopes of astatine, ranging in atomic weights from 207 to 218 are now known, the most stable, At^{210} and At^{211}, have half-lives of only 8.3 and 7.5 hrs., respectively. Chemical properties[1] have been determined only with tracer scale experiments, generally with solutions containing astatine at concentrations in the range 10^{-11} to 10^{-13} moles.

Oxidation states. A negative oxidation state is formed by reduction with zinc. This state is carried by silver iodide and the ion is doubtless At^-. There are two positive oxidation states, one obtained by oxidation with bromine and the other which requires an oxidizing agent of the strength of hypochlorite. It seems likely that these states are either $HAtO$ and $HAtO_3$, or $HAtO:$ and $HAtO_4$; probably the first pair. The zero state is obtained by the reduction of the positive states with SO_2. At pH13 it appears to disproportionate. The zero state is fairly volatile and soluble in organic solvents.

On the basis of these experiments the following tentative potential diagrams are constructed:

---

[1] G. L. Johnson, R. F. Leininger, and E. Segré, *J Chem. Phys.*, **17**, 1 (1948).

Acid Solution.

$$\overset{(-0.2)}{At^-}\!\!\!\!\!—\!\!\!\!\!\overset{(-0.7)}{At_2}\!\!\!\!\!—\!\!\!\!\!\overset{(-1.4)}{HAtO}\!\!\!\!\!—\!\!\!\!\!HAtO_3$$

Basic Solution.

$$\overset{(-0.2)}{At^-}\!\!\!\!\!—\!\!\!\!\!\overset{(0.0)}{At_2}\!\!\!\!\!—\!\!\!\!\!\overset{(-0.5)}{AtO^-}\!\!\!\!\!—\!\!\!\!\!AtO_3^-$$

Notes on the halogen potentials. The marked decrease in the oxidizing power of the free halogen from fluorine to iodine is to be noted. This leads to the replacement of a heavier halide by a lighter. For example,

$$Cl_2 + 2Br^- = Br_2 + 2Cl^-.$$

A number of other so-called replacements occur with the oxygen ions, such as

$$BrO_3^- + I^- = IO_3^- + Br^-,$$

but these, of course, are complicated reactions occurring in steps and are not simple replacements.

Most of these potentials are more negative than the water-oxygen couple, -1.23, and are capable, therefore, of liberating oxygen from water. With the exception of fluorine, these reactions, however, are slow.

The most powerful oxidizing couple among the oxygen ions is the periodate-iodate, but in alkaline solution the potential falls to a value somewhat less than the chloride-hypochlorite couple; hence hypochlorite will partially oxidize iodate, and if silver ion is present, the equilibrium may be displaced to give practically complete oxidation of the iodate to periodate.

CHAPTER 6

Sulfur, Selenium, Tellurium, and Polonium

Oxygen, the first member of Group VI, has been discussed in Chap. 4. Like oxygen, the other members of the group show a tendency to complete the octet of s-p electrons by the addition of two electrons, but the stability of the -2 oxidation state decreases with increasing atomic weight. With the lighter elements, the $+4$ and $+6$ states are the most stable, but the compounds of the latter increase in oxidizing power with the heavier elements. The $+2$ state is unstable with respect to the decomposition into the element and the $+4$ state, except in the case of polonium. Odd oxidation numbers are impossible with completed octets except by sharing a pair of electrons between two atoms of the group, for example, NaS_2, and are generally unstable with respect to the even states.

SULFUR

Oxidation states. Sulfur has an oxidation number of -2 in sulfides. It forms polysulfides, for example, S_3^{--}, in which the average sulfur oxidation number is negative; but in these compounds it is rather ambiguous to assign polar numbers because the sulfur atoms are linked by covalent bonds. The monoxide, SO, with oxidation number of $+2$, is known as an unstable gas molecule, and derivatives of the acid H_2SO_2, the sulfoxylates, exist. The average oxidation number of $+2$ also occurs in the thiosulfates and pentathionates. Hyposulfite, $S_2O_4^{--}$, corresponds to a value of $+3$ for the oxidation number, and sulfite, SO_3^{--}, is $+4$. The $+5$ state is represented by dithionate, and the sulfates are $+6$. The so-called persulfates are peroxy-compounds. Numerous compounds are known in which the average oxidation number is a positive fraction, as in $S_3O_6^{--}$ and

$S_4O_6^{--}$. The problem of assigning oxidation states in these compounds is similar to that of the polysulfides mentioned above. Compounds with the halogens are known in which the sulfur has oxidation states of $+1$, $+2$, $+4$, $+5$, and $+6$.

The sulfide-sulfur couple. The free energies of $H_2S(g)$, $H_2S(aq)$ and HS^- are taken in agreement with the Bureau of Standards values and are in close agreement with the older values of Lewis and Randall.[1] From these values we write

$$H_2S = S + 2H^+ + 2e^-, \qquad E^\circ = -0.141;$$
$$H_2S(aq) = H^+ + HS^-, \qquad K = 1.1 \times 10^{-7}.$$

The old value of Knox[2] for the second acid dissociation is 1.2×10^{-15}. Jellinek[3] reported 3×10^{-14} and Kubli[4] has found 3.63×10^{-13}. The interpretation of the heat of the second neutralization step depends upon the choice of the value for the constant. Although there is considerable support for the value given by Kubli, this would lead to a positive value for the entropy of S^{--}, which seems unlikely. Therefore we shall write

$$HS^- = H^+ + S^{--}, \qquad K = 1 \times 10^{-14}$$

and make the heat of formation of S^{--} and its entropy consistent with this constant.

$$S^{--} = S + 2e^-, \qquad E^\circ = 0.48.$$

However, as sulfur dissolves in sulfide to form polysulfide, this couple could not be attained in equilibrium. Because of its slowness, the acid couple potential cannot be measured directly. Hydrogen sulfide is oxidized rapidly and quantitatively to sulfur by iodine and ferric ion. More powerful oxidizing agents, such as bromine, will take the sulfur on to sulfate.

The polysulfides. The free energy and heat of formation of S^{--} lead to a value of -6 cal./deg. for the entropy of S^{--}. Using the Bichowsky and Rossini values for the heats of formation and as-

---

[1] G. N. Lewis and M. Randall, *Thermodynamics*, New York: McGraw-Hill Book Co., Inc., 1923.

[2] J. Knox, *Z. Elektrochem.*, **12**, 477 (1906).

[3] K. Jellinek, *Lehrbuch physik. Chem.*, **IV**, 62 (1931).

[4] H. Kubli, *Helv. Chem. Acta*, **29**, 1962 (1946).

TABLE 17

THERMODYNAMIC DATA ON SULPHUR[1]

(Heat and free energy of formation in kcal. Entropy of substance in cal./deg.)

Formula	Description	State	$\Delta H°$	$\Delta F°$	$S°$
S	$3s^2\,3p^4$ $(^3P_2)$	g	53.25	43.57	40.085
S	$(^3P_1)$	g	54.388		
S	$(^3P_0)$	g	54.888		
S	λ	liq	0.253		
S	μ	liq	0.67		
S	rhombic	c	0.0	0.0	7.62
S	monoclinic	c	0.071	0.023	7.78
S^+	$(^4S_{3/2})$	g	293.565		
S^{++}		g	834.79		
S^{--}		g	125.2		
S^{--}		aq	8.56	22.1	-6.4
S_2		g	29.86		
S_2^{--}		aq	9.3	21.8	(0.)
S_3^{--}		aq	7.8	21.1	(5.)
S_4^{--}		aq	5.3	19.4	(10.)
S_6		g	25.3		
S_8		g	24.1		
SO		g	19.02	12.78	53.04
SO_2		g	-70.76	-71.79	59.40
SO_2		aq	-80.86		
SO_3		g	-94.45	-88.52	61.24
SO_3^{--}		aq	-151.9	-116.1	-7
SO_4^{--}		aq	-216.90	-177.34	4.1
$S_2O_3^{--}$		aq	-145.7 (?)	-124.0	(8.)
$S_2O_4^{--}$		aq	-178.3	-143.4	28 (?)
$S_2O_5^{--}$		aq	-232	$-189.$	(25.)
$S_2O_6^{--}$		aq	-280.4	$-231.$	(30.)
S_2O_7		c	-194.3		
$S_2O_8^{--}$		aq	-324.3	$-262.$	(35.)
$S_3O_6^{--}$		aq	$-279.$	$-229.$	(33.)
$S_4O_6^{--}$		aq	-272.6 (?)	-244.3	(36.)
$S_5O_6^{--}$		aq	$-281.$	-228.5	(40.)
HS^-		aq	-4.22	3.01	14.6
H_2S		g	-4.815	-7.892	49.15
H_2S		aq	-9.4	-6.54	29.2
H_2S_2		liq	-3.6		
H_2S_5		liq	-2.0		
H_2SO_2		aq		$>-90.$	
HSO_3^-		aq	-151.9	-126.0	26.
HSO_4^-		aq	-211.70	-179.94	30.32
H_2SO_3		aq	-145.5	-128.59	56.
H_2SO_4		aq	-216.90	-177.34	4.1
$HS_2O_4^-$		aq		-140.0	
$H_2S_2O_4$		aq	$-164.$	-140.0	
$H_2S_2O_6$		aq	-280.0		

TABLE 17 (*Continued*)

THERMODYNAMIC DATA ON SULPHUR[1]

(Heat and free energy of formation in kcal. Entropy of substance in cal./deg.)

Formula	Description	State	$\Delta H°$	$\Delta F°$	$S°$
$H_2S_2O_7$		liq	*−302.7*		
$H_2S_2O_8$		aq	*−324.3*	*−262.*	35
$H_2S_4O_6$		aq	*−272.6*		
SF_6		g	*−262.*	*−237.*	*69.5*
SCl_4		liq	*−13.6*		
S_2Cl_2		g	*−5.70*		
S_2Cl_2		liq	*−14.4*	−5.9	(40.)
S_2Cl_4		liq	*−24.0*		
$SOCl_2$		liq	*−49.2*		
SO_2Cl_2		liq	*−93.0*		
SO_2Cl_2		g		−73.6	
S_2Br_2		liq	*−3.6*		
C_2H_4S		liq	19.52		43.30
CH_3SH		liq	−0.9	−0.4	
$(CH_3)_2SO$		liq	−30.3	−18.9	
$(CH_3)_2SO_2$		liq	−81.4	−64.7	
$(CH_3)_2S$		liq	−3.9	−2.7	

[1] Bureau of Standards values in *italics;* estimated values in parentheses.

suming the entropies S_2^{--}, 0; S_3^{--}, $+5$; and S_4^{--}, $+10$; the free energies are calculated: S_2^{--}, 21,800 cal.; S_3^{--}, 21,100 cal.; and S_4^{--}, 19,400 cal. The potentials of the following couples are of interest:

$$2S^{--} = S_2^{--} + 2e^-, \qquad E_B° = 0.48;$$

$$S^{--} + S_2^{--} = S_3^{--} + 2e^-, \qquad E_B° = 0.49;$$

$$S^{--} + S_3^{--} = S_4^{--} + 2e^-, \qquad E_B° = 0.52.$$

The hydrogen ions, for example, HS_2^-, are doubtless largely present in a one-molal alkali solution and the heats and free energies of the reactions have not been corrected for these hydrolysis effects as the ionization constants are not known. Except for this point the potentials are probably fairly good.

The sulfur-sulfurous acid couple. Starting with the free energy of $H_2SO_3(aq)$ as −128.59 kcal. as given by Powell,[1] we have adjusted the free energies of HSO_3^- and SO_3^{--} to give a reasonable fit with the free energies of ionization and with the entropies of formation

---

[1] R. E. Powell, University of California, unpublished calculations.

and ionization. Our values give

$$H_2SO_3 = H^+ + HSO_3^-, \qquad\qquad K = 1.25 \times 10^{-2};$$
$$HSO_3^- = H^+ + SO_3^{--}, \qquad\qquad K = 5.6 \times 10^{-8};$$
$$S + 3H_2O = H_2SO_3 + 4H^+ + 4e^-, \qquad E^\circ = -0.45;$$
$$S + 6OH^- = SO_3^{--} + 3H_2O + 6e^-, \qquad E_B^\circ = 0.66.$$

Yui[1] has given $K_1 = 1.27 \times 10^{-2}$ and $K_2 = 6.24 \times 10^{-8}$.

From these potentials sulfurous acid is a fairly good oxidizing agent, while sulfite ion is very much weaker. The mechanism of the reduction probably goes through hyposulfurous acid with the one-electron type of reducing agent.

The sulfite-sulfate couple. We have adopted the Bureau of Standards values for the free energies of $H_2SO_4(aq)$, HSO_4^-, and SO_4^{--}. The following equations may then be given:

$$HSO_4^- = H^+ + SO_4^{--}, \qquad\qquad K = 1.26 \times 10^{-2};$$
$$H_2O + H_2SO_3 = SO_4^{--} + 4H^+ + 2e^-, \qquad E^\circ = -0.17;$$
$$2OH^- + SO_3^{--} = SO_4^{--} + H_2O + 2e^-, \qquad E_B^\circ = 0.93.$$

Sulfuric acid in molal solutions is thus a poor oxidizing agent, considerably weaker than the sulfurous acid. The heat of concentration to form pure H_2SO_4, however, is 15 kcal. Hence, the concentrated acid becomes a stronger oxidizing agent, especially when heated, as the fugacity of the SO_2 which is formed increases rapidly with temperature. It should be noted that the free energy of H_2SO_4 is given as equal to SO_4^{--}. Thus in any actual solution the free energy of H_2SO_4 should be corrected for the concentration of HSO_4^- which is present.

Taube[2] and his co-workers have discussed the action of sulfite as a reducing agent with oxygen containing oxidizing agents. They suggest two mechanisms; one, the direct transfer of oxygen atoms, and the other, the formation of an intermediate compound which reacts with water to accomplish the oxygen transfer. (Cf. reduction of nitrate by sulfite as an example of the latter.)

Thiosulfate and tetrathionate. Bichowsky[3] determined the equilibrium in the reaction

$$SO_3^{--} + S(r) = S_2O_3^{--}.$$

[1] N. Yui, *Bul. Inst. Phys. Chem. Research Japan*, **19**, 1229 (1940).
[2] H. Taube, *et al.*, *Am. Chem. Soc. Paper*, Chicago, 1950.
[3] F. R. Bichowsky, *J. Am. Chem. Soc.*, **45**, 2225 (1923).

His value for the free energy of the reaction, -8430 cal., leads to $-124,800$ cal. for the free energy of $S_2O_2^{--}$. The accepted heat of formation of thiosulfate is inconsistent with the free energy data by about 12 kcal., and the value, $-124,000$ cal., will be taken arbitrarily as the free energy of thiosulfate.

$$3H_2O + S_2O_3^{--} = 2H_2SO_3 + 2H^+ + 4e^-, \qquad E° = -0.40;$$
$$6OH^- + S_2O_3^{--} = 2SO_3^{--} + 3H_2O + 4e^-, \qquad E_B° = 0.58.$$

However, with many oxidizing agents the thiosulfate is oxidized to tetrathionate, $S_4O_6^{--}$. Zimmermann and Latimer[1] have determined $\Delta H°$ as -7.76 kcal. for the oxidation of thiosulfate by iodine. From the estimated entropies of $S_2O_3^{--}$ and $S_4O_6^{--}$ we find

$$2S_2O_3^{--} + I_2(s) = S_4O_6^{--} + 2I^-, \qquad \Delta F° = -21.0 \text{ kcal.}$$

and combining with the potential of the iodine couple,

$$2S_2O_3^{--} = S_4O_6^{--} + 2e^-, \qquad E° = -0.08.$$

The free energy of formation of $S_4O_6^{--}$ is -244.3 kcal. and the potential for the tetrathionate-sulfurous acid couple

$$6H_2O + S_4O_6^{--} = 4H_2SO_3 + 4H^+ + 6e^-, \qquad E° = -0.51.$$

Any oxidizing agent which is capable of oxidizing tetrathionate to sulfurous acid should, of course, take the sulfurous acid on to sulfate. It is interesting to note that the above potential is about the same as the iodide-iodine couple. Since iodine will not oxidize tetrathionate, the first step in the mechanism of the $S_4O_6^{--}$ oxidation may have a potential which is more negative than the over-all value.

Connick and Awtrey[2] have studied the mechanism of the oxidation of thiosulfate by tri-iodide. They conclude that iodine and tri-iodide ion react rapidly with thiosulfate ion to form the intermediate $S_2O_3I^-$. The conversion is not complete because the $S_2O_3I^-$ also reacts rapidly with thiosulfate to give tetrathionate and iodide ions. When the ratio of the initial thiosulfate to iodine is less than 2, some $S_2O_3I^-$ remains in the solution after the above rapid reactions have consumed the thiosulfate. This $S_2O_3I^-$ either reacts with itself to form tetrathionate ion and iodine or is oxidized by iodine to give sulfate and iodide ions.

[1] H. W. Zimmermann, and W. M. Latimer, *J. Am. Chem. Soc.*, **61**, 1554 (1939).
[2] R. E. Connick and A. D. Awtrey, *J. Am. Chem. Soc.*, **73**, 1842 (1951).

Sorum and Edwards[1] have concluded that the oxidation of thiosulfate by peroxydisulfate occurs through a free radical chain mechanism.

The oxidation of thiosulfate to tetrathionate may be carried out by electrolysis of alkali sulfites, the highest efficiency being obtained at low hydrogen-ion concentration. The process always results in some sulfate formation, and the ratio of tetrathionate to sulfate varies with the presence of many substances. For example, the ratio is high in the presence of cobalt sulfate and low in the presence of molybdate. The reaction mechanism is doubtless complicated, and the ratio depends upon the potentials of the intermediate sulfur compounds and their relation to those of other oxidation-reduction couples which may be present either as added catalysts or formed by oxidation of the surface of the anode. The anodic oxidation potential is far higher than the reversible potential calculated above, the overvoltage being at least one volt.

Sulfoxylic acid. Salts of sulfoxylic acid, H_2SO_2, are known, and the acid is said to be unstable with respect to the reaction

$$2H_2SO_2 = S_2O_3^{--} + 2H^+ + H_2O.$$

From the free energies of thiosulfate and water, the free energy of sulfoxylic acid must be more positive than $-90,000$ cal. and

$$2H_2O + S = H_2SO_2 + 2H^+ + 2e^-, \qquad E^\circ < -0.5;$$
$$H_2O + H_2SO_2 = H_2SO_3 + 2H^+ + 2e^-, \qquad E^\circ > -0.4.$$

Hyposulfurous acid. We shall use the values of McMillan, Roberts, and Coryell[2] for the ΔH° and ΔF° of formation of hyposulfite ion, $S_2O_4^{--}$. They should be recalculated for changes in the heat of formation of SO_3^- and HSO_3^-, but in view of the uncertainties in these values, the corrections will not be made. Jellinek[3] gave for the acid dissociation constants

$$H_2S_2O_4 = H^+ + HS_2O_4^-, \qquad K = 0.45;$$
$$HS_2O_4^- = H^+ + S_2O_4^{--}, \qquad K = 3.5 \times 10^{-3}.$$

In view of the large value for the first ionization, it will be treated as complete. The free energy of the acid ion, $HS_2O_4^-$, from the value

[1] C. H. Sorum and J. O. Edwards, *Am. Chem. Soc. Paper*, Detroit, 1950.

[2] W. G. McMillan, J. D. Roberts, and C. D. Coryell, *J. Am. Chem. Soc.*, **64**, 398 (1942).

[3] K. Jellinek, *Das Hydrosulfit*, Stuttgart: Enke, 1911, p. 71.

of K_2 and the free energy chosen for hyposulfite, then, is -140.0 kcal. The potentials in acid and base derived from these free energies are

$$2H_2O + HS_2O_4^- = 2H_2SO_3 + H^+ + 2e^-, \qquad E^\circ = 0.08;$$
$$4OH^- + S_2O_4^{--} = 2SO_3^{--} + 2H_2O + 2e^-, \qquad E_B^\circ = 1.12.$$

Hyposulfite in alkaline solution is thus a powerful reducing agent. It is unstable with respect to the decomposition

$$2S_2O_4^{--} + H_2O = S_2O_3^{--} + 2HSO_3^-, \qquad \Delta F^\circ = -32.5 \text{ kcal.}$$

and the rate of the decomposition is more rapid in acid solution.

Hyposulfite may be prepared by cathodic reduction of bisulfite, HSO_3^-, solution. The solution must not be too acidic or the above decomposition will occur, and it must not be too alkaline since the reduction becomes difficult, as is indicated by the high positive value for the potential in molal hydroxide. The mechanism of the reduction is unknown, but many substances appear to catalyze the formation of the hyposulfite.

The thionic acids. The free energies of dithionate, $S_2O_6^{--}$, trithionate, $S_3O_6^{--}$, and penthathionate, $S_5O_6^{--}$, have been calculated from the heats of formation and estimated values for the entropies. A number of interesting oxidation-reduction potentials may be derived from these free energies.

The average oxidation number of dithionic acid is $+5$, and the following couples give the potential for the change to the $+4$ and $+6$ oxidation states.

$$2H_2SO_3 = S_2O_6^{--} + 4H^+ + 2e^-, \qquad E^\circ = -0.57;$$
$$2H_2O + S_2O_6^{--} = 2SO_4^{--} + 4H^+ + 2e^-, \qquad E^\circ = 0.22.$$

Hence the decomposition reaction

$$S_2O_6^{--} + H_2O = H_2SO_3 + SO_4^{--}, \qquad E^\circ = 0.78.$$

Although the energy of this reaction is favored in alkaline solution, the rate experimentally is greater in acid. If it is correct to assume that the value chosen for the free energy of $S_2O_6^{--}$ may be too large, the decomposition energy will have a somewhat larger negative value. Yost and Pomeroy[1] have studied the action of oxidizing agents upon dithionate and find it comparatively inert. The reaction rate depends

---

[1] D. M. Yost and R. Pomeroy, *J. Am. Chem. Soc.*, **49**, 703 (1927).

in general upon the rate of the decomposition into sulfurous acid and sulfate, the former being rapidly oxidized.

The conversion of sulfite to dithionate may be carried out by anodic oxidation and is in many ways similar to the oxidation of thiosulfate discussed above. The most efficient pH is about 8, and the overvoltage, or so-called anode polarization, is high. The yield is influenced by the presence of many substances, being high with fluoride and low with Mn^{++}.[1]

The potentials for the oxidation of trithionate and pentathionate are

$$3H_2O + S_3O_6^{--} = 3H_2SO_3 + 2e^-, \qquad E° = -0.30;$$
$$9H_2O + S_5O_6^{--} = 5H_2SO_3 + 8H^+ + 103e^-, \qquad E° = -0.41.$$

The reaction mechanisms are doubtless complicated and the over-all potentials probably not very significant. Any oxidizing agent capable of oxidizing these thionates will be sufficiently strong to oxidize the sulfurous acid to sulfate.

Since thiosulfate and pentathionate have the same average oxidation number for the sulfur, it is of interest to calculate the free energy of the conversion of thiosulfate to pentathionate.

$$5S_2O_3^{--} + 6H^+ = 2S_5O_6^{--} + 3H_2O, \qquad \Delta F° = -5 \text{ kcal.}$$

The free energy is not large, and considering the obvious complications of the mechanism it is not surprising that the rate of the reaction is slow.

Peroxydisulfate.   From the heat of formation of peroxydisulfate, $S_2O_8^{--}$, and the entropy of formation, assuming the entropy of the ion to be 35 cal./deg., the free energy of formation of $H_2S_2O_8$ (or $S_2O_8^{--}$, since it is a strong acid) is calculated to be -262.0 kcal.

$$2SO_4^{--} = S_2O_8^{--} + 2e^-, \qquad E° = -2.01.$$

This value places peroxydisulfate among the most powerful oxidizing agents. The di-acid hydrolyzes to give the mono-acid, H_2SO_5, called "Caro's acid." The data for this acid are insufficient to calculate its free energy. The complete hydrolysis of the di-acid gives hydrogen peroxide.

$$S_2O_8^{--} + 2H_2O = 2H^+ + 2SO_4^{--} + H_2O_2, \qquad \Delta F° = -10.77 \text{ kcal.}$$

---

[1] O. Essin, *Z. Elektrochem.*, **34**, 78 (1928).

The free energy of the reaction is not large and the reaction is reversed at high concentrations of sulfuric acid and hydrogen peroxide.

Peroxysulfate oxidations are generally slow at ordinary temperature but are catalyzed by silver ion, for example, the oxidation of manganous to permanganate in acid solution. The mechanism of the catalysis has been studied by Yost[1] who found that the rate-determining step was

$$S_2O_8^{--} + Ag^+ = 2SO_4^{--} + Ag^{+++},$$

followed by the rapid reduction of the $+3$ silver ion (see p. 189).

The commercial preparation of peroxysulfate is by the anodic oxidation of sulfuric acid (70 per cent) or ammonium or potassium acid sulfates. Highest efficiency is obtained at low temperatures, 5 to 10° C., with high current densities, and smooth platinum electrodes. With sulfuric acid both the mono- and di-acids are formed, and as the concentration of the former builds up, the efficiency decreases, the effect seemingly arising from the depolarizing action, that is, the reaction of the H_2SO_5 with the oxidized surface of the electrode and the consequent lowering of the overvoltage. The presence of fluoride raises the overvoltage and increases the efficiency. At low concentrations of acid, oxygen is evolved, but at high concentrations the activity of the water is lowered to such an extent that the oxidation of the sulfate occurs. With the ammonium sulfate process, using as high as 300 g of NH_4HSO_4 per liter, the efficiency is good (70 to 80 per cent) and the process has the added advantage that the ammonium peroxydisulfate separates from the bath because of its lower solubility. This appears to keep down the formation of the monosulfate. The potassium, and especially the sodium, peroxysulfates are more soluble, and therefore the ammonium sulfate process is generally employed.

The mechanism of the anodic oxidation of sulfate is unknown. It seems likely that it involves the oxidation of the sulfate ion to SO_4^- and the combination of two such ions. The action of fluoride in increasing the efficiency may be through the later formation of a fluoride on the anode, which thus makes more difficult the evolution of oxygen (see oxygen overvoltage).

Sulfur-halogen compounds. There are very few data available for the calculation of the free energy of the many compounds of sulfur

---

[1] D. M. Yost, *J. Am. Chem. Soc.*, **48**, 152 (1926).

with the halogens. The free energy of formation of the hexafluoride in water solution would have but little significance. The free energy of hydrolysis is

$$SF_6 + 4H_2O = SO_4^{--} + 8H^+ + 6F^-, \qquad \Delta F^\circ = -110 \text{ kcal.}$$

but the reaction is very slow.

Lewis and Randall calculate from the work of Trautz[1] that the free energy of formation of sulfuryl chloride (gas) from sulfur dioxide and chlorine is -1900 cal. This, combined with our value for sulfur dioxide, gives $-73,600$ cal. as the free energy of formation of $SO_2Cl_2(g)$. Its free energy of hydrolysis is

$$SO_2Cl_2(g) + 2H_2O = SO_4^{--} + 4H^+ + 2Cl^-, \qquad \Delta F^\circ = -51,800 \text{ cal.}$$

Bichowsky and Rossini give $-14,300$ cal. for the heat of formation of $S_2Cl_2(l)$. Estimating the entropy of the compound to be 40, the entropy of formation is -28 cal./deg., and the free energy of formation is -5900 cal. The potential for the reduction to chloride and sulfur then is

$$2S + 2Cl^- = S_2Cl_2 + 2e^-, \qquad E^\circ = -1.23.$$

Organic sulfur compounds. Not many free energies of the organic sulfur compounds are known. Waddington[2] and his co-workers gave data on C_2H_4S. Barrow and Pitzer[3] have summarized ΔH° and ΔF° data on CH_3SH, $(CH_3)_2S$, C_2H_5SH, $(C_2H_5)_2S$, $(CH_3)_2SO$, and $(CH_3)_2SO_2$. Various potentials may be calculated from these values, such as

$$(CH_3)_2SO + H_2O = (CH_3)_2SO_2 + 2H^+ + 2e^-, \qquad E^\circ = -0.23.$$

Freedman and Corwin[4] have discussed oxidation and reduction potentials of thio-disulfide systems and the reduction potential of the disulfide of ethylene thiourea.

Reduction of sulfur compounds in steps. For convenience, the half-reactions connecting one oxidation state with the higher and lower state have been summarized in the following diagrams. It is important to keep in mind that these couples are not generally subject

[1] M. Trautz, Z. Elektrochem., 14, 534 (1908).
[2] G. Waddington et al., J. Am. Chem. Soc., 71, 797 (1949).
[3] G. M. Barrow and K. S. Pitzer, Ind. and Eng. Chem., 41, 2737 (1949).
[4] L. D. Freedman and A. H. Corwin, J. Biol. Chem., 181, 601 (1949).

to rapid reversibility and, hence, the potentials, while valuable in many problems, cannot be used in the equilibrium sense. It may be noted that, in alkaline solution, sulfur is unstable with respect to disproportionation into S^{--} or (SS_4^{--}) and thiosulfate.

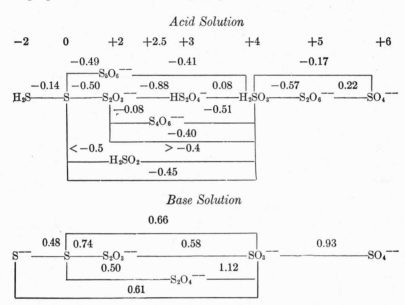

SELENIUM

Oxidation states. The oxidation state of selenium is -2 in the selenides, $+4$ in selenites, and $+6$ in selenates. Oxygen compounds corresponding to the $+2$, $+3$, $+5$ states and the polyacids of sulfur are not known. Polyselenides such as $NaSe_2$ and $NaSe_3$ exist but are less stable than the polysulfides. Compounds with the halogens are, in general, similar to those of sulfur with the halogens.

The selenide-selenium couple. We shall adopt the Bureau of Standards values for $\Delta H°$, $\Delta F°$, and $S°$ of $H_2Se(aq)$, but not their values for HSe^- and Se^{--} as the entropies appear to be unreasonable. De Hlasko[1] reported K_1 for H_2Se, and Lingane and Niedrach[2] have presented evidence for K_2. The latter value appears to be somewhat

---

[1] M. De Hlasko, *J. Chem. Phys.*, **20**, 167 (1923).
[2] J. J. Lingane and L. W. Niedrach, *J. Am. Chem. Soc.*, **70**, 4118 (1948).

TABLE 18

THERMODYNAMIC DATA ON SELENIUM[1]

(Heat and free energy of formation in kcal. Entropy of substance in cal./deg.)

Formula	Description	State	$\Delta H°$	$\Delta F°$	$S°$
Se	($^3P_2$)	g	*48.37*	*38.77*	*42.21*
Se	($^3P_1$)	g	*54.07*		
Se	($^3P_0$)	g	*55.63*		
Se	I, gray, hexagonal	c	0.0	0.0	*10.0*
Se	III, red, monoclinic	c	*0.2*		
Se		glass	*1.05*		
Se$^+$	($^4S_{3/2}$)	g	*274.70*		
Se^{++}	($^3P_0$)	g	*772.29*		
Se^{--}		aq	30.3	*42.6*	(0.)
Se$_2$		g	*33.14*	*21.15*	*60.22*
SeO		g	*9.48*		
SeO$_2$		c	−*55.00*	−41.5	(13.6)
SeO$_2$		aq	−*54.07*		
SeO$_3^{--}$		aq	−*122.39*	−*89.33*	*3.9*
SeO$_4^{--}$		aq	−*145.3*	−*105.42*	*5.7*
HSe$^-$		aq	16.8	23.5	(22.)
H$_2$Se		g	20.5	17.0	*52.9*
H$_2$Se		aq	18.1	18.4	39.9
HSeO$_3^-$		aq	−*123.5*	−*98.3*	*30.4* (?)
HSeO$_4^-$		aq	−*143.1*	−108.2	22.0
H$_2$SeO$_3$		c	−*126.5*		
H$_2$SeO$_3$		aq	−*122.39*	−101.8	*45.7*
H$_2$SeO$_4$		c	−128.6		
H$_2$SeO$_4$		aq	−*145.3*	−*105.42*	*5.7*
SeF$_6$		g	−*246.0*	−*222.*	*75.10*
SeCl$_2$		g	−*9.7*		
SeCl$_4$		c	−*45.0*	23.3	(44.)
Se$_2$Cl$_2$		liq	−*20.0*	−11.60	(45.)

[1] Bureau of Standards values in *italics;* estimated values in parentheses.

too small in view of the value 1×10^{-11} by Hagisawa[1] but we shall accept it and write

$$H_2Se(aq) = H^+ + HSe^-, \qquad K = 1.88 \times 10^{-4};$$
$$HSe^- = H^+ + Se^{--}, \qquad K = 1 \times 10^{-14};$$
$$H_2Se = Se + 2H^+ + 2e^-, \qquad E° = 0.40;$$
$$Se^{--} = Se + 2e^-, \qquad E°_B = 0.92.$$

[1] H. Hagisawa, *Bull. Inst. Phys. Chem. Research Japan*, **38**, No. 1034.

The soluble selenides are thus unstable with respect to oxidation by hydrogen ion but the reaction appears to be slow.

The selenium-selenite couple. Schott, Swift, and Yost[1] have determined the potential of the Se—H_2SeO_3 couple by direct equilibrium methods. The values of the Bureau of Standards are in approximate agreement.

$$H_2SeO_3 = H^+ + HSeO_3^-, \qquad\qquad K = 2.7 \times 10^{-3};$$
$$HSeO_3^- = H^+ + SeO_3^{--}, \qquad\qquad K = 2.5 \times 10^{-7};$$
$$Se + 3H_2O = H_2SeO_3 + 4H^+ + 4e^-, \qquad E° = -0.740;$$
$$Se + 6OH^- = SeO_3^{--} + 3H_2O + 4e^-, \qquad E_B° = 0.366.$$

Schott, Swift and Yost[2] were able to get an equilibrium with iodide and iodine; hence the couple is reversible and fairly rapid.

Von Hippel and Bloom[3] have plated metallic selenium from hot $18N$ H_2SO_4 solutions saturated with SeO_2. They discuss the equilibria

$$H_2SeO_3 = H^+ + HSeO_3^-$$
and $$H_2SeO_3 + H^+ = H_3SeO_3^+,$$

and conclude that high acid favors the deposition of the metal through the formation of the positive ion $H_3SeO_3^+$. These authors also discuss the phase relationships between the various allotropic modifications of the element.

Selenite-selenate couple. The Bureau of Standards values for the free energy of selenic acid and its ions are based in part upon the work of Sherrill and Izard,[4] who measured the equilibrium between the selenite-selenate couple and the chloride-chlorine and bromide-bromine couples. The Bureau of Standards values for H_2SeO_4 are taken equal to those of SeO_4^{--}; hence, in any actual solution of H_2SeO_4, its free energy must be corrected for the concentration of $HSeO_4^-$ which is present.

$$HSeO_4^- = H^+ + SeO_4^{--}, \qquad\qquad K = 8.9 \times 10^{-3};$$
$$H_2O + H_2SeO_3 = SeO_4^{--} + 4H^+ + 2e^-, \qquad E° = -1.15;$$
$$2OH^- + SeO_3^{--} = SeO_4^{--} + H_2O + 2e^-, \qquad E_B° = -0.05.$$

---

[1] H. F. Schott, E. H. Swift and D. M. Yost, *J. Am. Chem. Soc.*, **50**, 721 (1928).
[2] *Ibid.*
[3] A. T. von Hippel and M. C. Bloom, *J. Chem. Phys.* **18**, 1243 (1950).
[4] M. S. Sherrill and E. F. Izard, *J. Am. Chem. Soc.*, **50**, 1665 (1928).

Since equilibrium was established with the chlorine couple in four to seven days and with the bromine couple in fifty to seventy days, selenic acid is not a very rapid oxidizing agent. For some unknown reason the reduction with halide ions is faster than with more powerful reducing agents. For example, there is no appreciable reduction with H_2S, SO_2, or Fe^{++}.

Selenium halogen compounds. Yost and Claussen[1] reported $-246,000$ cal. as the heat of formation of selenium hexafluoride gas. Using $S°$ as for the sulfur hexafluoride, 75.1 cal./deg., the free energy is -222. kcal. and the free energy of its hydrolysis would be

$$SeF_6(g) + 4H_2O = SeO_4^{--} + 8H^+ + 6F^-, \qquad \Delta F° = -56 \text{ kcal.}$$

The Bureau of Standards gives -20.6 kcal. as the heat of formation of $Se_2Cl_2(l)$. Using the same entropy of formation as for the corresponding sulfur compound, -28 cal./deg., the free energy of formation is -11.6 kcal. The potential for reduction to chloride and selenium then is

$$2Se + 2Cl^- = Se_2Cl_2 + 2e^-, \qquad E° = -1.1.$$

Similar calculations may be made for $SeCl_2$ and $SeCl_4$.

TELLURIUM

Oxidation states. Like selenium, the -2, $+4$, and $+6$ oxidation states of tellurium are the only ones of importance. The $+2$ oxide, TeO, exists, and in cold hydrochloric acid it appears to form the salt $TeCl_2$, but when the solution is warmed it decomposes into the free element and a $+4$ complex chloride.

The telluride-tellurium couple. The free energy of formation of hydrogen telluride gas, H_2Te, is given as 33.1 kcal. The free energy of solution appears to be about 1 kcal. Hence, the free energy of $H_2Te(aq)$ is ca 34.1 kcal. De Hlasko[2] gave for the first dissociation constant

$$H_2Te = H^+ + HTe^-, \qquad K = 2.3 \times 10^{-3}.$$

Lingane and Niedrach[3] concluded from polarographic studies that

$$HTe^- = H^+ + Te^{--}, \qquad K = 1 \times 10^{-11}.$$

[1] D. M. Yost and W. H. Claussen, *J. Am. Chem. Soc.*, **55**, 885 (1933).
[2] M. de Hlasko, *J. chim. phys.*, **20**, 167 (1923).
[3] J. J. Lingane and L. W. Niedrach, *J. Am. Chem. Soc.*, **71**, 196 (1949).

TABLE 19

THERMODYNAMIC DATA ON TELLURIUM[1]

(Heat and free energy of formation in kcal. Entropy of substance in cal./deg.)

Formula	Description	State	$\Delta H°$	$\Delta F°$	$S°$
Te		g	_47.6_	_38.1_	_43.64_
Te		c, II	_0.0_	_0.0_	_11.88_
Te		amorp	_2.7_		
Te^+		g	_256.8_		
Te^{++}		g	_755.09_		
Te^{--}		aq		52.7	
Te_2^{--}		aq		38.75	
Te_2		g	_41.0_	_29.0_	_64.07_
HTe^-		aq		37.7	
H_2Te		g	_36.9_	_33.1_	_56.0_
H_2Te		aq		34.1	
TeO		g	_43.0_		
TeO_2		c	_−77.69_	_−64.60_	_16.99_
TeO_3^{--}		aq	_−142.1_	−108.0	(−2.)
H_6TeO_6		c		−167.9	
H_2TeO_3		c	_−144.7_	_−115.7_	_47.7_
H_2TeO_3		aq	_−144.7_		
$TeOOH^+$		aq		−61.78	
TeF_6		g	_−315._	_−292._	80.67
$TeCl_4$		c	_−77.2_	−56.7	(50)
$TeBr_4$		liq	_−49.8_		
$TeCl_6^{--}$				−137.4	

[1] Bureau of Standards values in _italics;_ estimated values in parentheses.

We may then write

$$H_2Te = Te + 2H^+ + 2e^-, \qquad E° = -0.72;$$
$$Te^{--} = Te + 2e^-, \qquad E_B° = 1.14.$$

Kasarnowsky[1] reports from direct cell measurements

$$Te_2^{--} = 2Te + 2e^-, \qquad E° = 0.84.$$

from which the free energy of Te_2^{--} is 38,750 cal. From the two half-reactions the following is calculated:

$$Te^{--} + Te = Te_2^{--}, \qquad \Delta F° = -14.0 \text{ kcal.}$$

The value for this free energy appears to be somewhat too large. We conclude that the heat of formation of H_2Te may be too large or that K_2 for the acid may be too small. As the high positive potentials

---

[1] J. Kasarnowsky, _Z. anorg. allgem. Chem.,_ **128**, 33 (1923).

indicate, -2 tellurium is a powerful reducing agent, and much of the difficulty in obtaining accurate data on these compounds arises from the inability of the experimenters to prevent some oxidation.

The tellurium-tellurous acid couple. Schuhmann[1] has determined by direct measurement the following couples:

$$2H_2O + Te = TeO_2(s) + 4H^+ + 4e^-, \qquad E° = -0.529;$$

$$2H_2O + Te = TeOOH^+ + 3H^+ + 4e^-, \qquad E° = -0.559.$$

The corresponding free energy values are $TeO_2(s)$, -64.6 kcal., and $TeOOH^+$, -61.78 kcal. This author also gave TeO_2 as the stable solid in equilibrium with water and reported

$$TeO_2 + H^+ = TeOOH^+, \qquad K = 8.9 \times 10^{-3};$$

$$TeO_2 + H_2O = TeOOH^+ + OH^-, \qquad K = 8.9 \times 10^{-17}.$$

Kasarnowsky[2] gave

$$TeO_2(c) + H_2O = H_2TeO_3(c), \qquad \Delta F° = 5550 \text{ cal}$$

From these values one calculates for the free energy of the H_2TeO_3, -115.7 kcal., and for the basic dissociation of $TeO(OH)_2$,

$$TeO(OH_2)(c) = TeOOH^+ + OH^-, \qquad K = 1 \times 10^{-12}.$$

Blanc[3] reported $K_1 = 2 \times 10^{-3}$ and $K_2 = 1 \times 10^{-8}$ for the two acid constants, but there are no accurate data on the solubility of the acid in water. The free energy of the ion TeO_3^{--} could be calculated directly from the heat of formation -142.1 kcal. if its entropy were known. Estimating -2 as this value, the calculated free energy is -108 kcal.

$$6OH^- + Te = TeO_3^{--} + 3H_2O + 4e^-, \qquad E_B° = 0.57.$$

The tellurous acid-telluric acid couple. From the thermal data tabulated by Bichowsky and Rossini,

$$4H_2O(l) + TeO_2(c) = H_6TeO_6(c) + H_2, \qquad \Delta H° = 45,600 \text{ cal.}$$

The entropy of H_6TeO_6 is not known, but estimating 47 for H_6TeO_6, $\Delta S°$ for the reaction is -6 cal./deg. and $\Delta F° = 47.2$ kcal.

$$4H_2O + TeO_2 = H_6TeO_6(c) + 2H^+ + 2e^-, \qquad E° = -1.02.$$

[1] R. Schuhmann, *J. Am. Chem. Soc.*, **47**, 356 (1925).
[2] J. Kasarnowsky, *Z. physik. Chem.*, **109**, 287 (1924).
[3] E. Blanc, *J. chim. phys.*, **18**, 28 (1920).

The free energy of solution of the orthotelluric acid is not known but it does not appear to be large, and this value for the solid can be used for any approximate calculations. The calculated potential is consistent with the fact that oxidizing agents of about the strength of chlorine are required to oxidize tellurous acid to telluric. Thermal data on the meta-acid H_2TeO_4 and the ion TeO_4^{--} give results which are in disagreement with chemical properties; hence it is impossible to give a potential for the tellurite-tellurate couple in alkaline solution. However, hypoiodite is capable of oxidizing tellurite; hence,

$$2OH^- + TeO_3^{--} = TeO_4^{--} + H_2O + 2e^-, \qquad E_B^0 = ca -0.4.$$

Like selenic acid, telluric acid is reduced much more readily by halide ions than by more powerful reducing agents, such as stannous and sulfur dioxide.

Yost and Russel[1] quote two values K_1 for H_6TeO_6:

$$H_6TeO_6 = H^+ + H_5TeO_6^-, \qquad K = 6.8 \times 10^{-7}, \quad 1.6 \times 10^{-9};$$

$$H_5TeO_6^- = H_4TeO_6^{--}, \qquad K = 4.1 \times 10^{-11}.$$

Halogen compounds of tellurium. Free energies may be calculated for TeF_6, $TeCl_4$, and $TeBr_4$. The complex ions, $TeCl_6^{--}$ and $TeBr_6^{--}$, exist in water solutions at moderate concentration of halide ions; and salts, such as $(NH_4)_2TeCl_6$, may be crystallized. Reichinstein[2] has measured the potential of tellurium against solutions of $TeCl_4$ in $2.5M$ HCl. Although the complex ion formula is uncertain, we shall write from his results

$$6Cl^- + Te = TeCl_6^{--} + 4e^-, \qquad E^0 = -0.55.$$

This would make the free energy of $TeCl_6^{--}$ $-137,400$ cal. If one calculates the free energy of $TeCl_4(s)$ from thermal data, assuming the entropy of the $TeCl_4$ to be 50, the free energy of the $TeCl_4$ is -56.7 kcal., and hence,

$$TeCl_4(s) + 2Cl^- = TeCl_6^{--}, \qquad \Delta F = -18. \text{ kcal.}$$

This equation is subject to a reinterpretation of the formula of the complex ion in Reichinstein's investigation.

[1] D. M. Yost and H. Russel, Jr., *Systematic Inorganic Chemistry*, New York: Prentice-Hall, Inc., 1946.
[2] D. Reichinstein, Z. *physik. Chem.*, **97**, 257 (1921).

POLONIUM

The standard state of the polonium element is the metallic solid. Nothing is known with regard to its thermal properties, as it has never been isolated in sufficient quantity to study.

Oxidation states. Our knowledge of the chemistry of polonium is based upon its radioactive properties, in the sense that its behavior toward various reagents can be studied by observing whether the activity goes with the precipitate or remains in solution. It forms a very unstable hydrogen compound, H_2Po, -2 state, and appears to exist in water solution as $+2$ polonium, Po^{++}. Claims are also made for a $+3$ ion. The oxidation state of $+4$ occurs in PoO_2, and hot chromic acid is said to oxidize the dioxide to the $+6$ state.

TABLE 20

THERMODYNAMIC DATA ON POLONIUM[1]

(Heat and free energy of formation in kcal. Entropy of substance in cal./deg.)

Formula	Description	State	$\Delta H°$	$\Delta F°$	$S°$
Po		g			(41.9)
Po		s	0.0	0.0	(15.5)
Po^{++}		aq	17.1	30.0	(4.)
PoO$_2$		c	−60.5	−46.6	(18.3)
H$_2$Po		g		>46.	
PoO$_3$		c		(−33.)	
PoO$_3^{--}$		aq		(−101.)	

[1] Bureau of Standards values in *italics;* estimated values in parentheses.

Polonium couples. From its chemical behavior, this estimate is made:

$$H_2Po(g) = Po + 2H^+ + 2e^-, \qquad E° > 1.0.$$

Paneth and Hevesy[1] and Haissinsky[2] have studied the potentials for the cathodic reduction of polonium to the metal and the anodic oxidation to the dioxide. From their work the probable values seem to be

$$Po = Po^{++} + 2e^-, \qquad\qquad E° = -0.65;$$
$$2H_2O + Po^{++} = PoO_2 + 4H^+ + 2e^-, \qquad E° = -0.8;$$
$$6OH^- + Po = PoO_3^{--} + 3H_2O + 4e^-, \qquad E°_B = 0.5.$$

[1] F. Paneth and F. von Hevesy, *Monatsh.*, **34**, 1593 (1913).
[2] M. Haissinsky, *J. chim. phys.*, **29**, 453 (1932).

Although the corresponding free energies have been listed, they are obviously highly tentative.

Summary of Group VI potentials. In order to show the trends exhibited by the oxidation-reduction potentials in the group, the values relating the -2, 0, $+4$, and $+6$ oxidation states have been summarized in the diagrams below.

The most striking characteristic of these potentials is the decrease in the power of the free elements as oxidizing agents. The acids of the $+4$ and $+6$ states increase in oxidizing power with increasing atomic weight with the exception that the potentials of the selenium acids are unduly high.

Acid Solution.

$$
\begin{array}{l}
\; -1.23 \\
H_2O\!\!-\!\!-\!\!-\!\!-\!\!-\!\!-\!\!-O_2 \\
\; -0.14 \qquad -0.45 \qquad\qquad -0.17 \\
H_2S\!\!-\!\!-\!\!-\!\!-\!\!-\!\!-\!\!-S\!\!-\!\!-\!\!-\!\!-\!\!-\!\!-\!\!-H_2SO_3\!\!-\!\!-\!\!-\!\!-\!\!-\!\!-SO_4^{--} \\
\; 0.40 \qquad\quad -0.74 \qquad\qquad -1.15 \\
H_2Se\!\!-\!\!-\!\!-\!\!-\!\!-\!\!-Se\!\!-\!\!-\!\!-\!\!-\!\!-\!\!-H_2SeO_3\!\!-\!\!-\!\!-\!\!-\!\!-SeO_4^{--} \\
\; 0.72 \qquad\quad -0.529 \qquad\quad -1.02 \\
H_2Te\!\!-\!\!-\!\!-\!\!-\!\!-Te\!\!-\!\!-\!\!-\!\!-\!\!-\!\!-TeO_2(c)\!\!-\!\!-\!\!-\!\!-\!\!-H_6TeO_6(c) \\
\; >1.0 \qquad (-0.74) \qquad\quad -1.5? \\
H_2Po\!\!-\!\!-\!\!-\!\!-\!\!-Po\!\!-\!\!-\!\!-\!\!-\!\!-\!\!-PoO_2(c)\!\!-\!\!-\!\!-\!\!-\!\!-PoO_3(c)(?)
\end{array}
$$

Base Solution.

$$
\begin{array}{l}
\; -0.401 \\
OH^-\!\!-\!\!-\!\!-\!\!-\!\!-\!\!-O_2 \\
\; 0.48 \qquad\quad 0.61 \qquad\qquad 0.91 \\
S^{--}\!\!-\!\!-\!\!-\!\!-\!\!-\!\!-S\!\!-\!\!-\!\!-\!\!-\!\!-\!\!-SO_3^{--}\!\!-\!\!-\!\!-\!\!-\!\!-SO_4^{--} \\
\phantom{S^{--}}\; 0.92 \qquad\quad 0.366 \qquad\quad -0.05 \\
Se^{--}\!\!-\!\!-\!\!-\!\!-\!\!-Se\!\!-\!\!-\!\!-\!\!-\!\!-SeO_3^{--}\!\!-\!\!-\!\!-\!\!-\!\!-SeO_4^{--} \\
\phantom{Se^{--}}\; 1.14 \qquad\quad 0.57 \qquad\qquad >-0.4 \\
Te^{--}\!\!-\!\!-\!\!-\!\!-\!\!-Te\!\!-\!\!-\!\!-\!\!-\!\!-TeO_3^{--}\!\!-\!\!-\!\!-\!\!-\!\!-TeO_4^{--} \\
\phantom{Te^{--}}\; >1.4 \\
Po^{--}\!\!-\!\!-\!\!-\!\!-\!\!-Po
\end{array}
$$

CHAPTER 7

Nitrogen, Phosphorus, Arsenic, Antimony, and Bismuth

The elements of Group V of the periodic system vary in properties from highly electronegative nonmetallic nitrogen to distinctly metallic bismuth. The stability of the -3 oxidation state decreases sharply as the atomic weight increases. In the $+3$ and $+5$ states of the oxygen acids, the elements are good oxidizing agents except in the case of phosphorus. The most powerful oxidizing agent of the group is the $+5$ bismic acid. The normal electronic state of the atoms of the group is $s^2p^3(^4S_{3/2})$.

NITROGEN

The oxidation states. Nitrogen forms compounds having all the oxidation states from -3 to $+5$. The most important compounds in the various states are: -3, ammonia, NH_3; -2, hydrazine, N_2H_4; -1, hydroxylamine, NH_2OH; $+1$, nitrous oxide, N_2O, and hyponitrous acid, $H_2N_2O_2$; $+2$, nitric oxide, NO; $+3$, nitrous acid, HNO_2; $+4$, nitrogen dioxide, NO_2, and nitrogen tetroxide, N_2O_4; and $+5$, nitric acid, HNO_3. In general, the compounds of the even numbers contain an even number of nitrogen atoms, but nitric oxide is an odd molecule and possesses but slight tendency to form a double molecule. Very few compounds are known in which the average oxidation number of the nitrogen is fractional. Hydrazoic acid, HN_3, is an example of such a compound.

Equilibria involving HNO_3, HNO_2, N_2O_4, NO_2, and NO. From Table 21, the free energy of nitrite ion is -8.25 kcal. Schumann[1] reported

$$HNO_2 = H^+ + NO_2^-, \qquad K = 4.5 \times 10^{-4}.$$

---

[1] M. Schumann, *Ber.*, 33, 527 (1900).

TABLE 21

THERMODYNAMIC DATA ON NITROGEN[1]

(Heat and free energy of formation in kcal. Entropy of substance in cal./deg.)

Formula	Description	State	$\Delta H°$	$\Delta F°$	$S°$
N	$(^4S_{3/2})$	g	*85.566*	*81.476*	*36.6145*
N⁺	$(^3P_0)$	g	*422.479*		
N⁺⁺	$(^2P_{1/2})$	g	*1106.71*		
N_2	$(1/\Sigma_g{}^+)$	g	0.0	0.0	*45.767*
$N_3{}^-$		aq	60.3	77.7	32. (?)
NO		g	*21.600*	*20.719*	*50.339*
NO_2		g	*8.091*	*12.390*	*57.47*
$NO_2{}^-$		aq	*−25.4*	−8.25	29.9
NO_3		g	*13.*		
$NO_3{}^-$		aq	*−49.372*	−26.43	35.0
N_2O		g	*19.49*	*24.76*	*52.58*
$N_2O_2{}^-$		aq	*−2.59*	*33.2*	*6.6*
N_2O_3		g	*20.0*		
N_2O_4		g	*2.309*	*23.491*	*72.73*
N_2O_5		c	*−10.0*	32.	27.1
NH		g	*59.*		
NH_2		g	*−11.04*	*−3.976*	*46.01*
NH_3		aq	*−19.32*	−6.36	26.3
$NH_4{}^+$		g	*20.*		
$NH_4{}^+$		aq	*−31.74*	−19.00	*26.97*
N_2H_4		liq	*12.05*		
N_2H_4		aq	8.16	30.56	(33.)
$N_2H_4 \cdot H_2O$		liq	−57.95		
$N_2H_4H_2{}^{++}$		aq	−4.0	22.50	19.
HN_3		g	70.3	78.5	*56.74*
HN_3		aq	60.50	71.30	(48.)
NH_4N_3		c	20.4	47.3	(31.3)
HNO_2		aq	−28.4	−12.82	
HNO_3		g			*63.62*
HNO_3		liq	*−41.404*	*−19.100*	*37.19*
HNO_3		aq	*−49.372*	*−26.43*	*35.*
NH_2OH		c	*−25.5*		
NH_2OH		aq	−21.7	−5.60	(40.)
$NH_2OH \cdot H^+$		aq	−30.7	−13.54	37.
NH_4OH		aq	*−87.64*	−63.05	*43.0*
$NH_2O_2{}^-$		aq	−9.4	18.2	34.0
$H_2N_2O_2$		aq	−13.7	8.6	52
NOCl		g	*12.57*	*15.86*	*63.0*
NOBr		g	*19.56*	*19.70*	*65.16*
N_4S		c	*127.6*		
$N_2H_4H^+$		aq	−1.7	21.0	31

[1] Bureau of Standards values in *italics;* estimated values in parentheses.

This makes the free energy of ionization 4570 cal. and the free energy of formation of nitrous acid -12.82 kcal. From Table 21 the free energy of nitrate ion is -26.43 kcal. Nitric acid will be treated as completely dissociated, so the same value is used for the acid. Before discussing nitric and nitrous acid potentials, a number of equilibria should be considered.

From Table 21,

$$2NO_2 = N_2O_4, \qquad \Delta F^\circ = -1.289 \text{ kcal.}$$

and the equilibrium constant for the reaction is 8.8. Hence at 25° C. the equilibrium mixture is largely N_2O_4, and equations will generally be written with tetroxide instead of the dioxide.

In alkaline solution, nitrogen tetroxide is unstable with respect to the decomposition into nitrite and nitrate.

$$N_2O_4 + 2OH^- = NO_2^- + H_2O + NO_3^-, \qquad \Delta F^\circ = -39.71 \text{ kcal.}$$

In cold water, low concentrations of N_2O_4 react to form a blue solution of nitric and nitrous acids. The free energy at 25° C. is

$$N_2O_4 + H_2O = HNO_2 + H^+ + NO_3^-, \qquad \Delta F^\circ = -6.07 \text{ kcal.}$$

However, in concentrated nitric acid the reaction is reversed and nitrous acid is oxidized to the tetroxide.

From the free energies of Table 21, we may also calculate

$$2HNO_2 = NO + NO_2 + H_2O, \qquad \Delta F^\circ = 2.46 \text{ kcal.}$$

This small positive free energy shows that there is a very appreciable pressure of NO and NO_2 in equilibrium with a nitrous acid solution, but a still more important reaction is the decomposition of nitrous acid into nitric acid and nitric oxide

$$3HNO_2 = H^+ + NO_3^- + 2NO + H_2O, \qquad \Delta F^\circ = -2.34 \text{ kcal.}$$

The direct experimental value for the equilibrium constant leads to a free energy of -2040 cal. as calculated by Lewis and Randall. The rate of the reaction is not rapid in cold dilute solutions of nitrous acid, but it becomes so upon heating. Hence, in warm concentrated solutions of the tetroxide the principal equilibrium is the following:

$$3NO_2 + H_2O = 2NO_3^- + 2H^+ + NO, \qquad \Delta F^\circ = -12.26 \text{ kcal.}$$

The free energy is not large however, and nitric oxide passed into concentrated nitric acid would obviously form an appreciable amount of NO_2 or N_2O_4.

The reduction of nitric acid. From the above equilibria it follows that the reduction products obtained upon the addition of a reducing agent to an excess of nitric acid, will depend very largely upon the concentration of the nitric acid. In many cases the first step is doubtless the reduction to nitrous acid.

$$H_2O + HNO_2 = NO_3^- + 3H^+ + 2e^-, \qquad E^\circ = -0.94.$$

But at low acid concentration, because of the decomposition of the nitrous acid, the net reaction is

$$2H_2O + NO = NO_3^- + 4H^+ + 3e^-, \qquad E^\circ = -0.96,$$

and at high acid concentrations,

$$2H_2O + N_2O_4 = 2NO_3^- + 4H^+ + 2e^-, \qquad E^\circ = -0.80.$$

The potential of this last couple changes rapidly with the concentration of hydrogen ion. Concentrated nitric acid is a rapid and powerful oxidizing agent, but in low hydrogen ion it is not only weak but also very slow in its reaction rate.

As an example of the effect of concentration upon the reduction products, one may cite the reduction of nitric acid by arsenious acid: with HNO_3 of density 1.45, the product is 1 part NO and 5 parts N_2O_4; with acid of density 1.35, the composition corresponds to $N_2O_3(NO + NO_2)$ and an acid density of 1.20 gives almost pure NO.

In view of these potentials, a powerful oxidizing agent is required to oxidize nitrous acid to nitric acid, and the reaction is quantitative with permanganate. Nitric oxide is, of course, readily oxidized to N_2O_4 by molecular oxygen, but it is remarkably inert to oxidation by many powerful agents, although PbO_2, MnO_2, and $KMnO_4$ will oxidize it slowly to nitric acid.

The nitrogen-tetroxide couples in acid solution are

$$2HNO_2 = N_2O_4 + 2H^+ + 2e^-, \qquad E^\circ = -1.07;$$
$$2H_2O + 2NO = N_2O_4 + 4H^+ + 4e^-, \qquad E^\circ = -1.03.$$

These values place the tetroxide about equal to bromine as an oxidizing agent in molal acid solution. Its action is much more rapid in general than that of nitric acid.

The nitrite-nitrate couple. Because of the decomposition of nitrogen tetroxide in alkali and of the greater stability of nitrite ion, the net half-reaction for the reduction of nitrate ion in hydroxide solution is

$$2OH^- + NO_2^- = NO_3^- + H_2O + 2e^-, \qquad E_B^o = -0.01.$$

The reduction of nitrate is slow with many reducing agents, but it goes with sodium amalgam and with ferrous hydroxide, and it may also be carried out electrolytically with copper or silver cathodes. Because of the more rapid reduction of nitrite, it is difficult to stop the reaction at the nitrite state even when no excess of reducing agent is used. The presence of cupric ions appears to favor the electrolytic reduction to lower oxidation states.

Nitrite may be oxidized to nitrate by comparatively weak oxidizing agents and also by anodic oxidation. The rate of the latter reaction is favored by low hydroxide concentration, contrary to the prediction from the over-all reaction potentials. However, the mechanism of the reaction is unknown and the accompanying oxidation of the water to oxygen is also favored by high hydroxide concentration.

The reduction of nitrous acid. Ferrous ion, a weak reducing agent, and titanous ion, a powerful reducing agent, both reduce nitrous acid to nitric oxide; while stannous ion, which is intermediate in potential, reduces nitrous acid to hydroxylamine when the solution is cold, and to nitrous oxide when the solution is hot. The first two are one-electron reducing agents, and the reduction to nitric oxide involves but one electron. Because of the remarkable inertness of nitric oxide, the reaction stops at this point. The potential of the nitric oxide-nitrous acid couple is

$$H_2O + NO = HNO_2 + H^+ + e^-, \qquad E^o = -1.00.$$

It is generally assumed that two-electron reducing agents such as stannous ion first form with nitrous acid some intermediate compound of +1 oxidation number. Both nitrous oxide, N_2O, and hyponitrous acid, $H_2N_2O_2$, correspond to this state, but the intermediate is thought to be nitroxyl, NOH, or possibly dihydroxylammonia, $NH(OH)_2$. From the electron structures the latter seems somewhat more reasonable, as it does not involve breaking an oxygen-nitrogen bond.

$$: \overset{\cdot\cdot}{\underset{\cdot\cdot}{O}} : \overset{\cdot\cdot}{\underset{\cdot\cdot}{N}} : \overset{\cdot\cdot}{O} : H \qquad : \overset{\cdot\cdot}{N} : \overset{\cdot\cdot}{\underset{\cdot\cdot}{O}} : H \qquad H : \overset{\cdot\cdot}{\underset{\cdot\cdot}{O}} : \overset{H}{\underset{\cdot\cdot}{N}} : \overset{\cdot\cdot}{\underset{\cdot\cdot}{O}} : H$$

(nitrous acid)　　　　　　(nitroxyl)　　　　　　(dihydroxylammonia)

Harteck[1] has prepared a form of HNO by the reaction of atomic hydrogen with nitric oxide, and atomic oxygen with ammonia at liquid air temperature. He has also claimed the preparation of NaNO by the reaction of sodium and nitric oxide in liquid ammonia.

The free energies of NOH and $NH(OH)_2$ are not known. The $\Delta H°$, $\Delta F°$, $S°$ values for hyponitrous acid have been given by Latimer and Zimmermann[2] based upon the heat of formation of $H_2N_2O_2(aq)$ as -11.3 kcal. Their values have been corrected to the new Bureau of Standards value for this heat. From this work we write

$$H_2N_2O_2 = H^+ + HN_2O_2^-, \qquad K = 9 \times 10^{-8};$$
$$HN_2O_2^- = H^+ + N_2O_2^-, \qquad K = 1 \times 10^{-11};$$
$$H_2N_2O_2 = N_2O + H_2O, \qquad \Delta F° = -37.5 \text{ kcal}.$$

This reaction is known to be highly irreversible.

$$H_2N_2O_2 + 2H_2O = 2HNO_2 + 4H^+ + 4e^-, \qquad E° = -0.833.$$

For comparison, the N_2O—HNO_2 couple is

$$N_2O + 3H_2O = 2HNO_2 + 4H^+ + 4e^-, \qquad E° = -1.29;$$
$$2NH_3OH^+ = H_2N_2O_2 + 6H^+ + 4e^-, \qquad E° = -0.496.$$

This small negative value should constitute a barrier to the reduction of nitrous acid to hydroxylamine by weak reducing agents.

$H_2N_2O_2$ is highly unstable with respect to N_2 and NO.

$$N_2 + 2H_2O = H_2N_2O_2 + 2H^+ + 2e^-, \qquad E° = -2.65;$$
$$H_2N_2O_2 = 2NO + 2H^+ + 2e^-, \qquad E° = -0.71.$$

Winkelblack[3] has given

$$NH_2OH(aq) + H_2O = NH_3OH^+ + OH^-, \qquad K = 6.6 \times 10^{-8}.$$

This leads to -13.54 kcal. as the free energy of NH_3OH^+ and an

[1] P. Harteck, *Ber.*, **66**, 423, 768 (1933).
[2] W. M. Latimer and H. W. Zimmermann, *J. Am. Chem. Soc.*, **61**, 1550 (1939).
[3] K. Winkelblack, *Z. physik. Chem.*, **36**, 574 (1901).

entropy of 37. cal./deg. for the ion. This latter value appears to be
too high.

Bray, Simpson, and MacKenzie[1] have studied the oxidation of
hydroxylamine by ferric ion which is powerful enough to oxidize it to
NOH but does not oxidize NOH to HNO_2. They found that at high
acid concentrations the product was quantitatively N_2O, the mechanism probably being the formation of NOH and its decomposition
into nitrous oxide,

$$2NOH = N_2O + H_2O.$$

At low hydrogen ion, nitrogen was formed, presumably through the
reaction

$$NH_3OH^+ + NOH = N_2 + 2H_2O + H^+.$$

The faster rate of decomposition of nitroxyl in acid may arise from its
slightly basic character and the formation of N^+ which then reacts
with NOH to link the nitrogens together. The ordinary splitting out
of water between two nitroxyl molecules would produce N·O·N and
not N·NO, which is the actual atomic arrangement in nitrous oxide.

More powerful oxidizing agents than ferric ion will, of course,
oxidize hydroxylamine to nitrous acid. Under these conditions
nitrous oxide may be formed by the reaction,

$$HNO_2 + NH_3OH^+ = N_2O + 2H_2O + H^+, \qquad \Delta F^\circ = -61.7 \text{ kcal.}$$

Under suitable conditions the product is hyponitrous acid,

$$HNO_2 + NH_3OH^+ = H_2N_2O_2 + H_2O + H^+, \qquad \Delta F^\circ = -21.7.$$

A possible mechanism for the formation of nitric oxide by the reduction of nitrous acid is through nitroxyl and its reaction with the
excess nitrous acid,

$$NOH + HNO_2 = 2NO + H_2O.$$

However, it is doubtful whether this is the case with a one-electron
reducing agent such as titanous ion, but it may be the explanation of
the action of stannous ion. With an excess of this reagent in low acid,
nitrous oxide is formed; but with excess nitrous acid, nitric oxide
results.[2]

---

[1] W. C. Bray, M. E. Simpson, and A. A. MacKenzie, J Am. Chem. Soc., 41,
1363 (1919).

[2] F. Raschig, Z. anorg. allgem. Chem., 155, 225 (1926).

There is some evidence of the existence of nitrohydroxylamic acid, $H_2N_2O_3$, in which the nitrogen is also in the $+2$ oxidation state. The acid is considered to be unstable with respect to decomposition into nitric oxide and water. The role which it plays, if any, in the oxidation of nitroxyl or the reduction of nitrous acid is unknown.

The hydroxylamine-ammonium couple. Combining the free energy value of ammonia gas (Table 21) with the values chosen by Lewis and Randall for the free energy of solution and the free energy of ionization of ammonium hydroxide,

$$NH_3(g) = NH_3(aq), \qquad \Delta F° = -2.39 \text{ kcal.;}$$
$$NH_4(aq) + H_2O = NH_4OH(aq), \qquad \Delta F° = 0;$$
$$NH_4OH = NH_4^+ + OH^-, \qquad K = 1.81 \times 10^{-5};$$
$$\Delta F° = 6.67 \text{ kcal.,}$$

we obtain the following free energies: $NH_3(aq)$, -6.36 kcal.; NH_4OH, -63.05 kcal.; and NH_4^+, -19.0 kcal. Bates and Pinching[1] have given 1.77×10^{-5} for the dissociation of NH_4OH. The potential for the hydroxylamine-ammonium ion couple then is

$$H_2O + NH_4^+ = NH_3OH^+ + 2H^+ + 2e^-, \qquad E° = -1.35.$$

This value would indicate that hydroxylamine is a powerful oxidizing agent, but actually its rate of reduction is slow with many powerful reducing agents. For example, there appears to be no reduction with stannous ion in acid solution. The reaction does go in acid, however, with zinc, ferrous, and titanous ions. On the other hand, very powerful oxidizing agents are required to oxidize ammonium ion as the potential requires, and in general any oxidizing agent which will oxidize ammonium ion to hydroxylamine will take it on up to nitric acid.

Hydroxylamine is unstable with respect to decomposition into ammonium ion and nitrous oxide.

$$4NH_3OH^+ = N_2O + 2NH_4^+ + 3H_2O + 2H^+, \qquad \Delta F° = -118.7 \text{ kcal.}$$

and the reaction is favored by alkali as the equation indicates. The reaction doubtless operates through nitroxyl so that some nitrogen may also be formed simultaneously by the reaction of the NOH with NH_3OH^+ as discussed above.

Bancroft[2] has presented evidence that nitrous acid may be reduced

[1] R. G. Bates and G. D. Pinching, *J. Am. Chem. Soc.*, **72**, 1393 (1950).

[2] W. D. Bancroft, *J. Phys. Chem.*, **28**, 475 (1924).

to ammonium without going through the hydroxylamine stage. As a hypothetical mechanism the formation of NH or N_2H_2 might be assumed. But this substance would certainly have a more positive free energy than hydroxylamine so that the reduction from the $+1$ to the -1 state would be difficult. It is, however, a possible process with powerful reducing agents.

The reduction of nitrous acid with sulfite. The one reducing agent for which the mechanism of the reduction of nitrous acid is best understood is sulfurous acid. The intermediate compounds are shown in the following scheme.

STEPS IN THE REDUCTION OF NITROUS
ACID WITH SULFITE

HNO_2

with HSO_3^- ↓

$HSO_3 \cdot NO$ with H^+ $HNO(H_2N_2O_2)$
(nitrosulfonic acid) $\longrightarrow$ (hyponitrous acid)

with HSO_3^- ↓

$(HSO_3)_2 \cdot NOH$ with H^+ NH_3OH^+
(hydroxylamine $\longrightarrow$ (hydroxylamine)
disulfonic acid)

with HSO_3^- ↓

$(HSO_3)_3 \cdot N$ with H^+ NH_4^+
(nitrilosulfonic acid) $\longrightarrow$ (ammonium)

The reactions with HSO_3^- are reversed in high hydroxide concentrations. With H^+, hydrolysis occurs with the formation of sulfuric acid and the products indicated by the arrows. These reactions may be looked upon as the successive replacement of the OH radical in orthonitrous acid $N(OH)_3$ by HSO_3 radicals and these in turn by H upon hydrolysis. The result is a series of two-electron reductions. Similarly the reduction of nitric acid, $HONO_2$, with sulfurous acid first forms nitrosyl sulfuric acid, HSO_3NO_2, which hydrolyzes to nitrous and sulfuric acids. At high hydrogen ion, nitrous acid is reduced by sulfurous acid to nitrous oxide.

The oxidation and reduction of hydrazine. Schwarzenbach,[1] and Ware, Spulnik, and Gilbert[2] have studied the dissociation of hydrazine. From this work and the free energies we write

$$N_2H_5^+ = N_2H_4 + H^+, \qquad K = 1.02 \times 10^{-8};$$
$$N_2H_6^{++} = N_2H_5^+ + H^+, \qquad K = 11.$$
$$N_2H_5OH = N_2H_5^+ + OH^-, \qquad K = 9.8 \times 10^{-7}.$$

The free energies are $N_2H_5^+$, 21.0 kcal.; $N_2H_6^{++}$, 22.5 kcal. The calculated entropies of the ions appear reasonable.

From these values, the potentials of the following half-reactions may be calculated:

$$2NH_4^+ = N_2H_5^+ + 3H^+ + 2e^-, \qquad E° = -1.275;$$
$$2OH^- + 2NH_4OH = N_2H_4 + 4H_2O + 2e^-, \qquad E_B° = -0.1;$$
$$2H_2O + N_2H_5^+ = 2NH_3OH^+ + H^+ + 2e^-, \qquad E° = -1.42;$$
$$2OH^- + N_2H_4 = 2NH_2OH + 2e^-, \qquad E_B° = -0.73;$$
$$N_2H_5^+ = N_2 + 5H^+ + 4e^-, \qquad E° = 0.23;$$
$$4OH^- + N_2H_4 = N_2 + 4H_2O + 4e^-, \qquad E_B° = 1.16.$$

It is obvious that hydrazine in acid solution should be a powerful oxidizing agent. The reaction rate is very slow, but it may be titrated quantitatively with strong reducing agents. However, powerful oxidizing agents are required to oxidize ammonia to hydrazine, chlorine being generally employed. In this oxidation the ammonia must be in excess to prevent the further oxidation of the hydrazine which goes very readily to nitrogen as the half-reaction potential indicates. The potential for the oxidation of hydrazine to hydroxylamine is very high, and there is no evidence that the reaction ever occurs.

Bray and Cuy[3] studied the oxidation of hydrazine and found that while the oxidation to nitrogen is quantitative with some reagents (as, for example, with iodine) one-electron oxidizing agents tend, as a limit, to form two molecules of NH_4^+ and one of N_2. As a mechanism Bray and Cuy assumed that N_2H_3 is the first product and that it

[1] G. Schwarzenbach, *Helv. Chem. Acta.*, **19**, 178 (1936).

[2] G. C. Ware, J. B. Spulnik and E. C. Gilbert, *J. Am. Chem. Soc.*, **58**, 1606 (1936).

[3] W. C. Bray and E. J. Cuy, *J. Am. Chem. Soc.*, **46**, 1786 and 1810 (1924).

decomposes according to the equation

$$2H^+ + 2N_2H_3 = N_2 + 2NH_4^+.$$

The oxidation takes place with ferric ion, so the N_2H_3 must be a weaker oxidizing agent than this substance.

$$N_2H_5^+ = N_2H_3 + 2H^+ + e^-, \qquad E^\circ > -0.6.$$

As the potential values predict, hydrazine is capable of oxidizing and reducing itself to form nitrogen and ammonia,

$$3N_2H_4 = N_2 + 4NH_3, \qquad \Delta F^\circ = -117.0 \text{ kcal.}$$

The alkaline solution is fairly stable in the absence of platinum, which catalyzes the reaction.

Hydrazine is not formed in the reduction of nitric acid or nitrates and appears to play no part in the ordinary mechanism of such reductions. It is said, however, to be formed in the reduction of the sulfite-nitric oxide complex, $K_2SO_3 \cdot 2NO$, by sodium amalgam; and Brackel[1] has described the reduction of $Ag_2N_2O_2$ with $KHSO_3$ to form hydrazine.

Nitrate to ammonia in alkaline solution. There is abundant evidence that the ordinary course of the reduction of nitrite in alkaline solution goes through the oxidation states, $+1$, -1, to -3, and the products under various conditions are hyponitrite, hydroxylamine, and ammonia. The potential values for the corresponding couples have been summarized in the potential diagram (see p. 104). It will be observed that the greatest potential to be overcome in the reduction is for the $+1$ to -1 step, while in the oxidation of ammonia the -3 to -1 step provides the highest barrier. The following experimental facts are of interest.

The cathodic reduction of concentrated nitrate with a mercury cathode described by Zorn[2] yields hyponitrite. The product may also be obtained by the reduction with sodium amalgam. It would appear that the union of two nitroxyls to form hyponitrous acid occurs less readily than the union of two NO^- ions to form $N_2O_2^{--}$, as hyponitrite is not readily formed in acid reduction. Hydroxylamine may be oxidized to hyponitrite by mercuric oxide (Hg—HgO, $E^\circ = -0.1$). The presence of mercury thus seems very definitely to favor the formation

---

[1] F. Brackel, *Ber.*, **33**, 2115 (1900).
[2] W. Zorn, *Ber.*, **12**, 1509 (1879).

of hyponitrite in alkaline solution, although it is not to be inferred that hyponitrite cannot be formed in its absence.

Although the cathodic reduction of nitrates in neutral or alkaline solution yields ammonia and no hydroxylamine, the reduction of nitrites on various cathodes gives a mixture of ammonia and hydroxylamine, according to the results of Suler.[1] The absence of hydroxylamine in the nitrate electrolysis must mean that nitrate is able to catalyze the reduction of hydroxylamine to ammonia in alkaline solutions. In view of the potentials, it is surprising that the reduction of nitrite ever stops at hydroxylamine, but this slowness as an oxidizing agent in alkaline solutions is in line with its similar behavior in acid solutions. Baudisch and Mayer[2] report that ferrous hydroxide reduces nitrite quantitatively to ammonia in slightly alkaline solutions when a threefold excess of the reducing agent is used. Without the excess, some nitrous oxide is formed.

Ammonium hydroxide is readily oxidized on various metal anodes to nitrite, and at high hydroxide concentration the oxidation does not go on to nitrate, as mentioned above. The presence of certain negative ions often leads to the formation of some nitrogen and nitrous oxide. Thus, Fichter[3] reports that the addition of ammonium carbonate to an ammonium hydroxide electrolyte with a platinum anode changes the oxidation product from nitrate to largely nitrogen and nitrous oxide.

The reduction of nitric and nitrous oxides. The inertness of nitric oxide in acid toward reduction by ferrous and titanous ions has been mentioned. It is, however, reduced by stannous to hydroxylamine and nitrogen and by stannite in alkali to hyponitrite, according to Divers and Haga.[4] A possible explanation of the difficulty in the reduction of nitric oxide by one-electron reducing agents is the high positive value for the NOH—NO couple. From analogy with hydroxyl and hydrogen peroxide we estimate

$$NOH = NO + H^+ + e^-, \qquad E^\circ = ca\ 0.3.$$

Thus even Ti^{+++} would not readily reduce nitric oxide over this barrier.

[1] B. Suler, *Z. Elektrochem.*, **7**, 831 (1901).
[2] O. Baudisch and P. Mayer, *Biochem. Zeit.*, **107**, 1 (1920).
[3] F. Fichter, *Z. Elektrochem.*, **18**, 647 (1912).
[4] E. Divers and T. Haga, *Chem. News*, **78**, 313 (1898).

Nichols and Derbigny[1] have studied the reduction of nitrous oxide by various reagents in acid solution. They report the reduction by Ti^{+++} to ammonia, by Sn^{++} to hydroxylamine, and by H_2SO_3 (slowly) to nitrogen. It is interesting to note the reduction by titanous in view of the fact that it does not react with nitric oxide.

Hydrazoic acid. Yost and Russel[2] gave

$$HN_3 = H^+ + N_3^-, \qquad K = 1.8 \times 10^{-5}.$$

The free energy of N_3^- is 77.7 kcal., and for the free energy of formation from hydrazine and nitrous acid we calculate

$$N_2H_4 + HNO_2 = HN_3 + 2H_2O, \qquad \Delta F^\circ = -58.7 \text{ kcal.}$$

The potential for the ammonium ion-hydrazoic acid couple is

$$3NH_4^+ = HN_3 + 11H^+ + 8e^-, \qquad E^\circ = -0.69.$$

Curtis and Darapsky[3] report the reduction of hydrazoic acid to ammonia by metals ranging from Al to Cu in reducing power. However, hydrazoic acid is a very much more powerful oxidizing agent in its reduction to nitrogen and ammonium.

$$NH_4^+ + N_2 = HN_3 + 3H^+ + 2e^-, \qquad E^\circ = -1.96.$$

The oxidation of chloride to chlorine by this couple is reported by Browne and Hoel.[4]

Cook[5] has studied the reduction by sodium amalgam and ferrous hydroxide. Under these conditions he found the products to be hydrazine and ammonia.

$$7OH^- + N_2H_4 + NH_3 = N_3^- + 7H_2O + 6e^-, \qquad E_B^\circ = 0.62.$$

Hydrazoic acid is also a powerful reducing agent.

$$HN_3 = \tfrac{3}{2}N_2 + H^+ + e^-, \qquad E^\circ = 3.1;$$
$$N_3^- = \tfrac{3}{2}N_2 + e^-, \qquad E_B^\circ = 3.4.$$

Sommer and Pincas[6] have studied the oxidation of hydrazoic acid

---

[1] M. L. Nichols and I. A. Derbigny, *J. Phys. Chem.*, **30**, 491 (1926).

[2] D. Yost and H. Russel, Jr., *Systematic Inorganic Chemistry*, New York: Prentice-Hall, Inc., 1946.

[3] T. Curtis and A. Darapsky, *J. prakt. Chem.*, **61**, 408 (1900).

[4] A. W. Browne and A. B. Hoel, *J. Am. Chem. Soc.*, **44**, 2117 (1922).

[5] W. T. Cook, *Proc. Chem. Soc.*, **19**, 213 (1904).

[6] F. Sommer and H. Pincas, *Ber.*, **49**, 259 (1916).

with ceric ion and found it quantitative in the oxidation to nitrogen. The oxidation by iodine is also quantitative if a trace of thiosulfate is present, and Raschig has discussed possible mechanism of the thiosulfate action.

From the potentials given, it is obvious that hydrazoic acid is unstable with respect to its decomposition into nitrogen and ammonia. The free energy of the reaction is very large.

$$3HN_3 = 4N_2 + NH_3, \qquad \Delta F^\circ = -202 \text{ kcal.}$$

The catalysis by platinum has been studied by Oliveri-Mandala.[1]

Nitrosyl chloride and nitrosyl bromide. Lewis and Randall[2] calculate 16,010 cal. for the free energy of formation of nitrosyl chloride gas from equilibrium data on the reaction between nitric oxide and chlorine. From thermal and spectroscopic data the value would appear to be 15.86 kcal., and this value will be used.

Blair, Brass, and Yost[3] found from the nitric oxide-bromine reaction that the free energy of formation of nitrosyl bromide gas is 19.26 kcal. The Bureau of Standards value is 19.7 kcal.

With water, the chloride and bromide rapidly hydrolyze,

$$NOCl(g) + H_2O = HNO_2 + H^+ + Cl^-, \qquad \Delta F^\circ = -37.65 \text{ kcal.}$$

$$NOBr(g) + H_2O = HNO_2 + H^+ + Br^-, \qquad \Delta F^\circ = 0.48 \text{ kcal.}$$

The free energies indicate that the hydrolysis is quite large, especially with the chloride. For this reason the behavior of solutions of these nitrosyl compounds as oxidizing and reducing agents will be essentially that of nitrous acid.

Ammoniated electron. The alkali metals dissolve in liquid ammonia to give blue solutions, which are regarded as containing the ammoniated electron.

$$Na = Na^+(ammo) + e^-(ammo).$$

Laitenen and Nyman[4] have given the potential of the electrode-electron couple against the H_2—H^+ couple as 1.89.

[1] E. Oliveri-Mandala, *Gazz. chim. Ital.*, **46**, 137 and 298 (1916).

[2] G. N. Lewis and M. Randall, *Thermodynamics*, New York: McGraw-Hill Book Company, Inc., 1923, p. 562. Compare F. P. Jahn, *J. Chem. Phys.*, **6**, 338 (1938).

[3] C. M. Blair, P. D. Brass and D. M. Yost, *J. Am. Chem. Soc.*, **56**, 1916 (1934).

[4] H. A. Laitenen and C. J. Nyman, *J. Am. Chem. Soc.*, **70**, 3002 (1948).

Potential Diagrams for Nitrogen

Acid Solution

Base Solution

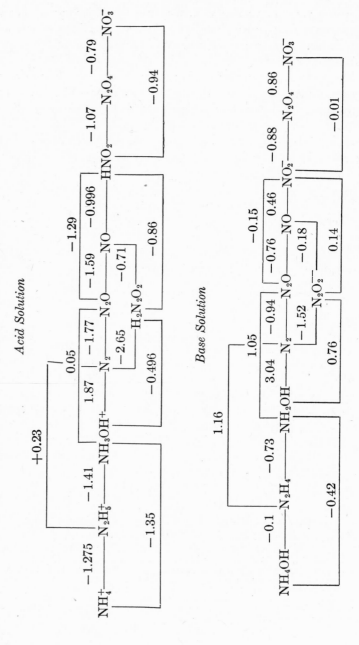

Summary of nitrogen potentials. The values for the potentials relating the various nitrogen oxidation states in acid and alkali
have been summarized in the potential diagrams. Most of the important facts regarding these potentials have already been presented.
The values for the reductions and oxidations to molecular nitrogen,
although of little chemical significance, are interesting from the energy
standpoint. With respect to N_2, nitric acid ($+5$ state) is the most
stable of the positive states, and ammonium (-3 state) is the most
stable of the negative states. On either side, the stability decreases
rapidly and regularly from the high state to the low. In spite of the
very favorable energy relations, only in the case of hydrazine is it
possible to go quantitatively to nitrogen. For this case the explanation
may be offered that the two nitrogens are already attached to each
other and the reaction does not therefore have to proceed through
atomic nitrogen with the resulting potential barrier. But such an explanation makes the case of hyponitrous acid particularly puzzling,
because here, too, the nitrogens are presumably attached to each
other, and yet, with a potential almost equal to that of fluorine, the
reduction to N_2 does not occur.

PHOSPHORUS

Oxidation states. The important compounds of the various oxidation states of phosphorous are: -3, phosphine, PH_3; -2, hydrogen
diphosphide, P_2H_4; $+1$, hypophosphorous acïd, H_3PO_2; $+3$, phosphorous acid, H_3PO_3; $+4$, hypophosphoric acid, $H_4P_2O_6$; and $+5$,
orthophosphoric acid, H_3PO_4. The oxides P_2O_3, P_2O_4, and P_2O_5 exist,
and claims are made for a suboxide, P_4O. The hydrogen phosphide,
$(P_2H)_x$—probably the tetraphosphide, P_4H_2—, is fairly stable, and
the compound PH, -1 state, is known as an unstable gas molecule.
Halides of the $+2$, $+3$, and $+5$ oxidation states have been prepared.

The free energies of phosphorus compounds. Rapid reversible equilibrium is practically never attainable in oxidation-reduction
reactions involving phosphorus or its compounds; hence, free energies
are not available from equilibrium data. The entropies of phosphine
and aqueous phosphoric acid and its ions are known, but for the other
oxygen acids and their ions we have no entropy values and have used
approximate values based upon similar compounds.

TABLE 22

THERMODYNAMIC DATA ON PHOSPHORUS[1]

(Heat and free energy of formation in kcal. Entropy of substance in cal./deg.)

Formula	Description	State	$\Delta H°$	$\Delta F°$	$S°$
P		g	75.18	66.71	38.98
P	white	c, III	0.0	0.0	10.6
P	red	c, II	-4.4	-3.3	(7.0)
P	black	c, I	-10.3		
P+		g	329.81		
P++		g	784.51		
P$_2$		g	33.82	24.60	52.13
P$_4$		g	13.12	5.82	66.90
P$_4$		liq	0.601		
PO		g	-9.7		
PO$_4$$^{----}$		aq	-306.9	-245.1	-52.
P$_2$O$_7$$^{----}$		aq	-543.1		
P$_4$O$_{10}$		c	-720.0		
PH$_3$		g	2.21	4.36	50.2
P$_4$H$_2$		c	6.9	16.0	(40.)
HPO$_3$		c	-228.2		
HPO$_3$		aq	-234.8 (?)	-215.8	(36.)
H$_2$PO$_2$$^-$		aq		-122.4	
HPO$_3$$^{--}$		aq	-233.8	-194.0	
HPO$_4$$^{--}$		aq	-310.4	-261.5	-8.6
H$_2$PO$_3$$^-$		aq		-202.35	(19.)
H$_2$PO$_4$$^-$		aq	-311.3	-271.3	21.3
H$_3$PO$_2$		c	-145.5		
H$_3$PO$_2$		aq	-145.6	-125.1	(38.)
H$_3$PO$_4$		c	-306.2		
H$_3$PO$_4$		aq	-308.2	-274.2	42.1
H$_3$PO$_3$		c	-232.2		
H$_3$PO$_3$		aq	-232.2	-204.8	(40.)
H$_4$P$_2$O$_6$		aq		-392.	
H$_4$P$_2$O$_7$		c	-538.0		
H$_4$P$_2$O$_7$		aq	-545.9		
PF$_3$		g			64.13
PCl$_3$		g	-73.22	-68.42	74.49
PCl$_3$		liq	-81.0	-68.6	
PCl$_5$		c	-110.7		
PCl$_5$		g	-95.35	-77.57	84.3
POCl$_3$		liq	-151.0		
POCl$_3$		g	-141.5	-130.3	77.59
PBr$_3$		g	-85.9	-41.2	83.11
PBr$_3$		liq	-47.5		
PBr$_5$		c	-66.0		
POBr$_3$		c	-114.6		
PH$_4$Br		c	-29.5		
PI$_3$		c	-10.9	-8.99	(46.)
P$_2$I$_4$		c	-19.76	-19.8	(44.2)
PH$_4$I		c	-15.8		
PN		g	-20.2	-25.3	50.45
P$_3$N$_5$		c	-75.7		

[1] Bureau of Standards values in *italics;* estimated values in parentheses.

The Bureau of Standards has chosen "white" phosphorus as their standard state in spite of the fact that the "red" or "violet" modifications are the more stable. We have adopted their value, although we employed the "red" phosphorus as the standard state in the First Edition. Thus, there is a difference of 4.4 kcal. in ΔH° between the two editions because of this change.

The phosphorous-phosphoric acid couple. Pitzer[1] has reviewed the data on the ionizations of H_3PO_4, and gives

$$H_3PO_4 = H^+ + H_2PO_4^-, \qquad K = 7.5 \times 10^{-3};$$
$$H_2PO_4^- = H^+ + HPO_4^{--} \qquad K = 6.2 \times 10^{-8};$$
$$HPO_4^{--} = H^+ + PO_4^{---}, \qquad K = 10^{-12}.$$

The Bureau of Standards free energies are in approximate agreement with these values for the various constants.

Kolthoff[2] found for phosphorous acid

$$H_3PO_3 = H^+ + H_2PO_3^-, \qquad K = 1.6 \times 10^{-2};$$
$$H_2PO_3^- = H^+ + HPO_3^-, \qquad K = 7 \times 10^{-7}.$$

For the free energies of the ions calculate $H_2PO_3^-$, -202.35 kcal., and HPO_3^{--}, -194.0 kcal. The evidence is fairly conclusive that the third hydrogen is attached to the phosphorus and is not replaceable.

These values lead to the following potentials for the phosphorous—phosphoric-acid couple.

$$H_2O + H_3PO_3 = H_3PO_4 + 2H^+ + 2e^-, \qquad E^\circ = 0.276;$$
$$3OH^- + HPO_3^{--} = PO_4^{---} + 2H_2O + 2e^-, \qquad E_B^\circ = 1.12.$$

From our value for the free energy of metaphosphoric acid we write

$$HPO_3 + H_2O = H_3PO_4, \qquad \Delta F^\circ = -1.5 \text{ kcal.}$$

The value seems to be of the right order of magnitude, but is not very significant, in view of the polymerization of the meta-acid. Yost and Russel[3] summarized the various acids and concluded that, in the formula $(HPO_3)n$ the value of n can be 2, 3, 4, 6, and possibly 1.

Davies and Monk[4] have reexamined the problem and have confirmed only the tri- and tetra-acid and a colloidal form which is the

[1] K. S. Pitzer, *J. Am. Chem. Soc.*, **59**, 2365 (1937).

[2] I. M. Kolthoff, *Rec. trav. chim., Pays-Bas*, **46**, 350 (1927).

[3] D. Yost and H. Russel, Jr., *Systematic Inorganic Chemistry*, New York: Prentice-Hall, Inc., 1946.

[4] C. W. Davies and C. B. Monk, *J. Chem. Soc.*, **413**, 423, 427 (1949).

former hexametaphosphoric acid. They have written the following constants:

$$HP_3O_9^{--} = H^+ + P_3O_9^{---}, \qquad K = 8.3 \times 10^{-8};$$
$$HP_4O_{12}^{---} = H^+ + P_4O_{12}^{----}, \qquad K = 1.8 \times 10^{-3};$$
$$Ca_2P_4O_{12} = Ca^{++} + CaP_4O_{12}^{--}, \qquad K = 2.2 \times 10^{-3};$$
$$CaP_4O_{12}^{--} = Ca^{++} + P_4O_{12}^{----}, \qquad K = 1.3 \times 10^{-5}.$$

With sodium hydroxide and the trioxide, the trimetaphosphate, $Na_5P_3O_{10}$ is formed and they give the constant

$$NaP_3O_{10}^{----} = Na^+ + P_3O_{10}^{-5}, \qquad K = 3 \times 10^{-3}.$$

The same authors found for the pyrophosphoric acid that the first two dissociations were complete and wrote for K_3 and K_4

$$H_2P_2O_7^{--} = H^+ + HP_2O_7^{---}, \qquad K = 2.7 \times 10^{-7};$$
$$HP_2O_7^{---} = H^+ + P_2O_7^{-4}, \qquad K = 2.4 \times 10^{-10}.$$

Hypophosphoric acid. There are no data available for the calculation of the free energy of hypophosphoric acid, $H_4P_2O_6$ (or H_2PO_3). However, the reaction

$$H_4P_2O_6 + H_2O = H_3PO_3 + H_3PO_4,$$

although slow in cold dilute solutions, goes if the solution is concentrated and somewhat acid. Considerable heat appears to be evolved. If we assume -30 kcal. as the free energy of the reaction, this would make the free energy of hypophosphoric acid, $H_4P_2O_6$, -392 kcal., and would give the following potentials:

$$2H_2O + H_4P_2O_6 = 2H_3PO_4 + 2H^+ + 2e^-, \qquad E^\circ = (0.9);$$
$$2H_3PO_3 = H_4P_2O_6 + 2H^+ + 2e^-, \qquad E^\circ = (-0.4).$$

These potentials are certainly approximately correct and throw considerable light on the problem of the phosphorous-phosphoric acid couple. Even a very powerful one-electron reducing agent, such as titanous ion, would be unable to reduce phosphate in acid solution to H_2PO_3. On the other hand, a fairly powerful one-electron oxidizing agent would be required to oxidize phosphorous acid to H_2PO_3. The reaction should not stop there, but, because of the ease of the next step, the H_2PO_3 should be oxidized to phosphoric acid. The assumptions appear to agree with the experimental facts. Linhart[1] found that

[1] G. A. Linhart, *Am. J. Sci.* (4), **35**, 353 (1913).

the reaction of phosphorous acid with mercuric chloride formed mercurous chloride, and the reaction was monomolecular with respect to the mercuric chloride. This first step of the reaction was slow and appeared to be followed by a rapid step giving phosphoric acid. It seems strange, however, that there is not some mechanism by which phosphoric acid can go directly to the phosphorous acid by the shift of an oxygen as, for example, in the reduction of nitric acid by sulfite. The answer probably is that no such reducing agent exists with a potential as low as the 0.2 required for the two-electron step.

Hypophosphorous acid. Kolthoff[1] records for the dissociation constant of hypophosphorous acid.

$$H_3PO_2 = H^+ + H_2PO_2^-, \qquad K = 0.01.$$

Only one of the hydrogens is replaceable, indicating that the other two are attached directly to the phosphorous. From this constant the free energy of $H_2PO_2^-$ is -122.4 kcal., and the potentials for the couples relating the acid to higher and lower oxidation states are

$$H_2O + H_3PO_2 = H_3PO_3 + 2H^+ + 2e^-, \qquad E^\circ = 0.50;$$
$$3OH^- + H_2PO_2^- = HPO_3^{--} + 2H_2O + 2e^-, \qquad E_B^\circ = 1.57;$$
$$2H_2O + P = H_3PO_2 + H^+ + e^-, \qquad E^\circ = 0.51;$$
$$2OH^- + P = H_2PO_2^- + e^-, \qquad E_B^\circ = 2.05.$$

Hypophosphorous acid is thus a very weak oxidizing agent and a very powerful reducing agent in both acid and basic solutions. A number of important decomposition reactions are considered in a later paragraph.

Hayward and Yost[2] have reviewed the kinetics of the oxidation of hypophosphorous acid and support the assumption that there are two forms of the acid, a normal and an active form, and that the rate-determining step in the reactions with oxidizing agents is the conversion of the normal to the active form.

Phosphine and other hydrogen phosphides. The solubility of phosphine in water is about $0.01M$ as given by Stock, Bottcher, and Lenger.[3] This would make the free energy of solution 2730 cal. The free energy of dissociation of phosphonium ion into phosphine and hydrogen ion must be close to zero, as the solution of the gas is not alkaline. One can then estimate the free energy of phosphonium ion,

[1] I. M. Kolthoff, *Rec. trav. chim.*, **46**, 350 (1927).

[2] P. Hayward and D. Yost, *J. Am. Chem. Soc.*, **71**, 915 (1949).

[3] A. Stock, W. Bottcher and W. Lenger, *Ber.*, **42**, 2855 (1909).

but, as it is unstable with respect to the phosphine gas, it will be simpler in writing all half-reactions in acid solution involving phosphine to use $PH_3(g)$. From the free energies derived above, we calculate

$$PH_3(g) = P + 3H^+ + 3e^-, \qquad E^\circ = -0.06;$$
$$3OH^- + PH_3(g) = P + 3H_2O + 3e^-, \qquad E_B^\circ = 0.89.$$

and, similarly for the tetraphosphide,

$$P_4H_2 = 4P + 2H^+ + 2e^-, \qquad E^\circ = 0.35;$$
$$2OH^- + P_4H_2 = 4P + 2H_2O + 2e^-, \qquad E_B^\circ = 1.18.$$

The energy thus favors the formation of phosphine over the formation of the tetraphosphide in the reduction of phosphorus. The data are insufficient to calculate the free energy of the diphosphide, but the value must be fairly positive as indicated by the fact that the following reaction occurs quite readily at room temperature.

$$5P_2H_4(l) = 6PH_3(g) + P_4H_2(c).$$

Phosphorus halogen compounds. The entropies and free energies of the liquid and solid phosphorous halogen compounds are not known. From the free energy of $PCl_3(g)$ and the free energy of vaporization, we calculate for $PCl_3(l)$, $\Delta F^\circ = -68.6$ kcal. In cold water the chloride hydrolyzes to phosphorous acid.

$$PCl_3 + 3H_2O = H_3PO_3 + 3Cl^-, \qquad \Delta F^\circ = -60.0 \text{ kcal.}$$

The free energies of a number of other halogen compounds may be estimated but, because of their hydrolysis to the corresponding acids, their chemistry in water solutions is essentially that of the acids. However the solid di-iodide, PI_2, is of interest since it is one of the few compounds of phosphorus having the $+2$ oxidation state. Its heat of formation is -5700 cal., and since all the substances are solids, the entropy of formation may be taken as zero, and the free energy equal to the heat. The hydrolysis reaction is

$$2PI_2(c) + 5H_2O = H_3PO_3 + H_3PO_2 + 4H^+ + 4I^-,$$
$$\Delta F^\circ = -78 \text{ kcal.}$$

The potential for the P, I^-—PI_2 couple would be about -0.1, but it is doubtless of little significance.

Summary of phosphorus potentials. The potential relations of the various phosphorus oxidation states are shown in the following schemes.

Acid Solution

| −3 | −2 | 0 | +1 | +3 | +4 | +5 |

$$
\begin{array}{ccccccc}
 & (0.0) & (0.1) & 0.51 & 0.50 & -0.38 & 0.94 \\
\text{PH}_3 & \!\!-\!\!-\!\! & \text{P}_2\text{H}_4 & \!\!-\!\!-\!\! & \text{P} & \!\!-\!\!-\!\! & \text{H}_3\text{PO}_2 & \!\!-\!\!-\!\! & \text{H}_3\text{PO}_3 & \!\!-\!\!-\!\! & \text{H}_4\text{P}_2\text{O}_6 & \!\!-\!\!-\!\! & \text{H}_3\text{PO}_4
\end{array}
$$

PH$_3$————P$_2$H$_4$————P————H$_3$PO$_2$————H$_3$PO$_3$————H$_4$P$_2$O$_6$————H$_3$PO$_4$

|� 0.065 ⎤ ⎡ 0.50 ⎤ ⎡ 0.276 ⎤|

Basic Solution

1.18

| (0.8) | (0.9) | 2.05 | 1.57 |

PH$_3$————P$_2$H$_4$————P————H$_2$PO$_2^-$————HPO$_3^{--}$————H$_2$P$_2$O$_6^{--}$————PO$_4^{---}$

⎡ 0.89 ⎤ ⎡ 1.73 ⎤ ⎡ 1.12 ⎤

The consideration of these potentials leads to a discussion of a number of important decomposition reactions,

Phosphorus is unstable with respect to its disproportionation into the +1 and −3 states.

$$4\text{P} + 6\text{H}_2\text{O} = \text{PH}_3 + 3\text{H}_3\text{PO}_2, \qquad \Delta F^\circ = -30.1 \text{ kcal.}$$

$$4\text{P} + 3\text{OH}^- + 3\text{H}_2\text{O} = 3\text{H}_2\text{PO}_2^- + \text{PH}_3, \qquad \Delta F^\circ = -80.0 \text{ kcal.}$$

The free energy for the reaction in alkaline solution is large and the reaction goes very readily.

Because of the enormous reducing power of phosphorus in alkaline solution (1.82 volts) it also liberates some hydrogen along with the products of the above reaction,

$$2\text{P} + 2\text{OH}^- + 2\text{H}_2\text{O} = 2\text{H}_2\text{PO}_2^- + \text{H}_2, \qquad \Delta F^\circ = -56.25 \text{ kcal.}$$

Hypophosphorous acid is unstable with respect to its decomposition into phosphorous acid and phosphine.

$$3\text{H}_3\text{PO}_2 = \text{PH}_3 + 2\text{H}_3\text{PO}_3, \qquad \Delta F^\circ = -29.9 \text{ kcal.}$$

This reaction occurs readily, and because of strong reducing potential the acid will also reduce water.

$$\text{H}_3\text{PO}_2 + \text{H}_2\text{O} = \text{H}_3\text{PO}_3 + \text{H}_2, \qquad \Delta F^\circ = -23.0 \text{ kcal.}$$

The decomposition of phosphorous acid into phosphine and phosphoric acid has a small positive free energy.

$$4\text{H}_3\text{PO}_3 = \text{PH}_3 + 3\text{H}_3\text{PO}_4, \qquad \Delta F^\circ = 0.9 \text{ kcal.}$$

However, because of the volatility of the phosphine the equilibrium may be displaced upon heating, and the decomposition occurs in hot solutions.

It is obvious also that, through these various steps, phosphorus is unstable with respect to its hydrolysis into the $+5$ and -3 oxidation states.

The most remarkable characteristic of the phosphorus potentials is their highly positive value. Even weak oxidation agents will oxidize phosphine all the way up to phosphorous acid, and from the over-all potentials these agents should take this acid up to phosphoric. Actually, oxidizing agents of about the strength of iodine are required for this last step, which seems to indicate that the mechanism is through the hypophosphoric acid as discussed above.

ARSENIC

Oxidation states. The important oxidation states of arsenic are: -3 in arsine, $+3$ in arsenious acid, and $+5$ in arsenic acid. The hydrogen arsenide, As_2H_2, -1, may be prepared. Very few definite compounds of the even oxidation states exist: the oxide As_2O_4 appears to be a compound of the $+3$ and $+5$ oxides, but the monosulfide AsS ($+2$) is a well-known mineral.

Arsine. Estimating the entropy of arsine as 52 in comparison to 50.35 for phosphine and using the Bureau of Standards value of 41.0 for the heat of formation, we find the free energy of arsine gas, $AsH_3(g)$, to be 42.0 kcal. In view of the slightly lower value for stibine, it is quite likely that this value for arsine is too high. But in the absence of definite evidence regarding the discrepancy it will be used. The potentials of the arsine-arsenic couples are

$$AsH_3 = As + 3H^+ + 3e^-, \qquad E^\circ = 0.60;$$
$$3OH^- + AsH_3 = As + 3H_2O + 3e^-, \qquad E^\circ_B = 1.43.$$

Arsine is thus a powerful reducing agent and should be readily oxidized by moderately strong oxidizing agents; the oxidation by hydrogen ion, however, is not rapid.

A metallic-arsenic cathode may be reduced to arsine, especially in alkaline solutions, according to the results of Grube and Kleber,[1] and arsenious acid is reduced to arsine efficiently at a mercury cathode.[2]

It is claimed that the reduction of arsenic trichloride by stannous chloride yields the solid arsenide, As_2H_2, which is unstable with re-

[1] G. Grube and H. Kleber, *Z. Elektrochem.*, **30**, 517 (1924).
[2] F. S. Aumonier, *J. Soc. Chem. Ind.*, **46**, 341 (1927).

TABLE 23

THERMODYNAMIC DATA ON ARSENIC[1]

(Heat and free energy of formation in kcal. Entropy of substance in cal./deg.)

Formula	Description	State	$\Delta H°$	$\Delta F°$	$S°$
As	($^4S_{3/2}$)	g	60.64	50.74	33.22
As	α gray metal	c	0.0	0.0	8.4
As	β	amor-phous	1.0		
As	γ yellow	c	3.53		
As$^+$	($^3P_0$)	g	304.24		
As^{++}	($^2P_{1/2}$)	g	771.03		
As$_2$		g	29.6	17.5	57.3
As$_4$		g	35.7	25.2	69.
AsO		g	4.79		
AsO$^+$		aq		−39.1	
AsO$_2^-$		aq		−83.7	
AsO$_4^{---}$		aq	−208.	−152.	−34.6
As$_2$O$_5$		c	−218.6	−184.6	25.2
As$_2$O$_5$		aq	−224.6		
As$_2$O$_5$·4H$_2$O		c	−500.3	(411.1)	(62.6)
As$_4$O$_6$	octahedral	c	−313.94	−275.36	51.2
As$_4$O$_6$	monoclinic	c	−312.8		
AsH$_3$		g	41.0	42.0	(52.)
HAsO$_2$		aq	−109.0	−96.25	30.3
HAsO$_4^{--}$		aq	−214.8	−169.	0.9
H$_2$AsO$_3^-$		aq	−170.3	−140.4	
H$_2$AsO$_4^-$		aq	−216.2	−178.9	28.
H$_3$AsO$_3$		aq	−177.3	−152.94	47.0
H$_3$AsO$_4$		c	−215.2		
H$_3$AsO$_4$		aq	−214.8	−183.8	49.3
AsF$_3$		g	−218.3	−214.7	69.08
AsF$_3$		liq	−226.8	−215.5	43.31
AsCl$_3$		g	−71.5	−68.5	78.2
AsCl$_3$		liq	−80.2	−70.5	55.8
AsBr$_3$		c	−46.61	−38.3	(38.5)
AsI$_3$		c	−13.7	−10.64	(49)
As$_2$S$_2$		g	−4.22		
As$_2$S$_2$		c	−31.9	−32.15	(32.9)
As$_2$S$_3$		c	−35.0	−32.46	(26.8)
AsN		g	7.		
NH$_4$H$_2$AsO$_4$		c	−251.47	−197.24	41.12
NH$_4$H$_2$AsO$_4$		aq	−247.9		

[1] Bureau of Standards values in *italics;* estimated values in parentheses.

spect to the decomposition into the elements. No data are available by which its free energy may be estimated.

The arsenic-arsenious acid couple. Schuhmann[1] has measured the electromotive force of the cell for which the net reaction is

$$As_2O_4(s) + 3H_2 = 2As + 3H_2O.$$

His result gives for the couple

$$3H_2O + 2As = As_2O_3 + 6H^+ + 6e^-, \qquad E° = -0.2340.$$

Arsenious oxide is slowly soluble to form the acid, $HAsO_2$, or some hydrate of this acid, and the molality of the saturated solution is 0.2067 at 25° C. Schuhmann has calculated the free energy of solution and, correcting a misprint in his value, this results in

$$2H_2O + As = HAsO_2(aq) + 3H^+ + 3e^-, \qquad E° = -0.2475.$$

The corresponding free energies are $As_4O_6(s)$, -275.36 kcal.; $HAsO_2(aq)$, -96.25 kcal.; and $H_3AsO_3(aq)$, -152.94 kcal. The more recent data on the dissociation of arsenious acid are fairly consistent. Hughes,[2] from glass electrode measurements reported that

$$H_3AsO_3 = H^+ + H_2AsO_3^- (AsO_2^- + H_2O), \qquad K = 6 \times 10^{-10}.$$

Britton and Jackson[3] agree. Based on this value, the free energy of AsO_2^- is -83.7 kcal., and the potential of the couple in alkaline solution is

$$4OH^- + As = AsO_2^- + 2H_2O + 3e^-, \qquad E_B° = -0.68.$$

From the values of these couples it is apparent that arsenic is a semi-noble metal.

Randall's[4] recalculation of the data by Washburn gives for the basic dissociation constant of arsenious acid

$$HAsO_2 = AsO^+ + OH^-, \qquad K = 5\ 0 \times 10^{-15}.$$

It is obvious from this value that the concentration of AsO^+ is not large except in high acid. The free energy of AsO^+ is -39.16 kcal.

---

[1] R. Schuhmann, *J. Am. Chem. Soc.*, **46**, 1444 (1924).
[2] W. S. Hughes, *J. Chem. Soc.*, 491 (1928).
[3] H. T. S. Britton and P. Jackson, *J. Chem. Soc.*, 1048 (1934).
[4] M. Randall, *International Critical Tables*, **VII**, 242.

The arsenious acid — arsenic acid couple. Liebhafsky[1] has reviewed the data of Roebuck on the equilibrium established in the oxidation of arsenious acid by tri-iodide. His value for the constant is

$$\frac{(H_3AsO_4)(H^+)^2(I^-)^3}{(I_3^-)(H_3AsO_3)} = 1.6 \times 10^{-1}.$$

The corresponding free energy of the reaction is 1085 cal. and the free energy of the arsenic acid, H_3AsO_4(aq), -183.8 kcal. Washburn[2] gives the approximate values for the three dissociation constants as $K_1 = 4.8 \times 10^{-3}$, $K_2 = 10^{-7}$, and $K_3 = 10^{-13}$. From the free energies we write

$$H_3AsO_4(aq) = H^+ + H_2AsO^-, \qquad K = 2.5 \times 10^{-4};$$
$$H_2AsO_4^- = H^+ + HAsO_4^{--}, \qquad K = 5.6 \times 10^{-8};$$
$$HAsO_4^{--} = H^+ + AsO_4^{---}; \qquad K = 3 \times 10^{-13}.$$

The potentials of the following couples may then be calculated:

$$2H_2O + HAsO_2 = H_3AsO_4 + 2H^+ + 2e^-, \qquad E^\circ = -0.559;$$
$$4OH^- + AsO_2^- = AsO_4^{---} + 2H_2O + 2e^-, \qquad E_B^\circ = 0.67.$$

The couple is capable of attaining a rapid reversible equilibrium and the mechanism of the oxidation of arsenite by iodine appears to be that of a direct oxygen shift through the medium of hypoiodous acid,

$$H_3AsO_3 + HIO = H_3AsO_4 + H^+ + I^-.$$

Arsenic sulfides. The chemistry of arsenious sulfide, As_2S_3, and arsenic sulfide, As_2S_5, and their acid ions, thioarsenite, AsS_2^- and thioarsenite, AsS_4^{---}, is of importance in analytical work. From the heat of formation of As_2S_3, we estimate the free energy to be -32.5 kcal. For the precipitation of the sulfide, we calculate

$$3H_2S + 2HAsO_2(aq) = 4H_2O + As_2S_3, \qquad \Delta F^\circ = -45.5 \text{ kcal.}$$

For the solution of $As_2S_3^{--}$ in sulfide, we write as an approximate value

$$As_2S_3 + S^{--} = 2AsS_2^-, \qquad \Delta F^\circ = \text{ca } -10 \text{ kcal.}$$

Hence,

$$As + 2S^{--} = AsS_2^- + 3e^-, \qquad E^\circ = \text{ca } 0.8.$$

The $+3$ sulfide is oxidized to thioarsenate by polysulfide. From the

[1] H. A. Liebhafsky, *J. Phys. Chem.*, **35**, 1648 (1931).
[2] E. W. Washburn, *J. Am. Chem. Soc.*, **30**, 31 (1908).

potential of S_2^{--} it can be stated that

$$2S^{--} + AsS_2^{--} = AsS_4^{--} + 2e^-, \qquad E_B^o > 0.6.$$

Arsenic trichloride. From the free energy of the trichloride, $AsCl_3$, it is found for the hydrolysis reaction that

$$AsCl_3(l) + 2H_2O = HAsO_2 + 3H^+ + 3Cl^-, \quad \Delta F^o = -6.42 \text{ kcal.}$$

Similar reactions may be written for the fluoride and bromide.

Summary of arsenic potentials. For convenience, the principal arsenic potentials are summarized in the following scheme:

Acid Solution

$$\underset{AsH_3}{} \overset{0.60}{\rule{2em}{0.4pt}} \underset{As}{} \overset{-0.2475}{\rule{3em}{0.4pt}} \underset{HAsO_2}{} \overset{-0.559}{\rule{3em}{0.4pt}} \underset{H_3AsO_4}{}$$

Basic Solution

$$\underset{AsH_3}{} \overset{1.43}{\rule{2em}{0.4pt}} \underset{As}{} \overset{0.68}{\rule{2em}{0.4pt}} \underset{AsO_2^-}{} \overset{0.67}{\rule{2em}{0.4pt}} \underset{AsO_4^{---}}{}$$

Arsenic, unlike phosphorus, will not disproportionate to give the $+3$ and -3 states.

$$4As + 3H_2O = As_2O_4 + 2AsH_3, \qquad \Delta F^o = 108 \text{ kcal.}$$

ANTIMONY

Oxidation states. The principal oxidation states are -3 in SbH_3, $+3$ in Sb_2O_3, and $+5$ in Sb_2O_5. The $+4$ oxide Sb_2O_4 is quite stable, and claims are made for existence of the corresponding hypoantimonic acid, $H_2Sb_2O_5$.

The stibine-antimony couple. The value given by Stock and Wrede[1] for the heat of formation of stibine, 34.0 kcal., appears to be reliable, although the older value of Berthelot and Petit is $2\frac{1}{2}$ times larger. The behavior of stibine and arsine upon heating certainly indicates that the latter is the more stable, and it may be that the Stock and Wrede value for stibine, which is less than the accepted value for arsine, is a little too low, but the inconsistency probably lies in the heat of formation of arsine. However, calculations will be made using

---

[1] A. Stock and F. Wrede, *Ber.*, **40**, 2923 (1907).

TABLE 24

THERMODYNAMIC DATA ON ANTIMONY[1]

(Heat and free energy of formation in kcal. Entropy of substance in cal./deg.)

Formula	Description	State	$\Delta H°$	$\Delta F°$	$S°$
Sb	($^4S_{3/2}$)	g	60.8	51.1	43.06
Sb	metal	c	0.0	0.0	10.5
Sb	explosive	c	2.44		
Sb$^+$	($^3P_0$)	g	261.52		
Sb^{++}	($^2P_{1/2}$)	g	678.1		
Sb$_2$		g	52.	40.	60.9
Sb$_4$		g	48.8		
SbO		g	45.		
SbO$^+$		aq		−42.0	
Sb$_2$O$_4$		c	−193.3	−165.9	
Sb$_4$O$_6$	Sb$_2$O$_3$	c	−336.8	−298.0	58.8
Sb$_2$O$_5$		c	−234.4	−200.5	29.9
Sb$_2$O$_5$		aq	−226.4		
SbH$_3$		g	34.	35.3	(53.)
SbO$_2^-$		aq		−82.5	
HSbO$_2$		aq		−97.5	
SbF		g	0.0		
SbF$_3$		c	−217.2	199.8	25.2
H$_3$SbF$_6$		aq	−444.3		
SbCl$_3$		g	−75.2	−72.3	80.8
SbCl$_3$		c	−91.34	−77.62	44.5 (?)
SbCl$_5$		g	−93.9		
SbCl$_5$		liq	−104.8		
SbOCl		c	−90.8		
SbBr$_3$		c	−62.1	54.4	(40.2)
SbI$_3$		c	−23.0	−22.5	(50.7)
SbS$_3^{--}$		aq	−4.	(−32.)	
Sb$_2$S$_3$	amorphous	c	−36.0	−32.0	(30.3)
SbS$_2^-$		aq		−13.	

[1] Bureau of Standards values in *italics;* estimated values in parentheses.

this heat of formation. Estimating the entropy of stibine as 53 cal./
deg., in comparison with 50.35 for phosphine, the free energy of stibine
is 35.3 kcal. Sand[1] and his co-workers found 37.1 at 20° C. from cathodic reduction potentials. For the stibine-antimony couple in acid
solution, it can be computed that

$$SbH_3(g) = Sb + 3H^+ + 3e^-, \qquad E° = 0.51.$$

Assuming no acid character for stibine, the potential for the couple in

[1] H. J. S. Sand, E. J. Weeks and S. W. Worrell, *J. Chem. Soc.*, **123**, 456 (1923).

basic solution would be $E_B^\circ = 1.34$. However, since stibine appears to form the sodium salt, Na_3Sb, in concentrated alkali, the calculated basic potential would be too large. $E_B^\circ < 1.34$. Because of this distinctly acid property of stibine and of the insolubility of many of the antimonides, a number of positive ions which would otherwise oxidize stibine form the antimonide; for example, Ag^+ forms Ag_3Sb.

The antimony-antimonous acid couple. Schuhmann has measured the electromotive force of the cell having the net reaction

$$Sb_2O_3(s) + 3H_2 = 2Sb + 3H_2O$$

and gives

$$3H_2O + 2Sb = Sb_2O_3 + 6H^+ + 6e^-, \qquad E^\circ = -0.152.$$

He has also measured this solubility and found for concentrations in the neighborhood of $1M$ that the positive ion in solution is SbO^+. For the antimony-antimonyl couple he records

$$Sb + H_2O = SbO^+ + 2H^+ + 3e^-, \qquad E^\circ = -0.212.$$

The corresponding free energies are Sb_4O_6, -298.0 kcal.; and SbO^+, $-42,000$ cal. For the basic dissociation of the oxide,

$$\tfrac{1}{2}Sb_2O_3 + \tfrac{1}{2}H_2O = SbO^+ + OH^-, \qquad K = 10^{-17}.$$

The solubility of the sesquioxide is given as 0.016 grams per liter at 15° C. by Schulze[1]. This would lead to a free energy of ca$-97,500$ cal. for $HSbO_2(aq)$. The acid dissociation has not been determined, but from the concentration of hydroxide required to prevent the hydrolysis of SbO_2^-, a value of $K = 10^{-11}$ would appear to be a close approximation. Hence,

$$HSbO_2(aq) = H^+ + SbO_2^-, \qquad \Delta F^\circ = 15,000$$

and the free energy of SbO_2^- would be $-82,500$ cal.

$$4OH^- + Sb = SbO_2^- + 2H_2O + 3e^-, \qquad E_B^\circ = 0.66.$$

Grube and Schweigardt[2] report 0.675 for this potential from cell measurements in $10M$ KOH. The metal may be precipitated by cathodic reduction in either acid or alkaline solution.

---

[1] H. Schulze, *J. prakt. Chem.*, **27**, 320 (1883).
[2] G. Grube and F. Schweigardt, *Z. Elektrochem.*, **29**, 257 (1923).

The antimonous-antimonic acid couple. From the free energy of the pentoxide, Sb_2O_5, we calculate

$$2H_2O + Sb_2O_3 = Sb_2O_5 + 4H^+ + 4e^-, \qquad E° = -0.692;$$

$$3H_2O + 2SbO^+ = Sb_2O_5 + 6H^+ + 4e^-, \qquad E° = -0.581.$$

Pauling[1] has summarized the evidence in favor of the formula $HSb(OH)_6$ for orthoantimonic acid. The free energy of this acid is not known. Likewise, the acid dissociation constants have not been determined, although the solutions of the oxide are known to be fairly acid. Grube and Schweigardt[2] report from cell measurements in $10M$ KOH

$$SbO_2^- + 2OH^-(10M) = SbO_3^- + H_2O + 2e^-, \qquad E = 0.589.$$

There is, however, no evidence that the $+5$ antimony is present as the meta-ion SbO_3^-, and the half-reaction might well be

$$SbO_2^- + 5OH^- = H_3SbO_6^{-4} + H_2O + 2e^-.$$

In the latter case the correction for the hydroxide activity would be considerably larger and the $E°$ value would probably be around 0.40.

The couple is capable of attaining rapid equilibrium in both acid and basic solutions. Antimonic acid will oxidize iodide but the reaction is reversed in alkaline solution. In the analytical methods using this reaction, tartrate is added to aid in keeping the $+3$ antimony in solution.

Antimony tetroxide. The data of Mixter[3] on the heat of formation of the oxide Sb_2O_4 is incompatible with its chemical properties. Using the value of Simon and Thaler,[4] -193.3 kcal., and the entropy of formation -91.7 cal./deg., the free energy is found to be -165.9 kcal.

$$H_2O + Sb_2O_4 = Sb_2O_5 + 2H^+ + 2e^-, \qquad E° = -0.48;$$

$$2H_2O + 2SbO^+ = Sb_2O_4 + 4H^+ + 2e^-, \qquad E° = -0.68.$$

The oxide in acid is thus unstable with respect to the $+3$ and $+5$ oxidation states; the decomposition is slow in acid but more rapid in alkaline. Strong hydroxides dissolve the oxide but there are no data for the free energies.

---

[1] L. Pauling, *J. Am. Chem. Soc.*, **55**, 1895 (1933).
[2] G. Grube and F. Schweigardt, *Z. Elektrochem.*, **29**, 257 (1923).
[3] W. G. Mixter, *Am. J. Sci.*, **28**, 103 (1909).
[4] A. Simon and E. Thaler, *Z. anorg. allgem. Chem.*, **162**, 253 (1927).

Antimony trichloride. From the free energy of formation of the trichloride, $SbCl_3(s)$, we calculate for the free energy of the hydrolysis

$$SbCl_2(s) + H_2O = SbO^+ + 2H^+ + 3Cl^-, \qquad \Delta F^\circ = -1500 \text{ cal.}$$

However, the reaction is complicated by the formation, at low hydrogen ion, of the solid basic chloride, $Sb_4O_5Cl_2$, and at high hydrochloric acid concentration of the complex chlorides $SbCl_4^-$ and $SbCl_6^{--}$. The free energies of the reactions which form these complex chlorides cannot be calculated from the present data.

The pentachloride, $SbCl_5$, is more highly hydrolyzed than the trichloride and forms the solid oxide, Sb_2O_5, with some of the acid, $HSb(OH)_6$, in solution.

The antimony sulfides. The heat of formation of the orange, precipitated antimonous sulfide, Sb_2S_3, and an estimated value for the entropy leads to the free energy of formation of 32.0 kcal.

$$2SbO^+ + 3H_2S(g) = Sb_2S_3 + 2H_2O + 2H^+, \quad \Delta F^\circ = -38 \text{ kcal.}$$

This free energy seems too large in view of the reversal of the equilibrium in concentrated HCl. However, the formation of the complex chlorides may be sufficient to account for it. The sulfide is soluble in sulfide ion,

$$Sb_2S_3 + S^{--} = 2SbS_2^-,$$

and the reaction is reversed in dilute acid solutions. From the equilibrium, the value $-13,000$ cal. may be taken as a rough estimate of the free energy of the thioantimonite ion SbS_2^-. The electrolytic reduction of the thioantimonite is employed in the quantitative estimation of antimony.[1]

$$Sb + 2S^{--} = SbS_2^- + 3e^-, \qquad E^\circ = ca \ 0.85.$$

This E° value is in agreement with the fact that the metal is oxidized to the thioantimonite by polysulfide, S_2^{--}, which has a potential of about 0.5.

There are no free energy data on the antimonic sulfide, Sb_2S_5. It is soluble in sulfide ion to form the thioantimonate, and, in acid, hydrogen sulfide reduces it to the antimonous sulfide. In alkaline solution thioantimonite is oxidized to the thioantimonate by S_2^{--}, and hence,

$$2S^{--} + SbS_2^- = SbS_4^{---} + 2e^-, \qquad E^\circ = 0.6.$$

---

[1] F. P. Treadwell and W. T. Hall, *Analytical Chemistry*, New York: John Wiley & Sons, Inc., 1935, **II**, 222.

Summary of antimony potentials. For convenience the potentials relating the principal antimony oxidation states are summarized in the following scheme:

$$\overset{0.51}{\text{SbH}_3}\underline{\quad}\overset{-0.212}{\text{Sb}}\underline{\quad\quad}\overset{-0.68}{\text{SbO}^+}\underline{\quad\quad}\overset{-0.48}{\text{Sb}_2\text{O}_4}\underline{\quad\quad}\text{Sb}_2\text{O}_5$$
$$\underline{\quad\quad\quad\quad -0.581 \quad\quad\quad\quad}$$

$$\overset{(1.34)}{\text{SbH}_3}\underline{\quad\quad}\overset{0.66}{\text{Sb}}\underline{\quad}\overset{(0.40)}{\text{SbO}_2^-}\underline{\quad\quad}\text{H}_3\text{SbO}_6^{-4}$$

BISMUTH

Oxidation states. The very unstable hydrogen compound BiH_3 (-3 state) and also the hydride $\text{Bi}_2\text{H}_2(-1)$ have been prepared. Many bismuthides of the type Na_3Bi are known. The oxide and halides of the $+2$ oxidation state may be prepared. The most stable state is the $+3$ as represented by Bi_2O_3 and its compounds. The oxide $\text{Bi}_2\text{O}_5(+5)$ is a very powerful oxidizing agent as is also the tetroxide, $\text{Bi}_2\text{O}_4(+4)$, which is probably to be considered as bismuthyl bismuthate, $\text{BiO}\cdot\text{BiO}_3$.

Bismuth-hydrogen compounds. Paneth[1] prepared bismuthine. He reports that at room temperature 80 per cent of the gas decomposed in 50 minutes and the decomposition was very rapid at 350° C; however, a stronger reducing agent than zinc, for example, Mg, must be used for the reduction of the metal.

$$\text{BiH}_3(\text{g}) = \text{Bi} + 3\text{H}^+ + 3e^-, \qquad E° > 0.8.$$

The bismuthine is acidic in properties and forms Ag_3Bi with silver nitrate. Weeks and Druce[2] have discussed the preparation of the solid hydride, Bi_2H_2. They found that, when heated in a vacuum, it decomposed according to the equation

$$3\text{Bi}_2\text{H}_2 = 4\text{Bi} + 2\text{BiH}_3.$$

The bismuth-bismuthyl couple. Swift[3] and Smith[4] studied the ionic species in a solution of Bi_2O_3 in perchloric acid and concluded

[1] F. Paneth, *Ber.*, **51**, 1704 and 1728 (1918).
[2] E. J. Weeks and J. G. F. Druce, *J. Chem. Soc.*, **127**, 1799 (1925).
[3] E. H. Swift, *J. Am. Chem. Soc.*, **45**, 371 (1923).
[4] D. F. Smith, *J. Am. Chem. Soc.*, **45**, 360 (1923).

TABLE 25

THERMODYNAMIC DATA ON BISMUTH[1]

(Heat and free energy of formation in kcal. Entropy of substance in cal./deg.)

Formula	Description	State	$\Delta H°$	$\Delta F°$	$S°$
Bi	$(^4S_{1/2})$	g	49.7	40.4	44.67
Bi	metal	c	0.0	0.0	13.6
Bi^+	$(^3P_0)$	g	219.1		
Bi^{++}	$(^2P_{1/2})$	g	605.3		
Bi_2		g	59.4	48.0	65.4
BiO		g	16.		
BiO		c	-49.85	-43.5	(17.)
BiO^+		aq		-34.54	
Bi_2O_3		c	-137.9	-118.7	36.2
Bi_2O_4		c		-109.0	
BiH		g	43.		
BiOOH				-88.4	
$Bi(OH)_3$		c	-169.6	$-137.$	(24.6)
BiCl		g	10.7	5.2	58.9
$BiCl_3$		g	-64.7	-62.2	85.3
$BiCl_3$		c	-90.61	-76.23	45.3
$BiCl_3$		aq	-101.6		
BiOCl		c	-87.3	-77.0	20.6
BiBr		g	12.7	3.8	61.6
BiI		g	16.	11.	63.4
$BiCl_4^-$		aq		-114.2	
Bi_2S_3		c	-43.8	-39.4	35.3

[1] Bureau of Standards values in *italics;* estimated values in parentheses.

that at moderate hydrogen-ion concentration the ion is BiO^+ or $Bi(OH)_2^+$ and at higher concentrations $BiOH^{++}$. By the direct cell measurements the potential of the bismuth-bismuthyl couple is found to be around -0.31 to -0.32. The higher value will be used.

$$H_2O + Bi = BiO^+ + 2H^+ + 3e^-, \qquad E° = -0.32.$$

This corresponds to a free energy of -34.54 kcal. for BiO^+. However, various authorities contend that BiO^+ is not the principal ion in acid solution. Graner and Sillén[1] wrote

$$2Bi^{+++} + H_2O = Bi_2O^{+4} + 2H^+, \qquad K = 6.5 \times 10^{-2}.$$

The free energy of formation of the oxide Bi_2O_3 is -118.7 kcal. It is not appreciably soluble in 1 molal hydroxide. Hence,

$$6OH^- + 2Bi = Bi_2O_3 + 3H_2O + 6e^-, \qquad E_B° = 0.46.$$

[1] F. Graner and L. G. Sillén, *Nature,* **160,** 715 (1947).

Baur and Lattmann[1] reported from direct cell measurements $E_B^o =$ 0.41. However, the formation of the monoxide (see below) as an intermediate step may have entered into their determination.

Bismuthyl hydroxide, BiOOH, may be precipitated, and its solubility is recorded as $5.8 \times 10^{-6}M$. If one were justified in assuming complete ionization into hydroxide and bismuthyl ions, the solubility product would be 3.3×10^{-11}. From the free energies,

$$\tfrac{1}{2}Bi_2O_3 + \tfrac{1}{2}H_2O = BiO^+ + OH^-, \qquad K = 4 \times 10^{-12}.$$

As the free energy of hydration of the oxide appears to be a small negative quantity, we shall write

$$BiOOH(s) = BiO^+ + OH^-, \qquad K = ca\ 1 \times 10^{-12}.$$

Bismuth trichloride and oxychloride. The oxychloride is of such importance in the chemistry of $+3$ bismuth that its free-energy relation will be considered at this point. Noyes and Chow[2] found for the reaction

$$\tfrac{3}{2}H_2 + BiOCl(c) = Bi + H_2O + H^+ + Cl^-, \qquad E^o = 0.16;$$

or

$$H_2O + Cl^- + Bi = BiOCl + 2H^+ + 3e^-, \qquad E^o = -0.16.$$

This corresponds to a free energy of $-77,000$ cal. for BiOCl. From the free energies we may calculate,

$$BiOCl = BiO^+ + Cl^-, \qquad \Delta F^o = 11,100\ cal.,$$
$$K = 7 \times 10^{-9}.$$

Considering the sensitivity of the oxychloride test for bismuth, this constant appears to be a little large. Feitknecht[3] calculated that

$$BiOCl + H_2O = Bi^{+++} + Cl^- + 2OH^-, \qquad K = 1.6 \times 10^{-31}.$$

However, there would seem to be some question about the validity of the determination of the concentration of Bi^{+++} upon which the constant is based.

Noyes, Hall, and Beattie[4] studied the solubility of the oxychloride in hydrochloric acid. For moderate concentrations of the acid, the ion

[1] E. Baur and W. Lattmann, *Z. Elektrochem.*, **40**, 582 (1934).
[2] A. A. Noyes and M. Chow, *J. Am. Chem. Soc.*, **40**, 739 (1918).
[3] W. Feitknecht, *Helv. Chem. Acta*, **16**, 1307 (1933).
[4] A. A. Noyes, F. W. Hall and J. A. Beattie, *J. Am. Chem. Soc.*, **39**, 2526 (1917).

$BiCl_4^-$ is probably formed and the ion $BiCl_5^{--}$ is formed at higher concentrations. They give

$$BiOCl + 2H^+ + 3Cl^- = H_2O + BiCl_4^-, \qquad K = 0.8.$$

From this value and the free energies of the other substances involved, the free energy of the complex chloride ion, $BiCl_4^-$, is $-114,200$ cal. The potential for the bismuth-complex-chloride couple becomes

$$4Cl^- + Bi = BiCl_4^- + 3e^-, \qquad E° = -0.16.$$

The free energy of the solid trichloride, $BiCl_3(c)$ is -76.23 kcal. We then find for the solubility of the chloride in chloride ion

$$BiCl_3(c) + Cl^- = BiCl_4^-, \qquad \Delta F° = -6.6 \text{ kcal.}$$

Based on the free energy of the oxide obtained above, the free energy of solution in hydrochloric acid is

$$Bi_2O_3(c) + H^+ + 8Cl^- = 2BiCl_4^- + 3H_2O, \qquad \Delta F° = -28.9 \text{ kcal.}$$

For the solubility product of bismuth sulfide, Kolthoff[1] reported

$$Bi_2S_3 = 2Bi^{+++} + 3S^{--}, \qquad K = 1.6 \times 10^{-72}.$$

Bismuth monoxide. The heat of formation of the monoxide, BiO, is given as -49.85 kcal. The potentials for the reduction and oxidation of the oxide are

$$H_2O + Bi = BiO + 2H^+ + 2e^-, \qquad E° = -0.285;$$
$$BiO = BiO^+ + e^-, \qquad E° = -0.39.$$

For the decomposition of the oxide

$$3BiO + 2H^+ = 2BiO^+ + Bi + H_2O, \qquad \Delta F° = 4.88 \text{ kcal.}$$

These values may not be very accurate, but they do show that the oxide is stable in low acid and should decompose in high acid. These appear to be the experimental facts. Moreover, the conditions for the formation of the oxide should be the reduction of $+3$ bismuth by a reducing agent, which is about the same strength as metallic bismuth, in a solution of low hydrogen ion. These conditions are met in the formation by reduction with Sn^{++}.

---

[1] I. M. Kolthoff, *J. Phys. Chem.*, **35**, 2720 (1931).

Bismuth tetroxide and pentoxide. Although it appears that the pentoxide, Bi_2O_5, and also its sodium salt can be prepared, they are very unstable and the commercial products are largely the tetroxide, Bi_2O_4, which is probably bismuthyl bismuthate $(BiO)BiO_3$. Baur and Lattmann[1] have studied the potential of the Bi_2O_3—Bi_2O_4 couple in alkaline solution. They found that Bi_4O_7 was an intermediate stage and reported for the potentials in $1M$ NaOH,

$$2OH^- + 2Bi_2O_3 = Bi_4O_7 + H_2O + 2e^-, \qquad E = -0.51;$$
$$2OH^- + Bi_4O_7 = 2Bi_2O_4 + H_2O + 2e^-, \qquad E = -0.62.$$

Correcting for the activity of the sodium hydroxide, we shall write

$$2OH^- + Bi_2O_3 = Bi_2O_4 + H_2O + 2e^-, \qquad E_B^\circ = -0.56.$$

We then calculate for the free energy of the tetroxide, $-109,000$ cal., and for the couple in acid solution.

$$2H_2O + 2BiO^+ = Bi_2O_4 + 4H^+ + 2e^-, \qquad E^\circ = -1.59.$$

Since the ratio H^+/e^- is 2 for low acid and probably 4 for high acid, the potential in concentrated acid becomes much larger and the tetroxide will oxidize manganous to permanganate under these conditions.

The potential for the Bi_2O_3—pure Bi_2O_5 is probably about the same.

TABLE 26

GROUP V POTENTIALS IN ACID SOLUTION

	-0.27		-1.45		-0.94	
NH_4^+	——————	N_2	——————	HNO_2	——————	NO_3^-

	0.065		0.50		0.276	
PH_3	——————	P	——————	H_3PO_3	——————	H_3PO_4

	0.60		-0.247		-0.56	
AsH_3	——————	As	——————	$HAsO_2$	——————	H_3AsO_4

	0.51		-0.212		-0.581	
SbH_3	——————	Sb	——————	SbO^+	——————	Sb_2O_5

	ca 0.8		-0.32		ca -1.6	
BiH_3	——————	Bi	——————	BiO^+	——————	Bi_2O_5

Trends in the Group V potentials. In order to compare the various elements of Group V, the potentials for the more important

[1] E. Baur and W. Lattmann, Z. Elektrochem., **40**, 582 (1934).

oxidation-reduction couples in acid solution have been summarized in Table 26.

The XH_3 compounds increase in reducing power with increasing atomic weight. As mentioned above, the discrepancy in the arsenic and antimony values is doubtless an error in some of the thermal data. The oxygen compounds of the group are good or even powerful oxidizing agents, with the exception of the compounds of phosphorus.

CHAPTER 8

Carbon, Silicon, Germanium, Tin, and Lead

The elements of this group have four valence electrons and, in the monatomic gas state, these are $s^2p^2(^3P_0)$. In their spectroscopic terms the elements are very much alike, but in the properties of their compounds there is but little similarity. The principal characteristic of the chemistry of carbon is its four tetrahedral electron pair bonds and the remarkable stability of these bonds with hydrogen, oxygen, nitrogen, sulfur, the halogens, and especially with other carbon atoms. The chemistry of silicon is very largely that of the dioxide and its many polyacids. With the heavier members of the family, the monoxide and dioxide become more basic, and the chemistry of the $+2$ and $+4$ ions assumes importance.

CARBON

Oxidation states. To carbon in methane and its oxidation products, the following oxidation numbers may be assigned: CH_4, -4; CH_3OH, -2; $HCHO$, 0; $HCOOH$, $+2$; and CO_2, $+4$. This procedure conforms to our system of assigning oxidation numbers to other elements, and the only singular fact in this series is the failure of carbon in the zero state to separate as graphite instead of existing as the pseudohydrate, formaldehyde. If these were the only hydrogen and oxygen compounds of carbon, this anomaly would present no serious problem. Instead, however, we have thousands of compounds in which it is futile to attempt a classification of the carbon atoms in terms of the oxidation state. Of course, one may always write a half-reaction relating a given compound to the element, as, for example, for benzoic acid,

$$C_6H_5COOH = 7C + 2H^+ + 2H_2O + 2e^-.$$

TABLE 27

THERMODYNAMIC DATA ON CARBON[1]

(Heat and free energy of formation in kcal. Entropy of substance in cal./deg.)

Formula	Description	State	$\Delta H°$	$\Delta F°$	$S°$
C	$(^3P_0)$	g	171.698	160.845	37.761
C	diamond	c	0.4532	0.6850	0.5829
C	graphite	c	0.0	0.0	1.3609
C+	$(^2P_{1/2})$	g	431.654		
C++	$(^1S_0)$	g	995.285		
C_2		g	234.7		
CO		g	−26.4157	−32.8079	47.301
CO_2		g	−94.0518	−94.2598	51.061
CO_2		aq	−98.69	−92.31	29.0
CH		g	142.1		
CH_3		g	32.		
CH_4		g	−17.889	−12.140	44.50
C_2H_2		g	54.194	50.0	47.997
C_2H_2		aq	50.6		
C_2H_4		g	12.496	16.282	52.45
C_2H_6		g	−20.236	−7.860	54.85
C_6H_6		g	19.820	30.989	64.34
C_6H_6		liq	11.718	29.756	41.30
$(HCOOH)_2$		g	−187.7	−163.8	83.1
HCOOH		g	−86.67	−80.24	60.0
HCOOH		liq	−97.8	−82.7	30.82
HCOOH		aq	−98.0	−85.1	39.1
HCOO−		aq	−98.0	−80.0	21.9
H_2CO_3		aq	−167.0	−149.00	45.7
HCO_3^-		aq	−165.18	−140.31	22.7
CO_3^{--}		aq	−161.63	−126.22	−12.7
CH_3COOH		liq	−116.4	−93.8	38.2
CH_3COOH		aq	−116.743	−95.51	
CH_3COO^-		aq	−116.843	−89.02	
$(COOH)_2$		c	−197.6	−166.8	28.7
$(COOH)_2$		aq	−195.57	−166.8	
$HC_2O_4^-$		aq	−195.7	−165.12	
$C_2O_4^{--}$		aq	−195.7	−159.4	10.6
HCHO		g	−27.7	−26.2	52.26
HCHO		aq		−31.0	
CH_3OH		g	−48.10	−38.70	56.8
CH_3OH		liq	−57.036	−39.75	30.3
CH_3OH		aq	−58.79	−41.70	31.63
C_2H_5OH		g	−56.24	−40.30	67.4
C_2H_5OH		liq	−66.356	−41.77	38.4
$C_6H_{12}O_6$		aq		−217.02	
CH_3CHO		g	−39.76	−31.96	63.5
CH_3CHO		aq	−49.88		

[1] Bureau of Standards values in *italics;* estimated values in parentheses.

TABLE 27 (Continued)

Formula	Description	State	$\Delta H°$	$\Delta F°$	$S°$
C_2H_5OH		aq	−68.85	−42.4	
$(CH_3)_2O$		g	−44.3	−27.3	63.72
$(CH_3)_2O$		aq	−52.2		
CN		g			48.40
C_2N_2		g	73.60	70.81	57.86
HCN		g	31.2	28.7	48.23
HCN		liq	25.2	29.0	26.97
HCN		aq	25.2 (?)	26.8	30.8 (?)
CN^-		aq	36.1	39.6	28.2
HCNO		aq	−35.1	−28.9	43.6
CNO^-		aq	−33.5	−23.6	31.1
CH_3NH_2		g	−6.7	6.6	57.73
$CH_3NH_3^+$		aq	−29.85		
$CO(NH_2)_2$		c	−79.634	−47.120	25.0
$CO(NH_2)_2$		aq	−76.30	−48.72	41.55
COS		g	−32.80	−40.45	55.34
CH_3SH		g	−2.97	0.21	60.90
CS_2		g	27.55	15.55	56.84
CS_2		liq	21.0	15.2	36.10
$(CH_3)_2S$		liq	−13.6	3.4	46.94
CNS^-		aq	17.2	21.2	(36.)
$(CNS)_2$				77.9	
CNCl		g	34.5	32.9	56.31
CNI		g	54.6	47.7	61.26
CH_3NO_2		liq	−26.7	−3.1	41.1
$NH_2CO_2NH_4$			−154.21	−109.47	39.70
CF_4		g	−162.5	−151.8	62.7
CCl_4		g	−25.50	−15.35	73.95
CCl_4		liq	−33.34	−16.43	51.25
$COCl_2$		g	−53.30	−50.31	69.13
CH_3Cl		g	−19.58	−13.96	55.97
CH_2Cl_2		g	−21.	−15.	64.68
CH_2Cl_2		liq	−27.9	−15.0	42.7
$CHCl_3$		g	−24.	−16.	70.86
$CHCl_3$		liq	−31.5	−17.1	48.5
CH_3Br		g	−8.2	−5.9	58.74
CH_3Br		liq	−21.8	−16.3	53.0
CH_3I		g	4.9	5.3	60.85
CH_3I		liq	−2.0	4.9	38.9
$(CH_3)_2S$		liq	−13.6	3.4	46.94
C_6H_6		liq	11.718	29.756	41.30
$C_6H_5CH_3$		liq		26.8	
$C_6H_5CO_2H$		s		−60.1	
$C_6H_5CO_2H$		aq		−57.95	
$C_6H_5CO_2^-$		aq		−52.25	
$C_6H_5NH_2$		liq		35.4	
$C_6H_5NH_3^+$		aq		29.4	

But as such a half-reaction has no chemical significance, this classification of carbon in benzoic acid as having an average oxidation number of $-\frac{2}{7}$ is not useful. However, there are many types of oxidation-reduction reactions in organic chemistry and fortunately it is not necessary to assign oxidation numbers in writing the corresponding half-reactions. A number of the more important cases will be considered.

The free energy of carbon compounds. The paucity of equilibrium data pertaining to carbon compounds has made the third law the most important and reliable source of free energies in this field. Parks and Huffman[1] in their excellent monograph have summarized the data on several hundred compounds. However, the most complete free energy tables are those of the Bureau of Standards.[2]

The oxidation of hydrocarbons. The potentials for the various steps in the oxidation of a hydrocarbon are of considerable interest, even though reversible equilibria cannot be attained at room temperature. The following half-reactions are calculated from the data in Table 27 for the oxidation of methane.

$$H_2O + CH_4(g) = CH_3OH(aq) + 2H^+ + 2e^-, \qquad E^\circ = -0.586;$$
$$CH_3OH(aq) = HCHO(aq) + 2H^+ + 2e^-, \qquad E^\circ = -0.19;$$
$$H_2O + HCHO(aq) = HCOOH(aq) + 2H^+ + 2e^-, \qquad E^\circ = -0.056;$$
$$HCOOH(aq) = CO_2(g) + 2H^+ + 2e^-, \qquad E^\circ = 0.196.$$

It is rather surprising that methyl alcohol has such a high oxidizing potential. The reduction of carbon dioxide to formaldehyde, $E^\circ = 0.1$, is of interest in connection with its absorption by plants. Hydrogen on a nickel catalyst will reduce HCO_3^- to HCO_2^-. The schematic representation of these potentials in acid and alkaline solutions is given below.

Acid

$$\overset{-0.58}{CH_4(g)}\rule[0.5ex]{2em}{0.4pt}\overset{-0.19}{CH_3OH(aq)}\rule[0.5ex]{2em}{0.4pt}\overset{0.01}{HCHO(aq)}\rule[0.5ex]{2em}{0.4pt}\overset{0.196}{HCO_2H(aq)}\rule[0.5ex]{2em}{0.4pt}CO_2(g)$$

Alkaline

$$\overset{0.25}{CH_4(g)}\rule[0.5ex]{2em}{0.4pt}\overset{0.59}{CH_3OH(aq)}\rule[0.5ex]{2em}{0.4pt}\overset{1.07}{HCHO(aq)}\rule[0.5ex]{2em}{0.4pt}\overset{1.01}{HCO_2^-(aq)}\rule[0.5ex]{2em}{0.4pt}CO_2^{--}$$

[1] G. S. Parks and H. M. Huffman, *Free Energies of Some Organic Compounds*, New York: Chemical Catalog. Co., 1932.

[2] Selected Values of Properties of Hydrocarbons, National Bureau of Standards, C. 461.

For the oxidation of ethane approximately the same values are obtained for corresponding steps, but here there is the added possibility of the oxidation of both carbon atoms.

$$H_2O + C_2H_6(g) = C_2H_5OH(aq) + 2H^+ + 2e^-,$$
$$E^\circ = -0.46;$$

$$C_2H_5OH(aq) = CH_3CHO(aq) + 2H^+ + 2e^-,$$
$$E^\circ = -0.192;$$

$$H_2O + CH_3CHO(aq) = CH_3COOH(aq) + 2H^+ + 2e^-,$$
$$E^\circ = 0.118;$$

$$2H_2O + CH_3COOH(aq) = H_2C_2O_4(aq) + 6H^+ + 6e^-,$$
$$E^\circ = -0.31;$$

$$H_2C_2O_4(aq) = 2CO_2(g) + 2H^+ + 2e^-,$$
$$E^\circ = 0.49.$$

From the last potential it should be relatively easy to oxidize oxalic acid to carbon dioxide; yet with as powerful an oxidizing agent as a permanganate the reaction is not rapid at room temperature.

Wurmser and Mayer-Reich[1] measured the lactic acid-pyruvic acid couple,

$$CH_3CHOHCOOH = CH_3COCOOH + 2H^+ + 2e^-, \quad E^\circ = -0.20.$$

A number of important free energy relations should also be noted. Formaldehyde is unstable with respect to the formation of glucose.

$$6HCHO(aq) = C_6H_{12}O_6(aq), \quad \Delta F^\circ = -30,900 \text{ cal.}$$

This reaction appears to be the net reaction in the synthesis of cellulose in plants, although the mechanism is very complicated.

Formaldehyde is also unstable with respect to its decomposition into carbon and water,

$$HCHO(aq) = C + H_2O, \quad \Delta F^\circ = -25,670 \text{ cal.}$$

but there is no evidence that this reaction occurs.

From the potentials it is obvious that formaldehyde should oxidize and reduce itself, and experimentally the reaction goes slowly with the formation of methyl formate.

The equilibrium between carbon monoxide and formic acid has been

---

[1] R. Wurmser and N. Mayer-Reich, *Compt. rend.*, **196**, 612 (1933).

studied by Branch.[1] From our free energy values we write

$$HCOOH(aq) = CO(g) + H_2O, \qquad \Delta F° = -3398 \text{ cal.}$$

For the oxidation of toluene to benzoic acid, we calculate from the free energies

$$2H_2O + C_6H_5CH_3(l) = C_6H_5COOH(aq) + 6H^+ + 6e^-,$$
$$E° = -0.21.$$

This value is comparable to $E° = -0.26$ for the CH_4—$HCOOH$ half-reaction.

Electrolytic reduction of acids, aldehydes, and alcohols. A number of investigations have been made on the electrolytic reduction of carbonic acid or bicarbonate. Fischer and Prziza[2] report a 98 per cent reduction of carbon dioxide at 5-atm. pressure in potassium sulfate solution with an amalgamated zinc cathode, the reduction product being formic acid. These authors were unable to reduce carbon monoxide under similar conditions.

With high overvoltage cathodes, formic acid may be reduced to formaldehyde and methyl alcohol, and oxalic acid reduced to glyoxalic acid and glycollic acid. In certain cases, esters may be reduced electrolytically with the replacement of the $\cdot\cdot$ CO $\cdot\cdot$ group by $\cdot\cdot$ CH$_2$ $\cdot\cdot$ to form an ether.[3] In general, the reduction of monobasic aliphatic acids is difficult.

Müller[4] has reviewed the experimental facts and discussed the theory of the reduction of ketones, in particular for acetone, $(CH_3)_2CO$. The reduction products are pinacol, $(CH_3)_2COHCOH(CH_3)_2$; isopropyl alcohol, $(CH_3)_2CHOH$; and propane, $CH_3CH_2CH_3$. The latter is produced with relatively high efficiency at amalgamated zinc and cadmium cathodes. This production of the propane is noteworthy in view of the fact that it is very difficult to reduce aldehydes or alcohols to the hydrocarbon. Müller has postulated a number of intermediates but little is actually known regarding the mechanism.

The cathodic reduction of an aldehyde forms the alcohol, and further reduction does not occur in spite of the favorable potential.

The anodic oxidation of certain aldehydes and alcohols in alkaline

[1] G. E. K. Branch, *J. Am. Chem. Soc.*, **37**, 2316 (1915).
[2] F. Fischer and O. Prziza, *Ber.*, **47**, 256 (1914).
[3] J. Tafel and G. Friedrichs, *Ber.*, **37**, 3187 (1904).
[4] E. Müller, *Z. Elektrochem.*, **33**, 253 (1927).

halide solutions results in the formation of the haloforms, for example,

$$C_2H_5OH + 3Cl^- + 7OH^- = CHCl_3 + CO_2 + 6H_2O + 10e^-.$$

A number of cases are given by Swann.[1] However, the reaction mechanism is probably through the formation of the hypohalite.

The electrolytic oxidation of alcohols, aldehydes, and acids. In agreement with the potential values, it is easier to oxidize an aldehyde to the acid than it is to oxidize the alcohol to the aldehyde; consequently it is difficult in the anodic oxidation of a primary alcohol in acid solution to build up an appreciable concentration of the aldehyde, because the oxidation goes on to form the acid, except in special cases. In alkaline solution the anodic oxidation of primary alcohols results in the formation of hydrogen and hydro-carbons as well as the aldehyde. From these results, it appears that the intermediate which is formed is unstable with respect to its own oxidation and reduction. This instability also exists in the alcohols; for example, methyl alcohol should decompose into methane and formaldehyde but the reaction, of course, does not occur with appreciable speed. Müller and Hochstetter[2] have discussed the mechanism of the aldehyde oxidation.

A somewhat similar result is obtained in the oxidation of aldehydes in alkaline solution. Thus, formaldehyde gives hydrogen and carbonate ion; and acetaldehyde yields formic acid, hydrocarbons, and some complex products. In acid solution, however, the aldehyde group is oxidized to carboxyl.

The anodic oxidation of acetic acid involves a number of points of unusual interest. Note, for example, that two distinct reactions may occur.[3] One, the Kolbe reaction, produces ethane and carbon dioxide.

$$2CH_3COOH \rightarrow C_2H_6 + 2CO_2 + 2H^+ + 2e^-, \qquad E^\circ = -0.12.$$

The other, the Hofer-Moest reaction, forms methyl alcohol and carbon dioxide.

$$H_2O + CH_3COOH \rightarrow CH_3OH + CO_2 + 2H^+ + 2e^-, \qquad E^\circ = -0.35.$$

The Kolbe reaction occurs with smooth platinum electrodes in concentrated acetate and acetic-acid mixtures and the anodic potential is

---

[1] S. Swann, Jr., *Trans. Elektrochem. Soc.*, **69**, 296 (1936).

[2] E. Müller and F. Hochstetter, *Z. Elektrochem.*, **20**, 367 (1914).

[3] S. Glasstone and A. Hickling, *J. Chem. Soc.*, 1878 (1934); F. Fichter, *Trans. Am. Electrochem. Soc.*, **56**, 467 (1929).

quite high, around -2.1 volts. The Hofer-Moest reaction is favored by the presence of high concentrations of alkali bicarbonates, sulfates, and other salts with negative ions which are not readily oxidized. It also occurs in acetic acid if salts of manganese, lead, or silver are present, as these substances appear to inhibit the Kolbe reaction.

Various theories of the oxidation mechanism are discussed in references cited. It seems probable that an intermediate is formed which may decompose to give the Hofer-Moest reaction, or if the conditions favor the stability of the intermediate, its concentration will build up until the rate of its reaction with acetic acid, to give the Kolbe reaction, becomes rapid. There is considerable uncertainty regarding the identity of the intermediate, but the strongest evidence points to a peroxyacetic acid, possibly CH_3CO_3H. On this assumption the following reactions may be written for an electrode of metal X, which has been oxidized to a surface layer of XOH.

$$XOH + CH_3COO^- = CH_3CO_3H + X + e^-,$$
$$CH_3CO_3H = CH_3OH + CO_2,$$
$$CH_3CO_2H + CH_3CO_3H = C_2H_6 + 2CO_2 + H_2O.$$

Higher fatty acids generally give the Kolbe reaction; and, in mixtures of two acids, hydrocarbons corresponding to R^1R^1, R^2R^2, and R^1R^2 are formed, as would be expected from the suggested mechanism.

Peroxycarbonate. The electrolysis of potassium carbonate solutions at low temperatures with a smooth platinum anode results in the formation of peroxycarbonate, $C_2O_6^{--}$. The diacid appears to hydrolyze slowly to form the monoacid, H_2CO_4. There are no experimental data regarding oxidizing power of the peroxycarbonates.

$$2H_2CO_3 = C_2O_6^{--} + 4H^+ + 2e^-, \qquad E° < -1.7.$$

Carbon as an oxidizing agent. Judging merely from the free energies, one would conclude that carbon was a fairly good oxidizing agent.

$$CH_4(g) = C + 4H^+ + 4e^-, \qquad E° = -0.13.$$

However, in view of the high energy of the C : C bonds in solid, it is not surprising that the activation energy is so large that, even at a high overvoltage, carbon cannot be reduced to methane.

Carbon is thermodynamically stable with respect to its hydrolysis.

$$2C + 2H_2O = CO_2 + CH_4, \qquad \Delta F = 6.73 \text{ kcal.}$$

The positive free energy is not large; and, again, except for the high activation energy, appreciable partial pressures of the gaseous products would be obtained. The following diagram summarizes the potential relationships between C, CH_4, CO, and CO_2 in acid solution:

$$\begin{array}{cccc} -0.13 & -0.51 & 0.116 \\ CH_4 \text{———} C \text{———} CO \text{———} CO_2 \end{array}$$

Carbon monoxide is thermodynamically unstable.

$$2CO = C + CO_2, \qquad \Delta F^\circ = -28.4 \text{ kcal.}$$

The ionization of carbonic acid. Harned and Davis[1] summarized the data on the ionization constants of H_2CO_3. From the free energies we write

$$H_2CO_3 = H^+ + HCO_3^-, \qquad K = 4.16 \times 10^{-7};$$
$$HCO_3^- = H^+ + CO_3^{--}, \qquad K = 4.84 \times 10^{-11}.$$

These constants are calculated for the practical assumption that all of the aqueous CO_2 is H_2CO_3. Olson and Youle[2] have corrected for the unhydrated CO_2 and give as the actual constant for the first dissociation

$$H_2CO_3 = H^+ + HCO_3^-, \qquad K = 2 \times 10^{-4}.$$

Unsaturated hydrocarbons. From the free energy data,

$$C_2H_6(g) = C_2H_4(g) + 2H^+ + 2e^-, \qquad E^\circ = -0.52.$$

A similar case of the single-bond—double-bond couple is the succinic acid-fumaric acid electrode which was measured directly by Borsook and Schott.[3] They found

$$HO_2CCH_2\text{—}CH_2CO_2H(aq) = HO_2CCH\text{=}CHCO_2H(aq)$$
$$+ 2H^+ + 2e^-, \qquad E^\circ = -0.44.$$

It is again interesting to note that while the activation energy of these more complicated molecules is lower, the magnitude of the potential remains the same as for the C_2H_6—C_2H_4 couple.

The cathodic reduction of the double bonds of the benzene ring can be accomplished in the case of a number of its derivatives, for example, the reduction of phenol to cyclohexanol.

[1] H. S. Harned and R. Davis, Jr., *J. Am. Chem. Soc.*, **65**, 2030 (1943).

[2] A. R. Olson and P. V. Youle, *J. Am. Chem. Soc.*, **62**, 1027 (1940).

[3] H. Borsook and H. F. Schott, *J. Biol. Chem.*, **92**, 535 (1931).

For the double-bond triple-bond potential, that is, the ethylene-acetylene couple, the computation from the free energies gives

$$C_2H_4(g) = C_2H_2(g) + 2H^+ + 2e^-, \qquad E^\circ = -0.73.$$

In spite of this favorable potential it is somewhat difficult to reduce acetylene. However, under suitable conditions it may be carried out electrolytically.

The following diagram summarizes the potentials for the reduction of carbon to ethane in acid solution.

$$\overset{-0.52}{C_2H_6\rule{1.2cm}{0.4pt}}\overset{-0.73}{C_2H_4\rule{1.2cm}{0.4pt}}\overset{-0.52}{C_2H_2\rule{1.2cm}{0.4pt}}C$$

Aniline-nitrobenzene. Parks and Hoffman, in their monograph, gave for the free energy of aniline (1) 35,400 cal., and for nitrobenzene (1) a rough estimate of 36,400 cal. The solubility of aniline in water is about $0.3M$ and the dissociation constant of the ion, $C_6H_5NH_3^+$, is 2×10^{-5}. As an approximate figure 29,400 cal. will be taken for the free energy of the acid ion. Hence,

$$2H_2O + C_6H_5NH_3^+ = C_6H_5NO_2 + 7H^+ + 6e^-, \qquad E^\circ = -0.87.$$

This potential is about the same as the value, -0.86, found for the NH_4^+—HNO_2 half-reaction. Haber and Schmidt[1] studied the electrolytic reduction of nitrobenzene and proposed a scheme which, with subsequent modification, became the following:

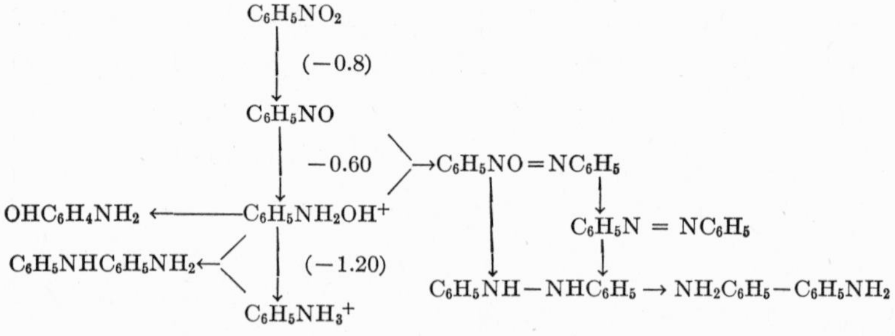

The first step, the formation of nitrosobenzene, requires a fairly high overvoltage. The second step, the formation of phenyl hydroxylamine, can attain a reversible equilibrium, and the potential of the couple has been measured.

$$C_6H_5NH_2OH^+ = C_6H_5NO + 3H^+ + 2e^-, \qquad E^\circ = -0.60.$$

---

[1] F. Haber and C. Schmidt, *Z. physik. Chem.*, **32**, 271 (1900).

The third step, the formation of aniline, is not reversible in the equilibrium sense. The potentials of the first and third steps have been estimated from the overall value and those of the corresponding simple nitrogen compounds. The formation of p-aminodiphenyl amine, $C_6H_5NHC_6H_5NH_2$; azoxybenzene, $C_6H_5NO:NC_6H_5$; and azobenzene, $C_6H_5N:NC_6H_5$ result from secondary reactions indicated by arrows. The azoxybenzene may be reduced to hydrazobenzene, $C_6H_5NH—NHC_6H_5$, which can rearrange to form benzidine. Also, rearrangement of the phenylhydroxylamine may occur to form p-aminophenol. Hydrazobenzene is not readily reduced to aniline, but a number of its substituted derivatives are. Reversible potentials have been measured for several of the substituted azobenzenes to the corresponding hydrazobenzenes and the $E°$ values are about -0.4 (see International Critical Tables).

A cathode with high overvoltage favors the reduction of nitrobenzene to aniline in acid solution,[1] apparently because phenylhydroxylamine is then rapidly reduced and cannot therefore enter into side reactions. The side reaction producing azoxybenzene is favored by alkaline solutions.[2]

A very complete review has been given by Swann[3] for the whole field of electrolytic organic oxidation and reduction reactions.

Cyanide, cyanate and cyanogen.   The CN group resembles the halogens in many respects and like them has the important oxidation states: -1 in HCN, 0 in C_2N_2 and $+1$ in HCNO. The dissociation constants of the acid and the potentials relating its states may be calculated from the free energies, Table 27.

$$HCN(aq) = H^+ + CN^-, \qquad K = 4 \times 10^{-10};$$
$$HCNO = H^+ + CNO^-, \qquad K = 1.2 \times 10^{-4};$$
$$HCN(aq) = \tfrac{1}{2}C_2N_2 + H^+ + e^-, \qquad E° = -0.37;$$
$$\tfrac{1}{2}C_2N_2 + H_2O = HCNO + H^+ + e^-, \qquad E° = -0.33;$$
$$CN^- + 2OH^- = CNO^- + H_2O + 2e^-, \qquad E_B = 0.97.$$

Cyanogen is unstable with respect to disproportionation in both acidic and basic solutions, but because of the high activation energy re-

[1] J. B. Conant, *International Critical Tables*, **VI**, 333.

[2] S. Glasstone and A. Hickling, *Electrolytic Oxidation and Reduction*, New York: D. Van Nostrand Co., Inc., 1936, p. 161.

[3] S. Swann, Jr., *Trans. Electrochem. Soc.*, **69**, 287 (1936).

quired to break the C ·· C bond the reaction is not rapid in acid.

$$C_2N_2 + 2OH^- = CN^- + CNO^- + H_2O, \qquad \Delta F° = -34.5 \text{ kcal.};$$
$$C_2N_2 + H_2O = HCN + HCNO, \qquad \Delta F° = -13.3 \text{ kcal.}$$

Thiocyanate. An accurate value for the free energy of thiocyanate cannot be given. From an approximate figure for the entropy we calculate $\Delta F° = 21.2$ kcal.

$$CN^- + S = CNS^-, \qquad \Delta F° = -17.9 \text{ kcal.}$$

The acid HCNS is strong as is ordinarily the case with hydrogen on a sulfur which is attached to a negative element. The most important potential is the oxidation to hydrogen cyanide and sulfurous acid.

$$3H_2O + HCNS = HCN(aq) + H_2SO_3 + 4H^+ + 4e^-,$$
$$E° = -0.55.$$

Bjerrum and Kirschner[1] found that free thiocyanogen was between bromine and iodine as an oxidizing agent and reported that

$$2CNS^- = (CNS)_2 + 2e^-, \qquad E° = -0.77.$$

Hydroquinone-quinone couples. The reversibility of hydroquinone-quinone electrodes and their extensive use in the determination of hydrogen-ion concentrations are well known. Hovorska and Dearing[2] have reported the potential

$$\text{(hydroquinone)} = \text{(quinone)} + 2H^+ + 2e^-, \qquad E° = -0.69938.$$

The potentials summarized in Table 28 have been taken from the papers of Conant and Fieser.[3]

For those cases in which a solid quinhydrone is formed as an intermediate, the over-all potential must obviously be measured in two

---

[1] N. Bjerrum and A. Kirschner, *Kgl. Danske Videnskab. Selskab. Math-fys.,* Series (8), **5**, 76 (1918).

[2] F. Hovorska and W. C. Dearing, *J. Am. Chem. Soc.,* **57**, 446 (1935).

[3] J. B. Conant and L. F. Fieser, *J. Am. Chem. Soc.,* **45**, 2198 (1923); *see also* E. Schreiner, *Z. physik. Chem.,* **117**, 64 (1925), and G. E. K. Branch and M. Calvin, *Theory of Organic Chemistry,* New York: Prentice-Hall, Inc., 1941.

steps. Thus, for benzoquinone,

$$C_6H_4O_2\cdot C_6H_4(OH)_2(c) = 2C_6H_4O_2(c) + 2H^+ + 2e^-,$$
$$E^\circ = -0.749;$$
$$2C_6H_4(OH)_2(c) = C_6H_4O_2\cdot C_6H_4O_2\cdot C_6H_4(OH)_2(c) + 2H^+ + 2e^-,$$
$$E^\circ = -0.613.$$

Many additional quinone derivatives have been studied for the purpose of determining the effect of substitution upon the potential, but most of this work has been in nonaqueous solutions. Among the more important of these researches are quinolinequinone and benzotriazole by Fieser and Martin,[1] naphthoquinones by Fieser and Fieser,[2] and various substituted quinones by Kvalnes.[3]

A very interesting review of the semiquinone problem has been given by Michaelis.[4]

TABLE 28

E° VALUES FOR SOME HYDROQUINONE–QUINONE COUPLES

Benzoquinone	-0.699	2-3 Dichloroquinone	-0.693
Toluquinone	-0.641	2-5 Dichloroquinone	-0.707
p-Xyloquinone	-0.606	2-6 Dichloroquinone	-0.716
Duroquinone	-0.498	Trichloroquinone	-0.688
Thymoquinone	-0.507	Tetrachloroquinone	-0.682
Monochloroquinone	-0.696	1-4 Naphthaquinone	-0.480

Diphenylbenzidine and inside indicators. Diphenylamine and its derivatives have become important as "inside" indicators for titrations with dichromate, ceric sulfate, and ferrous ion. Sarver and Kolthoff[5] have shown that diphenylamine is first oxidized irreversibly to diphenylbenzidine, and this is then oxidized reversibly to diphenylbenzidine violet. For this couple they gave

$$C_6H_5NHC_6H_4\text{—}C_6H_4NHC_6H_5 =$$
$$C_6H_5N{=}C_6H_4\text{—}C_6H_4N{=}C_6H_5 + 2H^+ + 2e^-, \qquad E^\circ = -0.76.$$

For the more soluble sulfonic acid derivative these authors report,

[1] L. F. Fieser and E. Martin, *J. Am. Chem. Soc.*, **57**, 1835 and 1840 (1935).
[2] L. F. Fieser and M. Fieser, *J. Am. Chem. Soc.*, **57**, 491 (1935).
[3] D. E. Kvalnes, *J. Am. Chem. Soc.*, **56**, 670, 2487 (1934).
[4] L. Michaelis, *Trans. Electrochem. Soc.*, **71**, 107 (1937).
[5] L. A. Sarver and I. M. Kolthoff, *J. Am. Chem. Soc.*, **53**, 2902 (1931).

$E° = -0.87$. The higher potential of this couple is advantageous because it is desirable to have an indicator which is not oxidized by ferric ion. Hammett, Walden, and Edmonds[1] investigated p-nitrodiphenylamine and 2-4 diaminodiphenylamine and give as $E°$ values, -1.06 and -0.70, respectively.

When an organic oxidation reduction indicator is employed in the titration of a reducing agent by a strong oxidizing agent, such as ceric sulfate, it is necessary to have the potential of the organic couple slightly more negative than that of the reducing couple. Because there is a wide range in the potentials of the reducing couples, it is desirable to have available a wide range of organic couples. Such a list has been prepared by Clark[2] and is given below.

	$E°$ in $1M$ H⁺
Indigo sulfonates.........................	-0.25 to -0.35
Methylene blue..........................	-0.5
Indophenols.............................	-0.55 to -0.65
Diphenylamine and other aromatic amines....	-0.7 to -1.0
Triphenylmethane dyes...................	-0.7 to -1.1
Ferrous O-phenanthroline	-1.15
Ferrous nitro-O-phenanthroline.............	-1.25

Potentials of biological interest. Clark, in the reference quoted above, has listed a number of couples of biological interest. Potentials for some of these at pH7 are: coenzyme I, 0.32; vitamin B₂, 0.22; vitamin E, -0.06; methamoglobin, -0.16; adrenaline, -0.39.

Indophenols. Clark[3] and his co-workers have measured the potentials of a number of leuco indophenol-indophenol couples. For the simplest type the reaction is

$$NH_2C_6H_4\text{—}NH\text{—}C_6H_4OH =$$
$$NH_2C_6H_4\text{—}N\text{=}C_6H_4\text{=}O + 2H^+ + 2e^-.$$

The $E°$ values are complicated functions of the hydrogen-ion concentration and range from -0.55 to -0.7.

Methylene blue. The same authors have studied Lauth's violet and its tetramethyl derivative, methylene blue. The potentials are nearly the same.

Methylene white = methylene blue + $2H^+ + 2e^-$, $E° = -0.53$.

[1] L. P. Hammett, G. H. Walden and S. M. Edmonds, *J. Am. Chem. Soc.*, **56**, 1092 (1934).

[2] W. M. Clark, *J. Appl. Physics*, **9**, 97, (1938).

[3] W. M. Clark, *Determination of Hydrogen Ions*, Baltimore: Williams and Wilkins, 1928, p. 384. *See also International Critical Tables*, **VI**, p. 333.

Indigo.   The potentials for a number of leuco-indigo—indigo couples have likewise been measured by Clark. The essential structural reaction is

$$C_6H_4 \underset{NH}{\overset{C(OH)}{<}} \underset{NH}{\overset{(OH)C}{>}} C_6H_4 =$$

$$C_6H_4 \underset{NH}{\overset{CO}{<}} C\!-\!C \underset{NH}{\overset{CO}{>}} C_6H_4 + 2H^+ + 2e^-.$$

For a number of derivatives, the $E°$ values range from -0.26 to -0.37.

Erioglaucine A.   Knop[1] has studied the oxidation of erioglaucine A and eriogreen B. The oxidation potentials are -0.71 and -0.72, respectively. These dyes have been used as indicators in oxidation-reduction titrations but as the oxidized form is not very stable, the ferrousphenanthroline complex (see p. 226) is to be preferred.

Nitroguanidine.   Smith and Sabetta[2] report the following for nitroso-nitroguanidine

$$H_2O + \underset{NHNO}{NH_2C\!\!=\!\!NH} = \underset{NHNO_2}{NH_2C\!\!=\!\!NH} + 2H^+ + 2e^-, \qquad E° = -0.88.$$

Xanthines.   Filitti[3] gave potentials for a number of xanthine couples.

$$H_2O + \begin{array}{c} NH\!-\!CO \\ | \quad\quad | \\ CH \quad C\!-\!NH \\ || \quad\quad || \quad > CH \\ N\!-\!\!\!-\!\!C\!-\!\!\!-\!N \end{array} = \begin{array}{c} NH\!-\!CO \\ | \quad\quad | \\ C\!=\!O \;\; C\!-\!NH \\ | \quad\quad || \quad > CH + 2H^+ + 2e^-, \\ NH\!-\!C\!-\!\!\!-\!N \end{array}$$

$$E° = 0.01.$$

Flavines, murexides, and porphyrexide.   Kuhn[4] and his co-workers have studied the oxidation and reduction of a large number of these complex nitrogen-carbon-oxygen ring structures. For the

[1] J. Knop, Z. anal. Chem., **77**, 111 (1929).
[2] G. B. L. Smith and V. J. Sabetta, J. Am. Chem. Soc., **54**, 1034 (1932).
[3] S. Filitti, J. chim. phys., **32**, 1 (1935).
[4] R. Kuhn, Ber., **68**, 1528 (1935); ibid., **69**, 1547 and 1557 (1936).

flavines, the $E°$ values for pH7 range from -0.1 to -0.2; for porphyrexide, -0.72; and for murexides, -0.02.

Safranine. Stiehler, Chen, and Clark[1] investigated a number of safranine derivatives. The $E°$ potentials are around -0.3.

Reactions of CCl_4, CF_4, $COCl_2$, Cs_2, COS, and $CO(NH_2)_2$. There are a large number of important reactions involving the simpler compounds of carbon with the halogens, sulfur, and nitrogen, and the free energies of many of these compounds have been included in Table 27. The free energy of CCl_4 is small; hence, as an oxidizing agent, it is almost as powerful as chlorine.

$$4H^+ + 4Cl^- + C = CCl_4 + 4H^+ + 4e^-, \qquad E° = -1.18.$$

However, at room temperature, CCl_4 is a slow oxidizing agent because of the energy required to break the C—Cl bond. At high temperatures with powerful reducing agents, very violent reactions may occur, as for example,

$$CCl_4(l) + N_2H_4(l) = C + 4HCl(g), \qquad \Delta F° = -100. \text{ kcal.}$$

The similar reaction with CF_4 has a $\Delta F°$ of about -130 kcal. The free energy of hydrolysis of CCl_4 to phosgene, $COCl_2$ is

$$CCl_4(l) + H_2O = COCl_2(g) + 2H^+ + 2Cl^-, \qquad \Delta F° = -30.0 \text{ kcal.}$$

As a result there is some danger of the formation of the highly toxic $COCl_2$, especially at a high temperature when carbon tetrachloride is in contact with water.

The basic dissociation constant of urea is 1.5×10^{-14}. It is rather readily oxidized.

$$CO(NH_2)_2 + H_2O \rightarrow CO_2 + 6H^+ + 6e^-, \qquad E° = -0.1.$$

SILICON

Oxidation states. The principal oxidation state, $+4$, is that of the dioxide, SiO_2, and the tetrahalides. The dioxide forms innumerable acids, the orthoforms of the mono-, di-, tri-, and tetra-acids being H_4SiO_4, $H_6Si_2O_7$, $H_8Si_3O_{10}$, and $H_{10}Si_4O_{13}$, respectively; and many dehydrated forms of these acids are also known, for example, meta-monosilicic acid, H_2SiO_3. In aqueous solutions these acids are often

[1] R. Stiehler, T. Chen and W. M. Clark, *J. Am. Chem. Soc.*, **55**, 891 (1933).

present in complicated equilibria; hence it appears that the difference in free energy between the various polyacids is small. Silicous acid, $H_2Si_2O_3$, is formed by the hydrolysis of the hydrogen halides, $SiHX_3$, and this acid may be classified as belonging to the $+2$ oxidation state. The monoxide exists as a stable gas molecule: in fact the evidence is fairly definite that SiO_2 decomposes into SiO and O_2 when it vaporizes. A number of hydrosilicons and their derivatives, analogous to the corresponding carbon compounds, are known, but they are relatively unstable and their free energies, with the exception of SiH_4, cannot be calculated at present.

Oxidation and reduction of silicon. Like the case of carbon, the bonds between the atoms in the solid silicon are so strong that the activation energies in reactions involving the free element are very

TABLE 29

THERMODYNAMIC DATA ON SILICON[1]

(Heat and free energy of formation in kcal. Entropy of substance in cal./deg.)

Formula	Description	State	$\Delta H°$	$\Delta F°$	$S°$
Si		g	88.04	77.41	40.120
Si		c	0.0	0.0	4.47
Si	amorphous	c	1.0		
Si$^+$		g	277.45		
Si^{++}		g	654.04		
SiO		g	−26.72	−32.77	49.26
SiO$_2$	quartz	c	−205.4	−192.4	10.00
SiO$_2$	cristobal-ite II	c	−205.0	−192.1	10.19
SiO$_2$	trid-ymite IV	c	−204.8	−191.9	10.36
SiO$_2$	vitreous	glass	−202.5	−190.9	11.2
SiH$_4$		g	−14.8	−9.4	48.7
H$_2$SiO$_3$		c	−270.7	−244.5	
H$_2$SiO$_4$		c	−320.6		
H$_2$Si$_2$O$_5$		c	−472.4		
H$_6$Si$_2$O$_7$		c	−611.2		
SiO$_3^{--}$		c		(−212.)	
SiF$_4$		g	−370.	−360.	68.0
SiF$_6^{--}$		aq	−558.5	−511.	−12. (?)
H$_2$SiF$_6$		aq	−557.2		
SiCl$_4$		g	−145.7	−136.2	79.2
SiCl$_4$		liq	−153.0	−136.9	57.2
SiBr$_4$		liq	−95.1		
SiI$_4$		c	−31.6		

[1] Bureau of Standards values in *italics;* estimated values in parentheses.

large. Consequently the oxidation-reduction couples of silicon are not thermodynamically reversible at low temperatures. However, the energy relations in the following cases are of some interest.

$$SiH_4(g) = Si + 4H^+ + 4e^-, \qquad E^\circ = -0.102;$$
$$4OH^- + SiH_4(g) = Si + 4H_2O + 4e^-, \qquad E_B^\circ = 0.73;$$
$$2H_2O + Si = SiO_2 + 4H^+ + 4e^-, \qquad E^\circ = 0.86;$$
$$3H_2O + Si = H_2SiO_3 + 4H^+ + 4e^- \qquad E^\circ = 0.84;$$
$$6F^- + Si = SiF_6^{--} + 4e^-, \qquad E^\circ = 1.2.$$

Only a very approximate value can be given for the free energies of the silicate ions in alkaline solution. Mulert[1] has given values for the heats of solutions of various hydrates of silicon dioxide but his data do not appear to be consistent with reasonable estimations of the free energies and entropies of solution. Several determinations of the ionization constants of the simpler silicic acids have been made. For H_2SiO_3, Joseph and Oakley[2] reported that

$$H_2SiO_3 = H^+ + HSiO_3^-, \qquad K = 10^{-10};$$
$$HSiO_3^- = H^+ + SiO_3^{--}, \qquad K = 10^{-12}.$$

These figures have been checked by Oka, Kawagaki, and Kadoya.[3] From the free energies of ionization and a rough figure for the solubility, we estimate ΔF° for SiO_3^{--} to be -212 kcal.

$$Si + 6OH^- = SiO_3^{--} + 3H_2O + 4e^-, \qquad E_B^\circ = 1.7.$$

From this potential, the free energy is favorable for the solution of silicon in alkali with the evolution of hydrogen. From the value of K_1 for H_2SiO_3, it appears that the formal charge on the Si must be zero and that the structure should be written with one double-bonded oxygen.

Silicon is thermodynamically unstable with respect to its disproportionation with water.

$$2Si + 2H_2O = SiH_4(g) + SiO_2, \qquad \Delta F^\circ = -88.4 \text{ kcal.}$$

Equilibria involving the silicon halides. Kubelka and Pristoupil[4] have investigated the reaction of the dioxide with hydrogen

[1] O. Mulert, Z. anorg. Chem., 75, 198 (1912).
[2] A. F. Joseph and H. B. Oakley, J. Chem. Soc., 127, 2813 (1925).
[3] Y. Oka, K. Kawagaki and R. Kadoya, J. Chem. Soc., Japan, 64, 718 (1943).
[4] P. Kubelka and V. Pristoupil, Z. anorg. allgem. Chem., 197, 391 (1931).

fluoride. They record

$$SiF_6^{--} + 2H_2O = SiO_2 + 4H^+ + 6F^-, \qquad K = 2 \times 10^{-27},$$
$$\Delta F° = 36,500 \text{ cal.}$$

This constant has been checked by Ryss,[1] and we have used the $\Delta F°$ for the reaction to calculate the free energy of SiF_6^{--}. With this free energy we calculate

$$SiF_6^{--} = SiF_4 + 2F^-, \qquad \Delta F° = 19. \text{ kcal.}$$

This is not consistent with the value of 8.3 kcal. found for this reaction by Ryss. At present we are unable to locate the source of the discrepancy, but is appears to be in the free energy of SiF_4. For the partial hydrolysis which occurs when the tetrafluoride is passed into water, the free energies give

$$3SiF_4(g) + 3H_2O = 2H_2SiF_6(aq) + H_2SiO_3(s), \quad \Delta F° = -14. \text{ kcal.}$$

For the hydrolysis of the tetrachloride our free energies give

$$SiCl_4(l) + 2H_2O = SiO_2 + 4H^+ + 4Cl^-, \quad \Delta F° = -66.5 \text{ kcal.}$$

GERMANIUM

Oxidation states. Germanium forms oxides of the $+2$ and $+4$ oxidation states, GeO and GeO_2. Both oxides are amphoteric. Evidence has been advanced indicating that germanous acid has a formic acid structure or at least may exist in this tautomeric form, but with hydrochloric acid it forms $GeCl_2$ and with hydrogen sulfide, GeS. Germane, GeH_4, and a number of hydrogen compounds analogous to the simple hydrocarbons are known, but no thermodynamic data have been obtained for them.

Germanium potentials. Nichols and Cooper[2] sought to measure the Ge—GeO_2 couple but concluded that the cell was not completely reversible. Laubengayer and Morton[3] studied the crystal forms of the dioxide. The tetragonal rutile type of the oxide is practically insoluble and much denser than the soluble hexagonal form, and the difference in energy between the two appears to be unusually large. No hydrates of the more soluble modification are known. Its solu-

---

[1] I. G. Ryss, *J. Gen. Chem. U.S.S.R.*, **16**, 331 (1946).

[2] M. L. Nichols and S. R. Cooper, *Ind. Eng. Chem., Anal. Ed.*, **7**, 350 (1935).

[3] A. W. Laubengayer and D. S. Morton, *J. Am. Chem. Soc.*, **54**, 2318 (1932).

TABLE 30

THERMODYNAMIC DATA ON GERMANIUM[1]

(Heat and free energy of formation in kcal. Entropy of substance in cal./deg.)

Formula	Description	State	$\Delta H°$	$\Delta F°$	$S°$
Ge		g	*78.44*	*69.50*	*40.106*
Ge		c	0.0	0.0	*10.14*
Ge$^+$		g	*267.32*		
Ge^{++}		g	*636.50*		
GeO		g	−22.8	−28.2	52.56
GeO		c	−73.	−66.	(12.)
GeO$_2$	precipitated	c	−141.	−127.	(12.)
H$_2$GeO$_3$		aq	−203.	−182.	(43.)
HGeO$_3^-$		aq	−198.	−170.	(21.)
GeCl		g	32.45		
GeCl$_4$		liq	−136.	−119.	60.
GeBr		g	*34.8*		
GeS		g	*1.35*		
GeI$_4$		c	−42.	−41.	(64.)
GeI$_2$		c	−27.	−26.	(36.)

[1] Bureau of Standards values in *italics;* estimated values in parentheses.

bility is given as 4.55 gram per liter at 25° C. From the heat of formation of the dioxide, we have calculated its free energy of formation using 12 cal./deg. as our estimated entropy. The other free energies have been adjusted to this value.

$$\text{Ge} + 2\text{H}_2\text{O} = \text{GeO}_2 + 4\text{H}^+ + 4e^-, \qquad E° = 0.15;$$
$$\text{Ge} + 3\text{H}_2\text{O} = \text{H}_2\text{GeO}_3(\text{aq}) + 4\text{H}^+ + 4e^-, \qquad E° = 0.131.$$

Pugh[1] has given the constants

$$\text{H}_2\text{GeO}_3(\text{aq}) = \text{HGeO}_3^- + \text{H}^+, \qquad K = 2.6 \times 10^{-9};$$
$$\text{HGeO}_3^- = \text{GeO}_3^{--} + \text{H}^+, \qquad K = 1.9 \times 10^{-13}.$$

For the potential in alkaline solution we may then write,

$$5\text{OH}^- + \text{Ge} = \text{HGeO}_3^- + 2\text{H}_2\text{O} + 4e^-, \qquad E_B° = 1.0.$$

Roth and Schwartz[2] measured the heat of hydrolysis of GeCl$_4$(l) and recorded 25 kcal. Estimating the entropy of the reaction as 27 cal. per degree, we find,

$$2\text{H}_2\text{O} + \text{GeCl}_4(\text{l}) = \text{GeO}_2 + 4\text{H}^+ + 4\text{Cl}^-, \qquad \Delta F° = -33 \text{ kcal.}$$

[1] W. Pugh, *J. Chem. Soc.*, 2001 (1929).
[2] W. A. Roth and O. Schwartz, *Z. physik. Chem.*, **134**, 456 (1928).

In hot concentrated hydrochloric acid the reaction is reversed and the dioxide may be converted to the volatile tetrachloride. The complex fluoride ion, GeF_6^{--}, forms, but there are no quantitative data.

In acid solutions halide complex ions of Ge^{++} are fairly stable in the absence of oxidizing agents but highly alkaline solutions evolve hydrogen with the oxidation of the germanium to $HGeO_3^-$. At the same time some decomposition into the metal and the germanate is said to occur. The uncomplexed Ge^{++} ion probably disproportionates. With reference to the Ge—GeO_2 couple, we estimate,

$$2H_2O + Ge^{++} = GeO_2 + 4H^+ + 2e^-, \qquad E^\circ = ca\ 0.3;$$

$$Ge = Ge^{++} + 2e^-, \qquad E^\circ = ca\ 0.0.$$

Jolly and Latimer[1] have studied the stability of GeI_2 and GeO_2. From their work the following potential diagram is constructed:

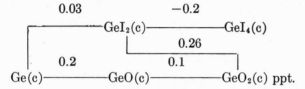

GeI_2 in contact with a water solution appears to be unstable with respect to disproportionation unless the solution has a high concentration of HI. At low acid it also tends to hydrolyze to GeO.

Both the +2 and +4 sulfides may be precipitated. The latter is readily soluble in sulfide ion with the formation of thiogermanate. No values for the equilibrium constants can be given.

The cathodic reduction of a germanium electrode in phosphoric acid results in the formation of some GeH_4. The compound appears to be endothermic and a fairly high temperature is required for its decomposition.

$$GeH_4 = Ge + 4H^+ + 4e^-, \qquad E^\circ > 0.3.$$

There are few elements whose chemistry is so little understood as is that of germanium. The almost complete lack of quantitative data is to be noted, and many of the qualitative facts upon which the approximate potentials have been estimated will doubtless be subject to reinterpretation.

---

[1] W. L. Jolly and W. M. Latimer, *Univ. of Calif. Rad. Lab. Report 1152* (1951).

TIN

Oxidation states. Tin exists in the $+2$ oxidation state, stannous and stannite compounds, and in the $+4$ state, stannic and stannate compounds. The hydrogen compound, SnH_4, may be prepared but it is thermodynamically unstable.

Tin-stannous potentials. The International Critical Tables chose for the Sn—Sn^{++} couple

$$Sn = Sn^{++} + 2e^-, \qquad E^\circ = 0.136$$

and the free energy of Sn^{++}, -6275 cal. Kapustinskii[1] gave $\Delta H^\circ = -5.4$ kcal., $\Delta F^\circ = -6.5$ kcal., and S° for Sn^{++}, -15.2 cal./deg. We shall continue to use the International Critical Tables value and shall not attempt to give ΔH° or S°. From the free energy of the hydroxide,

$$Sn(OH)_2(c) = Sn^{++} + 2OH^-, \qquad K = 3 \times 10^{-27}.$$

Garrett and Heiks,[2] in their careful investigation, gave 1.55×10^{-26}. These authors also wrote

$$Sn(OH)_2(c) = H^+ + HSnO_2^-, \qquad K = 3.78 \times 10^{-15}.$$

From the latter, ΔF° of $HSnO_2^-$ is -98.0 kcal.

$$Sn + 3OH^- = HSnO_2^- + H_2O + 2e^-, \qquad E_B^\circ = 0.91.$$

The free energy of SnS and our value for Sn^{++} give

$$SnS = Sn^{++} + S^{--}, \qquad K = 1 \times 10^{-26};$$
$$S^{--} + Sn = SnS + 2e^-, \qquad E^\circ = 0.94.$$

Stannous carbonate is hydrolyzed to the hydroxide.

For the dissociation of $SnCl_2$ Bjerrum[3] gave

$$SnCl_2 = Sn^{++} + 2Cl^-, \qquad K = 5.7 \times 10^{-3}.$$

Stannous-stannic potentials. An accurate value for the Sn^{++}—Sn^{+4} couple cannot be given as the activity coefficient and hydrolysis constant of stannic ion are not known. Huey and Tartar[4] reported -0.154 and we shall write

$$Sn^{++} = Sn^{+4} + 2e, \qquad E^\circ = -0.15.$$

[1] A. F. Kapustinskii, *J. Phys. Chem. U.S.S.R.*, **15**, 645 (1941).
[2] A. B. Garrett and R. E. Heiks, *J. Am. Chem. Soc.*, **63**, 562 (1941).
[3] J. Bjerrum, *Chem. Rev.*, **46**, 381 (1950).
[4] C. S. Huey and H. V. Tartar, *J. Am. Chem. Soc.*, **56**, 2585 (1934).

TABLE 31

THERMODYNAMIC DATA ON TIN[1]

(Heat and free energy of formation in kcal. Entropy of substance in cal./deg.)

Formula	Description	State	$\Delta H°$	$\Delta F°$	$S°$
Sn		g	*72.*	*64.*	*40.245*
Sn	gray	c	*0.6*	*1.1*	*10.7*
Sn	white	c	0.0	0.0	*12.3*
Sn^+		g	*242.57*		
Sn^{++}		g	*581.4*		
Sn^{++}		aq	−2.39	−6.275	−5.9
Sn^{++++}		aq		0.65	
SnO		c	*−68.4*	*−61.5*	*13.5*
SnO_2		c	*−138.8*	*−124.2*	*12.5*
$HSnO_2^-$		aq		−98.0	
$Sn(OH)_2$		c	*−138.3*	*−117.6*	*23.1*
SnF_6^{--}		aq	−474.7	−420.	(0.)
$Sn(OH)_4$		c	*−270.5*	*−227.5*	(29.)
$Sn(OH)_6^{--}$		aq		−310.5	
$SnCl_2$		c	*−83.6*	−72.2	(29.3)
$SnCl_4$		liq	*−130.3*	*−113.3*	*61.8*
$SnBr_2$		c	*−63.6*	−59.5	(34.9)
$SnBr_4$		liq	*−97.1*		
SnI_2		c	*−34.4*	−34.4	(40.3)
SnS		c	*−18.6*	*−19.7*	*23.6*
$Sn(SO_4)_2$		c	*−393.4*	−346.8	(37.1)

[1] Bureau of Standards values in *italics;* estimated values in parentheses.

The corresponding free energy of stannic ion is ca 650 cal. Prytz[1] attempted to measure the Sn—Sn^{+4} couple in perchlorate solution but we are unable to interpret his results.

The thermal data on stannic hydroxide (precipitated) do not appear to be very reliable, but we shall use the Bureau of Standards value, −270.5 kcal. An estimate of 29 for the entropy of the hydroxide is probably fairly close. This then gives −144 for the entropy of formation and −227.5 kcal. for the free energy.

$$Sn(OH)_4 = Sn^{+4} + 4OH^-, \qquad K = ca\ 10^{-57}.$$

From the rather sketchy data on the hydrolysis of stannate ion, $Sn(OH)_6^{--}$, we estimate

$$Sn(OH)_4 + 2OH^- = Sn(OH)_6^{--}, \qquad \Delta F° = −8.\ kcal.$$

[1] M. Prytz, Z. anorg. allgem. Chem., **219,** 89 (1934).

An approximate value for the free energy of stannate is then -310.5 kcal.

$$H_2O + 3OH^- + HSnO_2^- = Sn(OH)_6^{--} + 2e^-, \qquad E_B^o = 0.93.$$

From the free energies of stannite and stannate,

$$2H_2O + 2HSnO_2^- = Sn + Sn(OH)_6^{--}, \qquad \Delta F^o = -1.1 \text{ kcal.}$$

This energy appears very reasonable in view of the experimental decomposition of stannite solutions and is a gratifying check upon the validity of our free energies. No data can be given for the insoluble β stannic acid.

From the thermal data we estimate

$$SnF_6^{--} = Sn^{+4} + 6F^-, \qquad K = 1 \times 10^{-18};$$
$$Sn + 6F^- = SnF_6^{--} + 4e^-, \qquad E^o = 0.25.$$

For the free energy of hydrolysis of the tetrachloride we compute,

$$SnCl_4(l) + 4H_2O = Sn(OH)_4 + 4H^+ + 4Cl^-, \qquad \Delta F^o = -11.0 \text{ kcal.}$$

Since the hydroxide is quite soluble in hydrochloric acid, the actual chemical reaction forms considerable stannic ion in solution. The complex ion, $SnCl_6^{--}$, doubtless is present at high chloride concentrations but no value can be given for its free energy.

No quantitative work has been done on stannic sulfide or the thiostannates. From the fact that stannous sulfide is oxidized by polysulfide, we may write

$$2S^{--} + SnS = SnS_3^{--} + 2e^-, \qquad E^o > 0.6.$$

LEAD

Oxidation states. The plumbous ion, Pb^{++}, is stable in acid solution and forms salts with most negative ions; the hydroxide is amphoteric and plumbite ion is formed in alkaline solutions. The $+4$ oxide, PbO_2, is also amphoteric but is rather inert toward both H^+ and OH^-. The oxide, Pb_3O_4, is a plumbous orthoplumbate, Pb_2PbO_4; and Pb_2O_4 is probably $PbPbO_4$. Many investigators have claimed the existence of the $+1$ oxide, Pb_2O, but Van Arkel[1] has shown by X-ray analysis that it is a mixture of the tetragonal (red) PbO and the metal.

---

[1] A. E. Van Arkel, *Rec. trav. chim.*, **44**, 652 (1925).

Randall and Cann[1] reported 0.1213 for the Pb—Pb^{++} couple. Carmody[2] found 0.1263 and Fromherz[3] gave 0.1274. We shall write

$$Pb = Pb^{++} + 2e^-, \qquad E^\circ = 0.126.$$

The corresponding free energy of lead ion is -5810 cal. We calculate from the free energy of the hydroxide

$$Pb(OH)_2 = Pb^{++} + 2OH^-, \qquad K = 4.2 \times 10^{-15}.$$

Randall and Spencer[4] gave for their constant 8.7×10^{-16}.

There are three forms of the oxide, red, yellow, and black, with the red the most stable. The free energy of hydration is

$$PbO(r) + H_2O = Pb(OH)_2(c), \qquad \Delta F^\circ = 1.34 \text{ kcal.}$$

Hence the lead hydroxide is unstable with respect to the red oxide. The following equilibria were given by Garrett, Vellenga, and Fontana.[5]

$$PbO(r) + OH^- = HPbO_2^-, \qquad K = 4.6 \times 10^{-2};$$
$$Pb(OH)_2(aq) = H^+ + HPbO_2^- \qquad K = 1.2 \times 10^{-11};$$
$$Pb(OH)^+ = Pb^{++} + OH^-, \qquad K = 1.5 \times 10^{-8};$$
$$PbO(r) + H_2O = H^+ + HPbO_2^-, \qquad K = 4.6 \times 10^{-16}.$$

From the first equation, the free energy of $HPbO_2^-$ is -81.0 kcal.

$$Pb + 3OH^- = HPbO_2^- + H_2O + 2e^-, \qquad E_B^\circ = 0.54.$$

We may also write

$$PbO(r) + H_2O = Pb^{++} + 2OH^-, \qquad K = 4.5 \times 10^{-16}.$$

Plumbous halides. The potentials of cells having the reaction

$$Pb + 2AgX = PbX_2 + 2Ag$$

where X is Cl, Br, or I, have been measured by a number of investigators. Thus, for chloride and iodine, Gerke[6] reported the E° values

---

[1] M. Randall and J. Y. Cann, *J. Am. Chem. Soc.*, **52**, 589 (1930). Cf. J. Y. Cann and E. LaRue, *J. Am. Chem. Soc.*, **54**, 3456 (1932).

[2] W. R. Carmody, *J. Am. Chem. Soc.*, **51**, 2905 (1929); **54**, 210 (1932).

[3] H. Fromherz, *Z. physik. Chem.*, **153**, 382 (1931).

[4] M. Randall and H. M. Spencer, *J. Am. Chem. Soc.*, **50**, 1572 (1928).

[5] A. B. Garrett, S. Vellenga, and C. M. Fontana, *J. Am. Chem. Soc.*, **61**, 367 (1939).

[6] R. H. Gerke, *J. Am. Chem. Soc.*, **44**, 1684 (1922).

Table 32

THERMODYNAMIC DATA ON LEAD[1]

(Heat and free energy of formation in kcal. Entropy of substance in cal./deg.)

Formula	Description	State	$\Delta H°$	$\Delta F°$	$S°$
Pb		g	*46.34*	*38.47*	*41.890*
Pb	metal	c	0.0	0.0	*15.51*
Pb^+		g	*218.82*		
Pb^{++}		g	*566.89*		
Pb^{++}		aq	*0.39*	*−5.81*	*5.1*
Pb^{+4}		aq		72.3	
Pb_2		g	*78.*		
PbO	red	c	*−52.40*	*−45.25*	*16.2*
PbO	yellow	c	*−52.07*	*−45.05*	*16.6*
$HPbO_2^-$		aq		*−81.0*	
$Pb(OH)_2$		c	*−123.0*	*−100.6*	*21.*
PbO_2		c	*−66.12*	*−52.34*	*18.3*
Pb_3O_4		c	*−175.6*	*−147.6*	*50.5*
PbF_2		c	*−158.5*	*−148.1*	*29.*
PbF_4		c	*−222.3*	*−178.1*	(35.5)
$PbCl_2$		c	*−85.85*	*−75.04*	*32.6*
$PbBr_2$		c	*−66.21*	*−62.24*	*38.6*
$PbBr_2PbO$		c	*−122.3*		
PbI_2		c	*−41.85*	*−41.53*	*42.3*
PbI_3^-		aq		*−48.55*	
PbI_4^{--}		aq		*−63.02*	
PbS		c	*−22.54*	*−22.15*	*21.8*
PbS_2O_3		c	*−150.1*	*−134.0*	(35.4)
$PbSO_4$		c	*−219.50*	*−193.89*	*35.2*
PbS_3O_6		c	*−283.0*	*−213.8*	(55.4)
$PbSO_4 \cdot PbO$		c	*−282.5*	258.9	(48.7)
PbSe		c	*−18.0*	*−15.4*	(26.9)
$PbSeO_4$		c	*−148.*	*−122.*	(37.)
PbTe		c	*−17.5*	*−18.1*	(27.6)
$Pb(N_3)_2$		c	*104.3*	135.1	(49.5)
$Pb(NO_3)_2$		c	*−107.35*	*−60.3*	(50.9)
$Pb(OH)NO_3$		c	*−117.9*	*−72.6*	(37.7)
$Pb_3(PO_4)_2$		c	*−620.3*	*−581.4*	*84.43*
$PbHPO_3$		c	*−234.5*	*−208.3*	(31.9)
$PbCO_3$		c	*−167.3*	*−149.7*	*31.3*
PbC_2O_4		c	*−205.1*	*−180.3*	(33.2)
$PbO \cdot PbCO_3$		c	*−220.0*	*−195.6*	*48.5*
$2PbOPbCO_3$		c	*−273.*	*−242.*	*65.*
$Pb_3(OH)_2(CO_3)_2$				*−409.1*	
$Pb(C_2H_5)_4$		liq	*52.*		
$PbCrO_4$		c	*−225.2*	*−203.6*	(36.5)
$PbMoO_4$		c	*−265.8*	*−231.7*	(38.5)
$Pb(HCO_2)_2$		c	*−200.1*		(35.5)
$Pb(CH_3CO_2)_2$		c	*−230.5*		(40.)
$Pb(CNS)_2$		c	*27.5*		
$PbSiO_3$		c	*−258.8*	*−239.0*	*27.*
Pb_2SiO_4		c	*−312.7*	*−285.7*	*43.*

[1] Bureau of Standards values in *italics;* estimated values in parentheses.

0.490 and 0.2135; and for bromide, Cann and Sumner[1] gave 0.3525. Cann and Taylor[2] agree closely with Gerke's value for the iodine. Combining with our values for the Ag—AgX couples we find

$$2Cl^- + Pb = PbCl_2 + 2e^-, \qquad E^\circ = 0.268;$$
$$2Br^- + Pb = PbBr_2 + 2e^-, \qquad E^\circ = 0.280;$$
$$2I^- + Pb = PbI_2 + 2e^-, \qquad E^\circ = 0.365.$$

The corresponding free energies are consistent with the values in Table 32; the solubility products are:

$$PbCl_2 = Pb^{++} + 2Cl^-, \qquad K = 1.6 \times 10^{-5};$$
$$PbBr_2 = Pb^{++} + 2Br^-, \qquad K = 4.6 \times 10^{-6};$$
$$PbI_2 = Pb^{++} + 2I^-, \qquad K = 8.3 \times 10^{-9}.$$

From the free energy of PbF_2,

$$PbF_2 = Pb^{++} + 2F^-, \qquad K = 4 \times 10^{-8}.$$

Fromherz,[3] in his careful work on the lead halide activities, has shown the existence of relatively high concentrations of PbX^+ ions. He gave the following constants:

$$PbCl^+ = Pb^{++} + Cl^-, \qquad K = 0.775;$$
$$PbBr^+ = Pb^{++} + Br^-, \qquad K = 0.071;$$
$$PbI^- = Pb^{++} + I^-, \qquad K = 0.0345.$$

Concentrated solutions of halide ions dissolve the lead halides with the formation of the complex ions. Korenman[4] has given the constants for $PbCl_3^-$ and PbI_3^- as 4.2×10^{-2} and 3.6×10^{-6}, respectively.

Additional lead-plumbous couples and solubility products. The following couples and equilibrium constants are given in agreement with the free energies. Important references to the original work will also be given.

$$PbS = Pb^{++} + S^{--}, \qquad K = 7 \times 10^{-29};$$
$$Pb + S^{--} = PbS + 2e^-, \qquad E^\circ = 0.98.$$

[1] J. Y. Cann and R. A. Sumner, *J. Phys. Chem.*, **36**, 2615 (1932).
[2] J. Y. Cann and A. C. Taylor, *J. Am. Chem. Soc.*, **59**, 1989 (1937).
[3] H. Fromherz, *Z. physik. Chem.*, **153**, 382 (1931).
[4] I. M. Korenman, *J. Gen. Chem. U.S.S.R.*, **16**, 157 (1946).

Kolthoff[1] gave 3.4×10^{-28} for the constant.

$$PbSO_4 = Pb^{++} + SO_4^{--}, \qquad K = 1.3 \times 10^{-8};$$
$$Pb + SO_4^{--} = PbSO_4 + 2e^-, \qquad E° = 0.3563.$$

The potential is in agreement with the work of Shrawder and Cowperthwaite.[2]

The Pb—$PbSO_4$ couple is an important reference electrode and also one of the electrodes of the lead storage battery. Harned and Hamer[3] have given a general equation for the potential for the temperature range 0 to 60° C.

$$Pb_3(PO_4)_2 = 3Pb^{++} + 2PO_4^{---}, \qquad K = 1 \times 10^{-54};$$
$$PbHPO_4 = Pb^{++} + HPO_4^{--}, \qquad K = 8.7 \times 10^{-12}.$$

Jowett and Price[4] gave 3×10^{-44} and 4×10^{-12} for these constants.

$$PbCO_3 = Pb^{++} + CO_3^{--}, \qquad K = 1.5 \times 10^{-13};$$
$$Pb + CO_3^{--} = PbCO_3 + 2e^-, \qquad E° = 0.506.$$

Kelley and Anderson's[5] values are consistent with these data for $PbCO_3$.

Randall and Spencer[6] found for basic lead carbonate,

$$Pb_3(CO_3)_2(OH)_2 + 7OH^- = 3HPbO_2^- + 2CO_3^{--} + 2H_2O,$$
$$\Delta F° = 6.96 \text{ kcal.};$$
$$Pb(IO_3)_2 = Pb^{++} + 2IO_3^-, \qquad K = 3.2 \times 10^{-13}.$$

This is the value given by Geilmann and Holtje.[7]

$$Pb(BrO_3) = Pb^{++} + 2BrO_3^-, \qquad K = 2.9 \times 10^{-4}.$$

The data are those of MacDougall and Hoffman.[8]

$$PbCrO_4 = Pb^{++} + CrO_4^{--}, \qquad K = 2 \times 10^{-16}.$$

[1] I. M. Kolthoff, *J. Phys. Chem.*, **35**, 2720 (1931).

[2] J. Shrawder, Jr. and I. A. Cowperthwaite, *J. Am. Chem. Soc.*, **56**, 2343 (1934).

[3] H. S. Harned and W. J. Hamer, *J. Am. Chem. Soc.*, **57**, 33 (1935).

[4] M. Jowett and H. I. Price, *Trans. Faraday Soc.*, **28**, 668 (1932).

[5] K. K. Kelley and C. T. Anderson, *U. S. Bur. Mines Bull.*, **384**, (1934).

[6] M. Randall and H. M. Spencer, *J. Am. Chem. Soc.*, **50**, 1582, (1928).

[7] W. Geilmann and R. Holtje, *Z. anorg. allgem. Chem.*, **152**, 65 (1926).

[8] F. H. MacDougall and E. F. Hoffman, *J. Phys. Chem.*, **40**, 330 (1936).

Beck[1] reported 1.8×10^{-14}.

$$PbS_2O_3 = Pb^{++} + S_2O_3^{--}, \qquad K = 1.5 \times 10^{-4};$$
$$PbHPO_3 = Pb^{++} + HPO_3^{--}, \qquad K = 5.7 \times 10^{-7};$$
$$PbC_2O_4 = Pb^{++} + C_2O_4^{--}, \qquad K = 8.3 \times 10^{-12};$$
$$PbMoO_4 = Pb^{++} + MoO_4^{--}, \qquad K = 4 \times 10^{-6};$$
$$PbSeO_4 = Pb^{++} + SeO_4^{--}, \qquad K = 10^{-8};$$
$$PbSe = Pb^{++} + Se^{--}, \qquad K = 10^{-38};$$
$$PbTe = Pb^{++} + Te^{--}, \qquad K = 10^{-48};$$
$$Pb(N_3)_2 = Pb^{++} + 2N_3^{-}, \qquad K = 10^{-12}.$$

Plumbous-plumbic couples. The most critical investigation of any plumbous-plumbic couple appears to be the work of Harned and Hamer[2] on the $PbSO_4$—PbO_2 couple. They found

$$2H_2O + PbSO_4 = PbO_2 + SO_4^{-} + 4H^+ + 2e^-, \qquad E^\circ = -1.685.$$

This value, with those of the Pb—$PbSO_4$ and Pb—Pb^{++} couples, then gives

$$2H_2O + Pb^{++} = PbO_2 + 4H^+ + 2e^-, \qquad E^\circ = -1.455.$$

For the solubility of lead dioxide in $5.3N$ HNO_3, Cumming[3] gave 1.4×10^{-4} moles per liter. Using 1.1 for the activity coefficient of the nitric acid and 0.1 for the lead ion, a computation gives as a rough approximation

$$PbO_2 + 4H^+ = Pb^{+4} + 2H_2O, \qquad \Delta F^\circ = 10,850 \text{ cal.}$$

and for the free energy of Pb^{+4}, 72.3 kcal. Hence,

$$Pb^{+2} = Pb^{+4} + 2e^-, \qquad E^\circ = ca -1.7;$$
$$PbO_2 + 2H_2O = Pb^{+4} + 4OH^-, \qquad K = 10^{-64}.$$

From the free energies, one calculates

$$2OH^- + PbO(r) = PbO_2 + H_2O + 2e^-, \qquad E_B^\circ = -0.248.$$

However, the half-reaction cannot be measured directly in alkaline solution because of the formation of the intermediate oxide, Pb_3O_4,

[1] K. Beck, *Z. Elektrochem.*, **17**, 846 (1911).

[2] H. S. Harned and W. J. Hamer, *J. Am. Chem. Soc.*, **57**, 33 (1935).

[3] A. C. Cumming, *Z. Elektrochem.*, **13**, 19 (1907); *Trans. Faraday Soc.*, **2**, 199 (1907).

and probably also Pb_2O_3. Glasstone[1] wrote

$$Pb_2PbO_4 = 2Pb^{++} + PbO_4^{-4}, \qquad K = 5.3 \times 10^{-51}.$$

Grube[2] stated that both PbO_3^{--} and $Pb(OH)_6^{--}$ are present in alkaline solution and gave

$$2OH^-(8.4N) + PbO_2^{--} = PbO_3^{--} + H_2O + 2e^-, \qquad E_B = -0.208.$$

This would appear to correspond to an $E°$ of about -0.28 and this was approximately the figure estimated by Glasstone.

Elbs[3] and his co-workers prepared plumbic sulfate by the electrolysis of sulfuric acid (density 1.8) with a lead anode, and plumbic dichromate $Pb(Cr_2O_7)_2$ by a similar process, using concentrated chromic acid. With phosphoric acid they prepared $Pb(H_2PbO_4)_4$. The electrolysis of 100 per cent acetic acid yields the plumbic acetate, $Pb(C_2H_5O_2)_4$. By the action of cold concentrated hydrochloric acid upon the dioxide, the tetrachloride and the chloroplumbic acid, H_2PbCl_6, have been formed. There are no thermodynamic data for any of these plumbic compounds.

The lead storage battery. The cell reaction in the familiar lead storage battery is, for discharge,

$$PbO_2 + Pb + 4H^+ + 2SO_4^{--} = 2PbSO_4 + 2H_2O.$$

The $E°$ potential for the reaction may be obtained from the two half-reaction potentials given above, but, as the cell operates at fairly high

TABLE 33

CONSTANTS FOR THE EQUATION EXPRESSING THE E.M.F. OF THE LEAD STORAGE BATTERY AS A FUNCTION OF TEMPERATURE

M H_2SO_4	$E_{0°C}$	$a \times 10^6$	$b \times 10^8$
1	1.9174	56.1	108
2	1.9664	159	103
3	2.0087	178	97
4	2.0479	177	91
5	2.0850	167	87
6	2.1191	162	85
7	2.1507	153	80

[1] S. Glasstone, *J. Chem. Soc.*, **121**, 1469 (1922).

[2] G. Grube, *Z. Elektrochem.*, **28**, 285 (1922).

[3] K. Elbs and F. Fischer, *Z. Elektrochem.*, **7**, 343 (1900); K. Elbs and R. Nubling, *Z. Elektrochem.*, **9**, 776 (1903).

acid (density of $H_2SO_4 = 1.2$ to 1.3 when charged), the experimental values for the electromotive force are more significant. Harned and Hamer have represented these electromotive forces for the temperature range of 0 to 60° C. by the equation

$$E = E_{0°} + at + bt^2.$$

The constants for the equation are summarized in Table 33 for various molal concentrations of sulfuric acid. Although many theories have been proposed, little is actually known regarding the mechanism of the two-electron transfer which occurs at the lead dioxide plate.

Group potentials. The following diagrams summarize the group potentials.

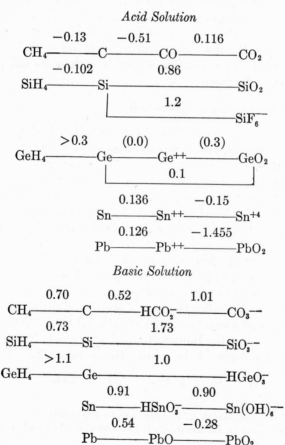

Acid Solution

```
              -0.13        -0.51          0.116
CH₄───────────C────────────CO────────────CO₂
              -0.102                 0.86
SiH₄──────────Si──────────────────────────SiO₂
                          1.2
                                          ─SiF₆⁻⁻

              >0.3          (0.0)           (0.3)
GeH₄──────────Ge────────────Ge⁺⁺───────────GeO₂
                          0.1

                        0.136        -0.15
             Sn──────────Sn⁺⁺─────────Sn⁺⁴
                        0.126        -1.455
             Pb──────────Pb⁺⁺─────────PbO₂
```

Basic Solution

```
       0.70          0.52           1.01
CH₄────────────C────────────HCO₂⁻────────────CO₃⁻⁻
       0.73                  1.73
SiH₄───────────Si──────────────────────────SiO₃⁻⁻
       >1.1                  1.0
GeH₄───────────Ge──────────────────────────HGeO₃⁻
                    0.91            0.90
             Sn──────────HSnO₃⁻────────Sn(OH)₆⁻⁻
                    0.54           -0.28
             Pb──────────PbO──────────PbO₂
```

CHAPTER 9

Gallium, Indium, and Thallium

The elements gallium, indium, and thallium resemble boron and aluminum in having two s electrons and one p electron in their valence shell. However, their important chemical properties are largely those of their $+3$ ions, and these ions are unlike boron and aluminum in that they do not have the noble-gas structure but are of the so-called "eighteen-electron" type. For this reason these elements will be discussed as a separate group.

GALLIUM

Oxidation states. The principal oxidation state is $+3$, which is represented by the ion, Ga^{+++}, in acid solution and $H_2GaO_3^-$ in alkaline solution. Halides of the $+2$ state may be prepared; and, since the positive ion has one s electron still remaining in the outer shell, it may double up to form an ion, Ga_2^{+4}, like mercurous, in which the two electrons constitute a bond holding the two gallium atoms together. The $+1$ oxide, Ga_2O, is formed by the reduction of the $+3$ oxide by the metal at high temperatures.

The gallium-gallic ion couple. Schwarz von Bergkampf[1] reports for the gallium-gallic ion couple by direct cell measurement, $E° = 0.52$. This corresponds to a free energy of -36.0 kcal. Saltman and Nachtrieb[2] have studied the heat of solution of the metal in acid and gave $\Delta H°$, -50.5 kcal.; ΔF, -38.8 kcal.; and $S°$ of Ga^{+++}, -76.0 cal./deg. We shall use the Bureau of Standards values although their entropy of the ion appears to be ʲoo negative and we write

$$Ga = Ga^{+++} + 3e^-, \qquad E° = 0.53.$$

---

[1] E. Schwarz von Bergkampf, *Z. Elektrochem.*, **38**, 847 (1932).
[2] W. M. Saltman and N. H. Nachtrieb, *Electrochem. Soc., Cleveland*, April 1950.

TABLE 34

THERMODYNAMIC DATA ON GALLIUM[1]

Formula	Description	State	$\Delta H°$	$\Delta F°$	$S°$
Ga		g	*66.0*	*57.0*	40.38
Ga	metal	c	0.0	0.0	*10.2*
Ga$^+$		g	*205.77*		
Ga^{++}		g	*680.21*		
Ga^{++}		aq		(−21.0)	
Ga^{+++}		g	*1388.5*		
Ga^{+++}		aq	*−50.4*	−36.6	−83.
GaO		g	*66.*		
GaO$_3^{--}$		aq		−148.	
Ga$_2$O$_3$		c	*−258.*	−237.2	(24.)
Ga$_2$O		c	*−82.*	−75.2	(22.)
Ga(OH)$^{++}$		aq		−89.8	
HGaO$_3^{--}$		aq		−164.	
Ga(OH)$_2^+$		aq		−142.1	
H$_2$GaO$_3^-$		aq		−178.	
Ga(OH)$_3$		c		−199.	(20.3)
GaCl		g	*9.*		
GaCl$_3$		c	*−125.4*	−117.8	(31.9)
GaBr$_3$		c	*−92.4*	84.5	(38.2)
GaI$_3$		c	*−51.2*		(48.7)
GaN		c	*−25.*	−18.6	(8.4)
Ga$_2$(C$_2$O$_4$)$_3$		c	*−515.*		(64.)

[1] Bureau of Standards values in *italics;* estimated values in parentheses.

Fricke and Meyring[1] have given the following data:

$$GaOH^{++} = Ga^{+++} + OH^-, \qquad K = 4 \times 10^{-12};$$
$$Ga(OH)_2^+ = GaOH^{++} + OH^-, \qquad K = 1.6 \times 10^{-11};$$
$$HGaO_3^{--} = GaO_3^{--} + H^+, \qquad K = 2 \times 10^{-12};$$
$$H_2GaO_3^- = HGaO_3^{--} + H^+, \qquad K = 4.8 \times 10^{-11}.$$

Although it is difficult to make an accurate combination of these values with the solubility of the hydroxide in acids and bases as given by Porter and Browning[2] and by Fricke and Blencke,[3] we shall write as approximate values for the freshly precipitated hydroxide

$$Ga(OH)_3(s) = Ga^{+++} + 3OH^-, \qquad K = ca\ 5 \times 10^{-37};$$
$$H_3GaO_3(s) = H_2GaO_3^- + H^+, \qquad K = ca\ 1 \times 10^{-15}.$$

[1] R. Fricke and K. Meyring, *Z. anorg. allgem. Chem.*, **176**, 329 (1928).
[2] L. E. Porter and P. E. Browning, *J. Am. Chem. Soc.*, **41**, 1491 (1919).
[3] R. Fricke and W. Blencke, *Z. anorg. allgem. Chem.*, **143**, 184 (1925).

Hence, the free energy of $Ga(OH)_3$ is ca $-198,300$ cal.; and $H_2GaO_3^-$, ca $-178,000$ cal. The potential in alkaline solution is

$$4OH^- + Ga = H_2GaO_3^- + H_2O + 3e^-, \qquad E_B^\circ = \text{ca } 1.22.$$

The metal dissolves readily in both acids and alkalies with the evolution of hydrogen.

The heat of combustion of the metal to form Ga_2O_3 is given as -255.8 kcal. Estimating the entropy of the oxide as 24 gives ΔS°, -70 cal./deg., and ΔF° of formation, $-235,000$ cal. The free energy of hydration then is 8500 cal. However, upon standing, the hydroxide goes over to a less soluble modification and the free energy of hydration to give this form is probably negative. Taube and Wilson[1] found

$$Ga^{+++} + Cl^- = GaCl^{++}, \qquad K = \text{ca } 1.$$

Gallous chloride. De Boisbaudran[2] has studied the preparation and properties of the dichloride, $GaCl_2$, or probably Ga_2Cl_4. The chloride may be prepared at high temperatures, and it is soluble in a small amount of water without decomposition, but the solution evolves hydrogen upon dilution. Also the chloride is said to be formed in solution by treating a concentrated solution of the gallic chloride with the metal. Upon dilution this solution evolves hydrogen. These facts indicate that the chloride is slightly dissociated in concentrated chloride solution, and that the undissociated chloride does not decompose water. These facts are consistent with the following potentials:

$$Ga^{++} = Ga^{+++} + e^- \qquad E^\circ = \text{ca } 0.65,$$
$$Ga = Ga^{++} + 2e^-, \qquad E^\circ = \text{ca } 0.45.$$

In the absence of a high concentration of chloride ion, the oxidation of Ga^{++} by water must be very rapid. The $+2$ state in alkaline solution appears to be unstable with respect to the decomposition into gallate and the metal. The free energy of Ga^{++} is ca $-21,000$ cal.

The $+1$ oxide. The heat of formation of the $+1$ oxide, Ga_2O, has been determined by Klemm and Schnick[3] as -82 kcal. Estimating the entropy of the oxide as 22 cal./deg., the ΔS° of formation is -22.1 and ΔF°, $-75,200$ cal.

$$H_2O + 2Ga = Ga_2O + 2H^+ + 2e^-, \qquad E^\circ = 0.4,$$
$$2H_2O + Ga_2O = Ga_2O_3 + 4H^+ + 4e^-, \qquad E^\circ = 0.5.$$

[1] H. Taube and A. S. Wilson, private communication.
[2] L. De Boisbaudran, *Compt. rend.*, **82**, 1098 (1876); *ibid.*, **83**, 636 and 824 (1876).
[3] W. Klemm and I. Schnick, *Z. anorg. allgem. Chem.*, **226**, 353 (1936).

These potentials are not very significant, as the relative solubilities of the two oxides in acids are not known. They do show, however, that the $+1$ oxide is unstable with respect to its decomposition into the $+3$ oxide and the metal.

INDIUM

Oxidation states. The only ion stable in water solutions is the In^{+++}. The halides of the $+1$ and $+2$ states may be prepared and the probable potentials of the In^+ and In^{++} or In_2^{+4} ions will be discussed.

The indium-indic ion couple. From the precise work of Hattox and De Vries[1] on the direct measurement of the indium-indic ion electrode in sulfate solutions, the following potential is obtained:

$$In = In^{+++} + 3e^-, \qquad E^\circ = 0.342.$$

The free energy of In^{+++} then is -23.7 kcal. The same authors found for the first step in the hydrolysis of the ion

$$In^{+++} + H_2O = InOH^{++} + H^+, \qquad K = 2 \times 10^{-4}.$$

The third law computation for the free energy of the hydroxide $In(OH)_3$ gives -18.2 kcal. and leads to the following solubility product and potential:

$$In(OH)_3 = In^{+++} + 3OH^-, \qquad K = 1 \times 10^{-33},$$
$$In + 3OH^- = In(OH)_3 + 3e^-, \qquad E_B^\circ = 1.0.$$

The metal dissolves fairly readily in acid solutions with the evolution of hydrogen.

The $+1$ and $+2$ oxidation states. The chlorides, InCl and InCl$_2$ or In$_2$Cl$_4$, may be prepared by the action of chlorine on the metal. From the reactions of these chlorides with hot water, as recorded by Thiel,[2] the following decompositions occur:

$$2In^{++} = In^{+++} + In^+,$$
$$2In^+ = In^{++} + In.$$

To account for these reactions, the approximate potentials must be

$$In^{++} = In^{+++} + e^-, \qquad E^\circ = ca\ 0.45,$$
$$In^+ = In^{++} + e^-, \qquad E^\circ = ca\ 0.35,$$
$$In = In^+ + e^-, \qquad E^\circ = ca\ 0.25,$$

[1] E. M. Hattox and T. De Vries, *J. Am. Chem. Soc.*, **58**, 2126 (1936).
[2] A. Thiel, *Z. anorg. Chem.*, **39**, 119 (1904); *loc. cit.*, **40**, 280 (1940).

TABLE 35

THERMODYNAMIC DATA ON INDIUM[1]

(Heat and free energy of formation in kcal. Entropy of substance in cal./deg.)

Formula	Description	State	$\Delta H°$	$\Delta F°$	$S°$
In		g	58.2	49.6	41.51
In		c	0.0	0.0	12.5
In^+		g	193.09		
In^{++}		g	629.62		
In^{+++}		g	1277.5		
In^{+++}		aq	−23.7	−32.0	−62.
InO		g	91.		
In_2O_3		c	−222.5	−200.5	(29.)
InH		g	51.	45.	49.6
$In(OH)^{++}$		aq		−55.5	
$In(OH)_3$		c	−214.	−182.	25.
InCl		g	−18.	−23.	59.3
InCl		c	−44.5	−39.2	(23.)
$InCl_2$		c	−86.8	−75.9	(29.2)
$InCl_3$		c	−128.4	−110.7	(33.)
$InCl_3$		aq	−152.0		
InBr		g	10.	1.	62.0
$InBr_3$		c	−96.5	88.5	(40.)
InI		g	20.	9.	63.8
InI_3		c	−55.0	−33.9	(50.5)
$In_2(SO_4)_3$		c	−695.	−613.4	(67.1)
InN		c	−4.8	2.7	(10.2)

[1] Bureau of Standards values in *italics;* estimated values in parentheses.

for the following reasons. The sum of the three $E°$ values must be 3×0.340 from the In—In^{+++} potential. In order to account for the decompositions, the $E°$ for the first couple must be greater than that for the second, and similarly the second must be greater than the third. The value of the third can hardly be negative since the metal dissolves readily in acid. As a check on this last point the free energy of InCl may be calculated from the thermal data. The Bureau of Standards selects −44.6 kcal. as the heat of formation. Taking the entropy of InCl as 23.2 in comparison with 23.0 for silver chloride, the entropy of formation is 18.0 cal./deg. and the free energy −39,200 cal. Hence,

$$Cl^- + In = InCl(c) + e^-, \qquad E° = 0.34.$$

The solubility of the InCl cannot be measured; but from the relations in this region of the periodic system, it should be more soluble than TlCl but probably less than one molal. This $E°$ value is then in approximate agreement with that chosen for the In—In$^+$ couple.

In the equilibrium between the metal and a solution of the ion, In^{+++}, there will be present appreciable concentrations of In$^+$ and In^{++}. In the absence of the metal, the ions of the lower oxidation states will rapidly disappear because of their decomposition or their oxidation by hydrogen ion. In alkaline solution the hydroxides, InOH and In(OH)$_2$, are unstable with respect to the formation of the less soluble In(OH)$_3$ and the metal.

THALLIUM

Oxidation states. Thallium forms compounds of the $+1$ oxidation state, thallous, and $+3$ state, thallic. A very unstable $+2$ bromide, TlBr$_2$, may be prepared, but this state has a high free energy of decomposition into the $+1$ and $+3$ states and is essentially nonexistent, although in some cases an appreciable concentration of $+2$ complex ions may be present in the equilibrium between thallous and thallic.

The thallium-thallous couple. The very precise measurements of Lewis[1] and his co-worker on the thallium-thallous ion electrode has led to the value,

$$Tl = Tl^+ + e^-, \qquad E° = 0.3363.$$

The corresponding free energy of Tl$^+$ is -7765 cal. Randall[2] gives,

$$Tl(OH)(c) = Tl^+ + OH^-, \qquad \Delta F° = 190 \text{ cal.},$$
$$K = 7.2 \times 10^{-1}.$$

The free energy of the solid hydroxide is then -45. kcal. and the potential of the couple in alkaline solution is

$$OH^- + Tl = Tl(OH)(c) + e^-, \qquad E_B° = 0.3445.$$

The free energy of hydration of the oxide is given as

$$Tl_2O(c) + H_2O(g) = 2Tl(OH)(c), \qquad \Delta F° = -3880 \text{ cal.}$$

---

[1] G. N. Lewis and M. Randall, *Thermodynamics*, New York: McGraw-Hill Book Company, Inc., 1923, p. 412.

[2] M. Randall, *International Critical Tables*, **VII**, 251.

TABLE 36

THERMODYNAMIC DATA ON THALLIUM[1]

(Heat and free energy of formation in kcal. Entropy of substance in cal./deg.)

Formula	Description	State	$\Delta H°$	$\Delta F°$	$S°$
Tl		g	44.5	36.2	43.23
Tl		c	0.0	0.0	15.4
Tl⁺		g	186.8		
Tl⁺		aq	1.38	−7.755	30.4
Tl⁺⁺		g	658.8		
Tl⁺⁺⁺		g	1348.1		
Tl⁺⁺⁺		aq	46.8	50.0	(−42.)
Tl₂O		c	−41.9	−32.5	23.8
TlH		g	49.	43.	51.39
Tl(OH)		c	−56.9	−45.5	17.3
Tl(OH)₃		c	−156.	−123.0	(24.4)
Tl₂SO₄		c	−221.7	−196.8	(52.8)
TlF		g	−33.		
TlCl		g	−15.	−21.	61.1
TlCl		c	−48.99	−44.19	25.9
TlBr		g	−4.	−13.	63.8
TlBr		c	−41.2	−39.7	28.6
TlI		g	8.	−3.	65.6
TlI		c	−29.7	−29.7	29.4
TlIO₃		c	−65.7	−47.6	(40.9)
Tl₂S		c	−20.8	−21.	(39.)
Tl₂Se		c	−18.	−19.8	(46.8)
Tl₂Te		c	−7.	−8.4	(47.3)

[1] Bureau of Standards values in *italics;* estimated values in parentheses.

From the free energies we calculate in approximate agreement with Randall

$$TlCl(c) = Tl^+ + Cl^-, \qquad K = 1.9 \times 10^{-4};$$
$$TlBr(c) = Tl^+ + Br^-, \qquad K = 3.6 \times 10^{-6};$$
$$TlI(c) = Tl^+ + I^-, \qquad K = 8.9 \times 10^{-8};$$
$$Cl^- + Tl = TlCl(c) + e^-, \qquad E° = 0.557;$$
$$Br^- + Tl = TlBr(c) + e^-, \qquad E° = 0.658;$$
$$I^- + Tl = TlI(c) + e^-, \qquad E° = 0.753.$$

Kolthoff[1] has given for the solubility product of Tl₂S,

$$Tl_2S = 2Tl^+ + S^{--}, \qquad K = 1.2 \times 10^{-24}.$$

[1] I. M. Kolthoff, *J. Phys. Chem.*, **35**, 2720 (1931).

The value of the constant from our free energies is 10^{-21}, and the potential for the Tl—Tl_2S couple

$$S^{--} + 2Tl = Tl_2S + 2e^-, \qquad E_B^o = 0.93.$$

In agreement with our free energies, we also calculate

$$Tl_2Se = 2Tl^+ + Se^{--}, \qquad K = 10^{-35},$$
$$Tl_2Te = 2Tl^+ + Te^{--}, \qquad K = 3 \times 10^{-34}.$$

For thallous iodate we calculate

$$TlIO_3 = Tl^+ + IO_3^-, \qquad K = 3 \times 10^{-6}.$$

Noyes and Abbot[1] studied equilibria between a number of thallous salts at 40° C. The following are values for the concentration products at that temperature.

$$TlBrO_3 = Tl^+ + BrO_3^-, \qquad K = 3.9 \times 10^{-4};$$
$$TlCNS = Tl^+ + CNS^-, \qquad K = 5.8 \times 10^{-4}.$$

The thallous-thallic couple. Noyes and Garner[2] measured the oxidation potential of the thallous-thallic couple in nitric acid solutions and gave -1.230 as the E^o value. Partington and Stonehill[3] have measured the same potential in sulfuric acid at 25° C. and deduce -1.2207 as the true value. Sherrill and Haas[4] chose perchloric acid as the electrolyte because of the freedom from complex formation of the perchlorate and have expressed their E^o value as a function of the total ionic strength of the cell.

$$E^o = 1.2466 + 0.0076u + 0.00482u^2.$$

These authors point out that the extrapolation to zero ionic strength in their measurements is large, but in the absence of a better value, we shall write

$$Tl^+ = Tl^{+++} + 2e^-, \qquad E^o = -1.25.$$

This would make the free energy of thallic ion Tl^{+++}, 50.0 kcal. The same authors estimate for the solubility product of thallic hydroxide

$$Tl(OH)_3 = Tl^{+++} + 3OH^-, \qquad K = 1.5 \times 10^{-44}.$$

[1] A. A. Noyes and C. G. Abbot, *Z. physik. Chem.*, **16**, 130 (1895).
[2] C. S. Garner and A. A. Noyes, *J. Am. Chem. Soc.*, **58**, 1268 (1936).
[3] J. R. Partington and H. I. Stonehill, *Trans. Faraday Soc.*, **31**, 1365 (1935).
[4] M. S. Sherrill and A. J. Haas, Jr., *J. Am. Chem. Soc.*, **58**, 953 (1936).

Hence one computes for the free energy of the hydroxide, $Tl(OH)_3(c)$, -123. kcal. This gives for the potential of the thallous-thallic couple in alkaline solution

$$2OH^- + TlOH(c) = Tl(OH)_3(c) + 2e^-, \qquad E_B^\circ = 0.05.$$

The solubility product of $Tl(OH)$, calculated from the Bureau of Standards value for the heat, -122.6 kcal., is 10^{-16}. The source of this discrepancy is not known.

In neutral solution thallous sulfate may be oxidized quantitatively on a platinum anode to the thallic hydroxide by using a fairly high overvoltage. At lower voltages a black form of the oxide Tl_2O_3 is said to form, and the same product is obtained in hot alkaline solutions. In slightly acid solutions of the thallous sulfate, Gallo and Ceuni[1] report the anodic oxidation to a peroxide complex, Tl_3O_5.

For the $TlCl$—$TlCl_3$ couple in HCl Hughes and Garner[2] wrote

$$TlCl + 2.5Cl^- = TlCl_{3.5}(aq) + 2e^-, \qquad E^\circ = -0.980 + 0.00508\mu.$$

This is in agreement with the chemical facts that thallic solutions do not oxidize chloride ion but do oxidize iodide.

Summary of Group 3 potentials. For comparison of the potentials of the three elements of the group the following diagrams are given.

Acid Solution

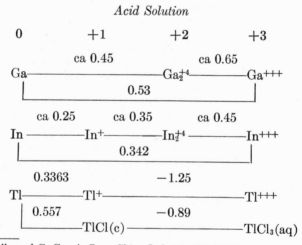

[1] G. Gallo and G. Ceuni, *Gazz. Chim. Ital.*, **39**, 285 (1908).
[2] R. H. Hughes and C. S. Garner, *J. Am. Chem. Soc.*, **64**, 1644 (1942).

Basic Solution

ca 1.22
Ga————————————————————H₂GaO₃⁻

1.0
In ————————————————————In(OH)₃

0.05
Tl————————TlOH————————————Tl(OH)₃

The principal point of interest is the increasing oxidizing power of the +3 ion with increasing atomic weight. The increasing stability of the +1 state and the decreasing stability of the +2 state may also be noted.

CHAPTER 10

Zinc, Cadmium, and Mercury

Like the alkaline earths, the elements of this group have two s electrons in their valence shell, but they are unlike the alkaline earth elements in that the kernels are of the 18-electron type instead of octets. Mercury forms -ous compounds in which the mercury atom has lost only one of the s electrons; and, as a result, two such atoms combine to form a double ion with an electron pair bond; $Hg:Hg^{++}$.

Oxidation states. Zinc forms compounds in which the oxidation state is $+2$. There is some evidence for the $+1$ state as an intermediate in the reduction of Zn^{++}, but it is not stable in water solutions.

Free energies and potentials of zinc. The Bureau of Standards free energy for Zn^{++} is in close agreement with the conclusions of Shrawder, Cowperthwaite, and La Mer.[1]

The potential of the Zn—Zn^{++} couple is

$$Zn = Zn^{++} + 2e^-, \qquad E° = 0.763.$$

Dietrich and Johnston[2] report for the zinc-zinc hydroxide electrode against the mercury-mercuric oxide electrode in alkali

$$Zn + HgO + H_2O = Zn(OH)_2 + Hg(l), \qquad E° = 1.348.$$

This gives,

$$Zn + 2OH^- = Zn(OH)_2(c) + 2e^-, \qquad E°_B = 1.245.$$

and

$$Zn(OH)_2(c) = Zn^{++} + 2OH^-, \qquad K = 4.5 \times 10^{-17}.$$

There are several unstable forms of zinc hydroxide, and these authors

---

[1] J. Shrawder, I. A. Cowperthwaite, and V. K. La Mer, *J. Am. Chem. Soc.*, **56**, 2348 (1934).

[2] H. G. Dietrich and J. Johnston, *J. Am. Chem. Soc.*, **49**, 1419 (1927).

TABLE 37

THERMODYNAMIC DATA ON ZINC[1]

(Heat and free energy of formation in kcal. Entropy of substance in cal./deg.)

Formula	Description	State	$\Delta H°$	$\Delta F°$	$S°$
Zn		g	*31.19*	*22.69*	*38.45*
Zn		c	0.0	0.0	*9.95*
Zn^+		g	*249.251*		
Zn^{++}		g	*664.902*		
Zn^{++}		aq	*−36.43*	*−35.184*	*−25.45*
Zn^{+++}		g	*1581.*		
ZnO		c	*−83.17*	−76.05	*10.5*
ZnO_2^{--}		aq		−93.03	
$Zn(NH_3)_4^{++}$		aq		−73.5	
$Zn(OH)^+$		aq		−78.8	
$Zn(OH)_2$		c	*−153.5*	−132.6	(19.9)
ZnCl		g	*1.*	*−5.0*	58.3
$ZnCl_2$		c	*−99.40*	*−88.255*	*25.9*
$ZnBr_2$		c	*−78.17*	*−74.142*	*32.84*
ZnI		g	*15.*	*3.0*	*63.0*
ZnI_2		c	*−49.98*	*−50.01*	*38.0*
ZnS	sphalerite	c	*−48.5*	*−47.4*	*13.8*
ZnS	wurtzite	c	*−45.3*	−44.2	(13.8)
ZnS	precip.	c	*−44.3* (?)	−43.2 (?)	
$ZnSO_4$		c	*−233.88*	*−208.31*	*29.8*
$ZnSO_4·H_2O$		c	*−310.6*	*−269.9*	*34.9*
$ZnSO_4·6H_2O$		c	*−663.3*	*−555.0*	*86.8*
$ZnSO_4·7H_2O$		c	*−735.1*	*−611.9*	*92.4*
ZnSe		c	*−34.*	−34.7	(22.3)
$Zn(N_3)_2$		c	*50.8*		
Zn_3N_2		c	*−6.9*		
$Zn(NO_3)_2$		c	*−115.12*	−71.42	(46.3)
$Zn(CH_3)_2$		liq	*−5.5*		
$Zn(C_2H_5)_2$		liq	*−4.*		
$Zn(CHO_2)$		c	*−225.0*		
$Zn(CH_3CO_2)_2$		c	*−258.1*		
$Zn(CN)_2$		c	*18.4*	29.	(22.9)
$Zn(CN)_4^{--}$		aq	82.0	100.4	
$ZnSiO_3$		c	*−294.6*	−274.8	(21.4)
Zn_2SiO_4		c	*−360.8*		
$ZnCO_3$		c	*−194.2*	−174.8	*19.7*

[1] Bureau of Standards values in *italics;* estimated values in parentheses.

carefully prepared the stable orthorhombic crystalline modification for their work. From their value of the solubility product and the measured solubility, $1 \times 10^{-6}M$, it appears that the saturated solution contains considerable non-ionized zinc hydroxide. The free energy of the solid hydroxide is $-132,640$ cal. as calculated from these potentials. This value is in reasonable agreement with the thermal data.

Kolthoff and Kameda[1] found for the hydrolysis of zinc ion

$$Zn^{++} + H_2O = Zn(OH)^+ + H^+, \qquad K = 2.45 \times 10^{-10}.$$

Their value for the solubility product, 1×10^{-17}, is in approximate agreement with that given above.

From the solubility of the hydroxide in alkali, Dietrich and Johnston calculate,

$$Zn^{++} + 4OH^- = ZnO_2^{--} + 2H_2O, \qquad \Delta F^\circ = -21,090 \text{ cal.},$$
$$K = 2.8 \times 10^{15}.$$

$$Zn(OH)_2 = ZnO_2^{--} + 2H^+, \qquad K = 1.0 \times 10^{-29}.$$

This makes the free energy of zincate ion, ZnO_2^{--}, $-93,030$ cal., and the potential of the zinc-zincate couple.

$$4OH^- + Zn = ZnO_2^{--} + 2H_2O + 2e^-, \qquad E_B^\circ = 1.216.$$

For the dissociation,

$$Zn(NH_3)_4^{++} = Zn^{++} + 4NH_3(aq),$$

Euler[2] gives 2.6×10^{-10} from electromotive-force measurements, and Wijs[3] gives 9.8×10^{-10} from the partial pressure of ammonia over solutions of the complex ion. Bjerrum[4] chose 3.4×10^{-10} and we shall use his value. Hence the free energy of formation of the ion $Zn(NH_3)_4^{++}$ is -73.5 kcal. and for the half-reaction,

$$4NH_3(aq) + Zn = Zn(NH_3)_4^{++} + 2e^-, \qquad E_B^\circ = 1.04.$$

Euler also determined the dissociation constant of the complex cyanide, $Zn(CN)_4^{--}$, and found $K = 1.3 \times 10^{-17}$. Kunschert[5] gave 1.287 as the E° value of the zinc-complex cyanide couple which corresponds to 1.2×10^{-18} for the constant. He assumed the formula of the ion to be $Zn(CN)_4^{--}$. We shall write

$$4CN^- + Zn = Zn(CN)_4^{--} + 2e^-, \qquad E^\circ = 1.26.$$

Kunschert measured the potential of the zinc-complex oxalate

[1] I. M. Kolthoff and T. Kameda, *J. Am. Chem. Soc.*, **53**, 835 (1931).
[2] H. Euler, *Ber.*, **36**, 3400 (1903).
[3] H. J. de Wijs, *Rec. trav. chim.*, **44**, 663 (1925).
[4] J. Bjerrum, *Chem. Rev.* **46**, 381 (1950).
[5] F. Kunschert, *Z. anorg. Chem.*, **41**, 341 (1904).

couple. Attempting to recalculate his results, we find the dissociation constant approximately $K = 10^{-9}$ and the potential of the couple:

$$3C_2O_4^{--} + Zn = Zn(C_2O_4)_3^{-4} + 2e^-, \qquad E° = \text{ca } 1.02.$$

From the free energies of the zinc sulfides the solubility products are

$$ZnS(\text{sphalerite}) = Zn^{++} + S^{--}, \qquad K = 7.0 \times 10^{-26};$$
$$ZnS(\text{wurtzite}) = Zn^{++} + S^{--}, \qquad K = 1.6 \times 10^{-23}.$$

Precipitated zinc sulfide appears to be slightly more soluble than wurtzite and its solubility seems to depend somewhat upon the pH at which it is precipitated.

$$Zn + S^{--} = ZnS \text{ (wurtzite)} + 2e^-, \qquad E° = 1.44.$$

From the free energy of ZnSe,

$$ZnSe = Zn^{++} + Se^{--}, \qquad K = 10^{-31}.$$

Kelley and Anderson[1] in their study of the carbonate data give -174.78 kcal. for the free energy of formation of zinc carbonate. Making use of the free energies of the ion,

$$ZnCO_3 = Zn^{++} + CO_3^{--}, \qquad K = 2 \times 10^{-10};$$
$$Zn + CO_3^{--} = ZnCO_3 + 2e^-, \qquad E° = 1.06.$$

Ageno and Valla[2] gave 2.1×10^{-11} for the solubility product.

Sillén and Liljequist[3] have studied the zinc complex halide ions. For $3M$ $NaClO_4$ solution they gave

$$Zn^{++} + Cl^- = ZnCl^+, \qquad K = 0.65;$$
$$Zn^{++} + Br^- = ZnBr^+, \qquad K = 0.25;$$
$$Zn^{++} + I^- = ZnI^-, \qquad K = 0.05.$$

In both acidic and basic solution, the zinc couple is more positive than the corresponding hydrogen couple, although the difference is smaller in the basic solution. However, because of the very high overvoltage of hydrogen on zinc the metal does not dissolve rapidly in hydrogen ion unless it is in contact with some substance on which hydrogen gas can be liberated at a lower overvoltage. Likewise, because of the overvoltage, zinc ion or zincate may be reduced to the

[1] K. K. Kelley and C. T. Anderson, *U. S. Bur. Mines Bull.*, No. 384 (1935).
[2] F. Ageno and E. Valla, *Atti. Accad. Lincei*, **20**, 705 (1911).
[3] L. G. Sillén and B. Liljequist, *Svensk. Kem. Tid.*, **56**, 85 (1944).

metal in water solutions and both the voltage and overvoltage are more favorable at low hydrogen-ion concentration. The quantitative estimation of zinc by cathodic precipitation may be made in a solution buffered by acetate and acetic acid, but the determination is more satisfactory when the electrolyte is zincate or the complex cyanide.

CADMIUM

Oxidation states. Like that of zinc, cadmium's only important oxidation state is the $+2$. The hydroxide is considerably more basic than zinc hydroxide. There is some evidence for the existence of the $+1$ oxide, Cd_2O, and chloride, Cd_2Cl_2.

The cadmium-cadmium ion couple. Harned and Fitzgerald[1] have reviewed the literature on the cadmium cadmium-ion couple and gave $E° = 0.402$. From the Bureau of Standards free energy

$$Cd = Cd^{++} + 2e^-, \qquad E° = 0.403.$$

From measurements on the cell whose reaction is

$$Cd + HgO + H_2O = Cd(OH)_2 + Hg,$$

Ishikawa and Shibata[2] obtained $-42,100$ for the free energy of the reaction and calculated for the solubility product, $K = 1.17 \times 10^{-14}$. Wijs[3] reported 2.8×10^{-14} and 2.1×10^{-14}. We shall use the Bureau of Standards value for the free energy, which is -112.46 kcal.

$$Cd(OH)_2 = Cd^{++} + 2OH^-, \qquad K = 2.0 \times 10^{-14};$$
$$2OH^- + Cd = Cd(OH)_2 + 2e^-, \qquad E_B° = 0.809.$$

There appears to be no appreciable formation of cadmate ion in dilute hydroxide solutions.

For the dissociation constant of the cadmium ammonia-complex ion, Wijs[4] reported 2.5×10^{-7}, and Euler,[5] 1×10^{-7}. Bjerrum[6] chose 7.5×10^{-8}. Based on this value, the free energy of $Cd(NH_3)_4^{++}$ is -53.73 kcal. and

$$4NH_3 + Cd = Cd(NH_3)_4^{++} + 2e^-, \qquad E_B° = 0.61.$$

[1] H. Harned and M. E. Fitzgerald, *J. Am. Chem. Soc.*, **58**, 2624 (1936).
[2] F. Ishikawa and E. Shibata, *Science Rep. Tohoku Imp. Univ.*, **21**, 499 (1932).
[3] H. J. de Wijs, *Rec. trav. chim.*, **44**, 663 (1925).
[4] H. J. de Wijs, *ibid.*
[5] H. Euler, *Ber.*, **36**, 3400 (1903).
[6] J. Bjerrum, *Chem. Rev.*, **46**, 381 (1950).

TABLE 38

THERMODYNAMIC DATA ON CADMIUM[1]

(Heat and free energy of formation in kcal. Entropy of substance in cal./deg.)

Formula	Description	State	$\Delta H°$	$\Delta F°$	$S°$
Cd		g	26.97	18.69	40.067
Cd	metal α	c	0.0	0.0	12.3
Cd	metal γ	c		0.14	
Cd^+		g	235.802		
Cd^{++}		g	627.117		
Cd^{++}		aq	−17.30	−18.58	−14.6
Cd^{+++}		g	1436.		
Cd_2		g	51.04		
CdO		c	−60.86	−53.79	13.1
CdH		g	62.54	55.73	50.76
$Cd(OH)_2$		c	−133.26	−112.46	22.8
CdF_2		c	−164.9	−154.8	27.
CdCl		g	4.6	−1.8	60.36
$CdCl_2$		c	−93.00	−81.88	28.3
$CdCl^+$		aq		−51.8	5.6
$CdCl_2$	un-ionized	aq		−84.3	17.
$CdCl_3^-$		aq		−115.9	50.7
CdBr		g	−12.	−22.	63.09
$CdBr_2$		c	−75.15	−70.14	31.9
$CdBr_2·4H_2O$		c	−356.32	−297.69	74.7
CdI		g	19.6	8.1	64.97
CdI_2		c	−48.0	−48.0	40.2
$CdI_2·CdO·$ H_2O		c	−178.7		
CdS			−34.5	−33.60	17.
$CdSO_4$		c	−221.36	−195.99	32.8
$CdSO_4·H_2O$		c	−294.37	−254.84	41.1
$CdSO_4·$ $\frac{8}{3}H_2O$		c	−411.82	−349.63	57.9
CdTe		c	−24.30	−23.82	22.6
$Cd(N_3)_2$		c	107.8		
Cd_3N_2		c	38.6		
$Cd(NO_3)_2$		c	−107.98	−61.	(47.3)
$CdCO_3$		c	−178.7	−160.2	25.2
$CdCO_3$	amorphous	c	−177.5		
$Cd(CN)_2$		c	39.0	49.7	(24.9)
$Cd(NH_3)_4^{++}$				−53.73	
$Cd(CN)_4^{--}$				111.	
$Cd(NH_2)_2$			−14.71		

[1] Bureau of Standards values in *italics;* estimated values in parentheses.

From Bjerrum's value for the dissociation constant of the complex cyanide, we write

$$Cd(CN)_4^{--} = Cd^{++} + 4CN^-, \qquad K = 1.4 \times 10^{-19};$$

$$Cd + 4CN^- = Cd(CN)_4^{--} + 2e^-, \qquad E° = 1.09.$$

From the free energy of formation of the sulfide CdS,

$$CdS = Cd^{++} + S^{--}, \qquad K = 1.0 \times 10^{-28},$$

and for the potential of the cadmium-cadmium sulfide couple

$$Cd + S^{--} = CdS + 2e^-, \qquad E° = 1.24.$$

A similar calculation for the telluride, CdTe, gives

$$CdTe = Cd^{++} + Te^{--}, \qquad K = 10^{-42}.$$

Since the potential required to oxidize cadmium sulfide to the ion and free sulfur is of interest for many analytical procedures, that value is given here although it belongs under the sulfur potentials.

$$CdS = Cd^{++} + S + 2e^-, \qquad E° = -0.32.$$

A fairly powerful oxidizing agent is thus required to effect the oxidation.

Kelley[1] has given -163.4 kcal. for the free energy of the carbonate but we shall use the Bureau of Standards figure (-160.2) and calculate

$$CdCO_3 = Cd^{++} + CO_3^{--}, \qquad K = 5.2 \times 10^{-12};$$

$$Cd + CO_3^{--} = CdCO_3 + 2e^-, \qquad E° = 0.74.$$

Cadmium orms a complex ion with iodide, CdI_4^{--}. The dissociation constant has been studied by a number of investigators. Bates and Vosburgh[2] found

$$CdI_4^{--} = Cd^{++} + 4I^-, \qquad K = ca\ 5 \times 10^{-7}.$$

The free energies and entropies of $CdCl^+$, $CdCl_2(aq)$, and $CdCl_3^-$ in Table 38 are from the paper by King.[3] The corresponding dissociation constants are

$$CdCl^+ = Cd^{++} + Cl^-, \qquad K = 4 \times 10^{-2};$$

$$CdCl_2(aq) = Cd^{++} + 2Cl^-, \qquad K = 6.1 \times 10^{-3};$$

$$CdCl_3^- = Cd^{++} + 3Cl^-, \qquad K = 4 \times 10^{-3}.$$

[1] K. K. Kelley and C. T. Anderson, *U.S. Bur. Mines Bull.*, No. 384 (1935).
[2] R. G. Bates and W. C. Vosburgh, *J. Am. Chem. Soc.*, **60**, 137 (1938).
[3] E. L. King, *J. Am. Chem. Soc.*, **71**, 322 (1949).

The electrolytic reduction of cadmium is best accomplished from a solution of the complex cyanide, and this is the basis of the quantitative procedure.[1]

Cadmium in the +1 state.   From the very meager data regarding the chemical properties of Cd_2O and Cd_2Cl_2, one concludes that the ion Cd_2^{++} is capable of reducing water readily; hence,

$$Cd_2^{++} = 2Cd^{++} + 2e^-, \qquad E° > 0.6.$$

The value of the $Cd—Cd^{++}$ couple then fixes that of the $Cd—Cd_2^{++}$ couple as

$$2Cd = Cd_2^{++} + 2e^-, \qquad E° < 0.2.$$

MERCURY

Oxidation states.   Mercury forms compounds of the double mercurous ion, Hg_2^{++}, $+1$ oxidation state, and the mercuric ion, Hg^{++}, $+2$ state. Even at very low concentrations, the aqueous mercurous ion appears to be undissociated.

The mercury-mercurous ion couple.   We shall use the potential value given by Christensen.[2]

$$2Hg = Hg_2^{++} + 2e^-, \qquad E° = -0.789.$$

The free energy of mercurous ion corresponding to the $E°$ is 36.35 kcal. The couple is capable of rapidly attaining equilibrium and, when used as an electrode, is readily reversible.

X-ray examination of freshly precipitated "mercurous oxide" shows only mercury and mercuric oxide. Also the heat of formation of Hg_2O is, within the experimental errors, that of HgO. We believe that the evidence is conclusive that Hg_2O cannot exist in contact with an aqueous solution.

The mercury-mercurous halide couples.   Randall and Young[3] give for the mercury-mercurous chloride couple

$$2Cl^- + 2Hg = Hg_2Cl_2 + 2e^-, \qquad E° = -0.2676.$$

These authors studied the effect of oxygen upon the potential and

---

[1] F. P. Treadwell and W. T. Hall, *Analytical Chemistry*, New York: John Wiley & Sons, Inc., 1935, vol. 2, p. 197.

[2] M. T. Christensen, Univ. New Zealand Thesis 1947.

[3] M. Randall and L. E. Young, *J. Am. Chem. Soc.*, **50**, 989 (1928).

TABLE 39

THERMODYNAMIC DATA ON MERCURY[1]

(Heat and free energy of formation in kcal. Entropy of substance in cal./deg.)

Formula	Description	State	$\Delta H°$	$\Delta F°$	$S°$
Hg		g	*14.54*	*7.59*	*41.80*
Hg	metal	liq	0.0	0.0	*18.5*
Hg^+		g	*257.126*		
Hg^{++}		g	*698.56*		
Hg^{++}		aq	41.59	*39.38*	−5.4
Hg_2		g	*27.1*		
Hg_2^{++}		aq		36.35	
HgO	red	c	−21.68	−13.990	*17.2*
HgO	yellow	c	−21.56	−13.959	*17.5*
HgH		g	*58.06*	*52.60*	*52.42*
$HHgO_2^-$		aq		−45.42	
$Hg(OH)_2$		aq		−65.70	
HgF		g	*14.*		
HgCl		g	*19.*	*14.*	*62.2*
$HgCl_2$		c	−55.0	−44.4	(34.5)
Hg_2Cl_2		c	−63.32	−50.35	*46.8*
HgBr		g	*23.*	*18.*	*65.0*
$HgCl_4^{--}$		aq		−107.7	
$HgBr_4^{--}$		aq	−99.9	−88.0	84. (?)
Hg_2Br_2		c	−49.42	−42.714	*50.9*
$HgBr_2$		c	−40.5	−35.22	(37.2)
HgI		g	*33.0*	*23.*	*67.1*
HgI_2	red	c	−25.2	−24.07	(42.6)
HgI_2	yellow	c	−24.55	−23.1	(42.6)
HgI_4^{--}		aq	−55.4	−51.15	(90.) (?)
Hg_2I_2		c	−28.91	−26.60	*57.2*
HgS	red,cinnabar	c	−13.90	−11.67	*18.6*
HgS	black	c	−12.90	−11.05	*19.9*
Hg_2S				−1.6	
HgS_2^{--}				11.6	
$HgSO_4$		c	−168.3	−141.0	(32.6)
Hg_2SO_4		c	−177.34	−149.12	*47.98*
$(Hg_2N)_2O$		c	76.3		
Hg_2NOH		c	2.5		
$Hg_2NOH \cdot 2H_2O$		c	−139.2		
Hg_2NBr		c	15.0		
Hg_2CO_3		c		−105.8	
HgC_2O_4		c	−161.8	−126.2	(33.1)
$Hg(CN)_2$		c	62.5	74.3	(27.4)
$Hg(CN)_4^{--}$		aq	126.0	141.3	(64.) (?)
$Hg(ONC)_2$		c	64.0		
$Hg(CNS)_2$		c	48.0		
Hg_2CrO_4		c		−155.75	
$Hg_2C_2O_4$		c		−140.7	
$Hg_2(CH_3CO_2)_2$		c		−154.5	
$Hg_2(IO_3)_2$		c		−46.8	
$Hg_2(CNS)_2$		c		50.8	
$Hg_2(CN)_2$		c		62.2	
$Hg(IO_3)_2$				−41.2	

[1] Bureau of Standards values in *italics;* estimated values in parentheses.

found that in the presence of air the potential is at least a millivolt lower. This error applies also to the decinormal and normal potassium chloride calomel electrodes, which have been so widely used as reference couples. Their values for these electrodes are:

DN in air, -0.3354;   absence of air, -0.3341.

N in air, -0.2825;   absence of air, -0.2812.

The free energy of formation of mercurous chloride, Hg_2Cl_2, is $-50,310$ cal. and the solubility product

$$Hg_2Cl_2 = Hg_2^{++} + 2Cl^-, \qquad K = 1.1 \times 10^{-18}.$$

The generally accepted value for the standard saturated KCl calomel electrode is -0.2415.

Ishikawa and Ueda[1] report $-42,700$ cal. for the free energy of formation of mercurous bromide, which is in exact agreement with the value selected by Randall.[2]

$$2Br^- + 2Hg = Hg_2Br_2 + 2e^-, \qquad E^\circ = -0.1397.$$

The solubility product of the salt is

$$Hg_2Br_2 = Hg_2^{++} + 2Br^-, \qquad K = 1.3 \times 10^{-22}.$$

Bates and Vosburgh[3] found for the potential of the mercury-mercurous iodide couple

$$2I^- + 2Hg = Hg_2I_2 + 2e^-, \qquad E^\circ = 0.0405.$$

We then compute for the solubility product

$$Hg_2I_2 = Hg_2^{++} + 2I^-, \qquad K = 4.5 \times 10^{-29}.$$

Additional mercury-mercurous salt couples. Brodsky[4] has determined the solubility product of mercurous carbonate. His value and the corresponding potential are:

$$CO_3^{--} + 2Hg = Hg_2CO_3 + 2e^-, \qquad E_B^\circ = -0.44;$$
$$Hg_2CO_3 = Hg_2^{++} + CO_3^{--}, \qquad K = 9.0 \times 10^{-17}.$$

The potential of the mercury mercurous-sulfate couple,

$$SO_4^{--} + 2Hg = Hg_2SO_4 + 2e^-, \qquad E^\circ = -0.6151,$$

---

[1] F. Ishikawa and Y. Ueda, *Science Rep. Tohoku Imp. Univ.*, **22**, 263 (1933).
[2] M. Randall, *International Critical Tables*, **VII**, 260.
[3] R. G. Bates and W. C. Vosburgh, *J. Am. Chem. Soc.*, **59**, 1189 (1937).
[4] A. E. Brodsky, *Z. Elektrochem.*, **35**, 837 (1929).

is given by Harned and Hamer.[1] Using our value for the Hg—Hg_2^{++} couple, the solubility product is

$$Hg_2SO_4 = Hg_2^{++} + SO_4^{--}, \qquad K = 1 \times 10^{-6}.$$

Larson and MacDougall[2] reported for the mercury-mercurous acetate couple

$$2Hg + 2CH_3CO_2^- = Hg_2(CH_3CO_2)_2 + 2e^-, \qquad E^\circ = -0.51.$$

For the solubility product,

$$Hg_2(CH_3CO_2)_2 = Hg_2^{++} + 2CH_3CO_2^-, \qquad K = 3.6 \times 10^{-10}.$$

DeVries and Cohen[3] found

$$2Hg + H_2PO_4^- = Hg_2HPO_4 + H^+, \qquad E^\circ = -0.638.$$

For the iodate couple, Takaro[4] gave

$$Hg_2 + 2IO_3^- = Hg_2(IO_3)_2 + 2e^-, \qquad E^\circ = -0.394;$$
$$Hg_2(IO_3)_2 = Hg_2^{++} + 2IO_3^-, \qquad K = 1.94 \times 10^{-14}.$$

Brodsky recalculated the work of a number of early investigators to give the following approximate values for the solubility products:

$$Hg_2CrO_4 = Hg_2^{++} + CrO_4^{--}, \qquad K = 2 \times 10^{-9};$$
$$Hg_2C_2O_4 = Hg_2^{++} + C_2O_4^{--}, \qquad K = 1 \times 10^{-13};$$
$$Hg_2C_4H_4O_6 = Hg_2^{++} + C_4H_4O_6^{--}, \qquad K = 1 \times 10^{-10};$$
$$Hg_2(CNS)_2 = Hg_2^{++} + 2CNS^-, \qquad K = 3 \times 10^{-20};$$
$$Hg_2(CN)_2 = Hg_2^{++} + 2CN^-, \qquad K = 5 \times 10^{-40};$$
$$Hg_2S = Hg_2^{++} + S^{--}, \qquad K = 10^{-45}.$$

The mercurous-mercuric couple. Carter and Robinson[5] measured the potential of the mercurous-mercuric couple in perchloric acid against a calomel electrode at 18° C. and reported E°, -0.913. Popoff and his co-workers[6] have also measured the potential of the couple in perchloric acid, using a hydrogen electrode. They found $E^\circ = -0.905$. The extrapolation of the measured potentials to

[1] H. S. Harned and W. J. Hamer, *J. Am. Chem. Soc.*, **57**, 31 (1935).

[2] W. D. Larson and F. H. MacDougall, *J. Phys. Chem.*, **41**, 493 (1937).

[3] T. DeVries and D. Cohen, *J. Am. Chem. Soc.*, **71**, 1114 (1949).

[4] I. Takaro, *Chem. Zent.*, **II**, 301 (1944).

[5] S. R. Carter and R. Robinson, *J. Chem. Soc.*, 267 (1927).

[6] S. Popoff, J. A. Riddick, V. I. Wirth and L. D. Ough, *J. Am. Chem. Soc.*, **53**, 1195 (1933).

infinite dilution would appear to give a slightly lower value, and it would appear that the potential is probably around -0.915. However, we shall use the Bureau of Standards value for the free energy of Hg^{++}, and this with our value for Hg_2^{++} gives

$$Hg_2^{++} = 2Hg^{++} + 2e^-, \qquad E^\circ = -0.920.$$

From this value we compute for the free energy of mercuric ion 39,415 cal., and for the equilibrium between mercury, mercuric, and mercurous ions,

$$Hg + Hg^{++} = Hg_2^{++}, \qquad \Delta F^\circ = -3.03 \text{ kcal.}$$
$$K = 166.$$

This equilibrium is readily reversible and if the mercuric compound of a given ion is much less soluble than the corresponding mercurous compound, the latter becomes unstable with respect to the decomposition into mercury and the mercuric compound. For the mercury-mercuric couple,

$$Hg = Hg^{++} + 2e^-, \qquad E^\circ = -0.854.$$

Since the Hg^{++}—Hg_2^{++} couple is a stronger oxidizing agent than the Hg^{++}—Hg couple, reducing agents will first reduce mercuric ion to mercurous, but as the value for the Hg^{++}—Hg couple is about the same, excess of the reducing agent will take the mercurous ion on down to mercury. It also follows from these potentials that fairly powerful oxidizing agents, such as bromine water or hot nitric acid, are required to oxidize mercurous ion to mercuric.

The mercury-mercuric oxide couple. Because of the instability of mercurous oxide, the reduction of mercuric oxide goes directly to mercury. From the free energies, the potential is

$$Hg + 2OH^- = HgO(r) + H_2O + 2e^-, \qquad E^\circ_B = -0.098;$$
$$HgO(r) + H_2O = Hg^{++} + 2OH^-, \qquad K = 3 \times 10^{-26}.$$

Garrett and Hirschler[1] gave the following values:

$$HgO(r) = HgO(y), \qquad \Delta F^\circ = 31 \text{ cal.;}$$
$$HgO(r) + OH^- = HHgO_2^-, \qquad K = 3.15 \times 10^{-5};$$
$$HgO(r) + H_2O = Hg(OH)_2(aq), \qquad K = 2.25 \times 10^{-4};$$
$$Hg(OH)_2(aq) = HgOH^+ + OH^-, \qquad K = 10^{-14};$$
$$Hg(OH)_2(aq) = Hg^{++} + 2OH^-, \qquad K = 1.2 \times 10^{-22}.$$

---

[1] A. B. Garrett and A. E. Hirschler, *J. Am. Chem. Soc.*, **60**, 305 (1938).

The mercury-mercuric sulfide couple.   The third-law calculation of the free energy of the black form of mercuric sulfide gives
-11.05 kcal.   From this we find

$$HgS = Hg^{++} + S^{--}, \qquad K = 1.6 \times 10^{-54};$$
$$Hg + S^{--} = HgS + 2e^-, \qquad E_B^\circ = 0.75.$$

Goates, Cole and Gray[1] gave -10.22 kcal. for the free energy from
cell measurements and this may be more accurate than the third-law
value. The potential required to oxidize mercuric sulfide to mercuric
ion and sulfur is of interest:

$$HgS = S + Hg^{++} + 2e^-, \qquad E^\circ = 1.09.$$

Knox[2] gave

$$HgS_2^{--} = Hg^{++} + 2S^{--}, \qquad K = 1.96 \times 10^{-55}.$$

From this constant and the solubility product, we calculate

$$HgS + S^{--} = HgS_2^{--}, \qquad K = 3.8.$$

The sulfide is thus soluble in moderate sulfide concentrations.
   The mercuric cyanide and halide complex ions.   The data
of Sherrill[3] on the cyanide and halide mercuric-complex ions are given
in the following summarization:

	CN^-	I^-	Br^-	Cl^-
$\dfrac{(Hg^{++})(X^-)^4}{(HgX_4^{--})}$	4×10^{-42}	5.3×10^{-31}	2.3×10^{-22}	1.1×10^{-16}.

From these data, the following potentials have been calculated:

$$4CN^- + Hg = Hg(CN)_4^{--} + 2e^-, \qquad E^\circ = 0.37;$$
$$4I^- + Hg = HgI_4^{--} + 2e^-, \qquad E^\circ = 0.04;$$
$$4Br^- + Hg = HgBr_4^{--} + 2e^-, \qquad E^\circ = -0.21;$$
$$4Cl^- + Hg = HgCl_4^{--} + 2e^-, \qquad E^\circ = -0.48.$$

Korshunov and Shchennekova[4] report for $Hg(CNS)_4^{--}$

$$Hg(CNS)_4^{--} = Hg^{++} + 4CNS^-, \qquad K = 5 \times 10^{-20}.$$

---

[1] J. R. Goates, A. G. Cole and E. L. Gray, *J. Am. Chem. Soc.*, **73**, 3596 (1951).
[2] J. Knox, *Trans. Faraday Soc.*, **4**, 29 (1908).
[3] M. S. Sherrill, *Z. physik. Chem.*, **43**, 735 (1903); **47**, 103 (1904).
[4] A. Korshunov and M. K. Shchennekova, *J. Gen. Chem. U.S.S.R.*, **19**, 1820
(1949).

It is of interest to know the potential of the reduction of mercuric chloride solutions to mercurous chloride, but it is difficult to write an equation for the net reaction because of the complex nature of the mercuric chloride solution. Sherrill gives for the composition of the saturated solution: $HgCl_2(aq)$, 2.6×10^{-1}; $HgCl^+$, 2.7×10^{-4}; Hg^{++}, 3.5×10^{-8}; and $HgCl_4^{--}$, 1.6×10^{-6}, all in moles per liter. Using our free energy of the solid, we shall write

$$Cl^- + \tfrac{1}{2}Hg_2Cl_2 = HgCl_2(\text{sat. sol.}) + e^-, \qquad E^\circ = -0.53.$$

Johnson, Quarfort, and Sillén[1] have made a careful study of the mercuric chloride solution. These authors give the following constants:

$$HgCl^+ = Hg^{++} + Cl^-, \qquad K = 1.8 \times 10^{-7}$$
$$HgCl_2 = Hg^{++} + 2Cl^-, \qquad K = 6.0 \times 10^{-14}$$
$$2HgCl^+ = Hg^{++} + HgCl_2 \qquad K = 5.5 \times 10^{-1}$$
$$HgCl_3^- = HgCl_2 + Cl^-, \qquad K = 1.4 \times 10^{-1}$$
$$HgCl_4^{--} = HgCl_2 + 2Cl^-, \qquad K = 1.4 \times 10^{-2}$$
$$HgCl_3^- = Hg^{++} + 3Cl^-, \qquad K = 8.3 \times 10^{-15}$$
$$HgCl_4^{--} = Hg^{++} + 4Cl^-, \qquad K = 8.3 \times 10^{-16}$$
$$2HgCl_2 = HgCl^+ + HgCl_3^-, \qquad K = 4.3 \times 10^{-5}.$$

Their value for $HgCl_4^{--}$ is doubtless to be preferred to that quoted above by Sherrill.

Additional mercuric couples. There are not sufficient data to calculate the free energy of the complex mercuric ammono-basic salts. Franklin[2] found for the reaction

$$HgNH_2Cl + NH_4^+ + Cl^- = Hg(NH_3)_2Cl_2$$

that equilibrium was established at $0.49N$ ammonium chloride. The whole problem of the free energies of these chlorides and other salts should be investigated by third-law methods.

For the mercuric ammonia complex, Bjerrum[3] gave

$$Hg(NH_3)_4^{++} = Hg^{++} + 4NH_3(aq) \qquad K = 5.2 \times 10^{-20}.$$

---

[1] A. Johnson, I. Quarfort, and L. Sillén, *Acta Chem. Scand.*, **1**, 46, 473 (1947).
[2] E. C. Franklin, *J. Am. Chem. Soc.*, **29**, 40 (1907).
[3] J. Bjerrum, *Chem. Rev.*, **46**, 381 (1951).

Takacs[1] gives for the potential of the mercury-mercuric iodate couple

$$2IO_3^- + Hg = Hg(IO_3)(s) + 2e^-, \qquad E^\circ = -0.394;$$
$$Hg(IO_3)_2 = Hg^{++} + 2IO_3^-, \qquad K = 3.0 \times 10^{-13}.$$

Summary of group potentials. For comparisons within the group, the potentials are summarized in the following diagrams.

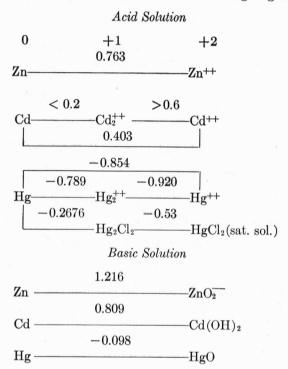

Acid Solution

Basic Solution

The change from the electropositive character of zinc to the noble-metal character of mercury is to be noted. The other important relation is the increasing stability of the +1 state with respect to its decomposition into the +2 state and the metal.

[1] I. Takacs, *Chem. Zent.*, **II**, 301 (1944).

CHAPTER 11

Copper, Silver, and Gold

The elements of subgroup I have one s electron in the valence level, but the group of 10 d electrons which has just been filled in the outer shell of the kernel is still fairly unstable. For this reason it is possible to remove one or two electrons from this group in addition to the one s electron. Hence these elements form compounds in which the oxidation state is $+1$, $+2$, or $+3$, although there is considerable variation in the relative stabilities of these various states with the different elements. The $+2$ and $+3$ ions form co-ordination complexes with one s, two p, and one d orbitals to give a square planar geometry while the $+1$ ions ordinarily form linear complex ions with one s and one p orbital.

Oxidation states. Copper forms compounds of the $+1$ state, cuprous; and the $+2$ state, cupric. The existence of the $+3$ oxidation state is shown by the formation of salts of the acid oxide, Cu_2O_3, but it and the $+3$ ion are such powerful oxidizing agents that they are very unstable in water solution.

Cuprous and cupric free energies. We have accepted the Bureau of Standards value for the free energy of cuprous ion, Cu^+, as it is in close agreement with the value given by Fenwick.[1] However, we believe that their heat of formation of the ion is in error, as the entropy can hardly be as low as -6.3.[2] The values for cuprous and cupric oxides are in agreement with the work of Randall, Nielsen, and West.[3] The free energy of CuCl is in approximate agreement with the work of Nielsen and Brown[4] and the values of CuBr and CuI with the work of Ishikawa, Yamazaki, and Murooka.[5]

[1] F. Fenwick, *J. Am. Chem. Soc.*, **48**, 860 (1926).

[2] Z. Z. Hugus has calculated the entropy of Cu^+ from equilibrium data by E. Heinerth [*Z. Elektrochem.*, **37**, 61 (1931)] and obtained the values 8.3 ± 2.0 cal./deg.

[3] M. Randall, R. F. Nielsen, and G. H. West, *Ind. Eng. Chem.*, **23**, 388 (1931).

[4] R. F. Nielsen and D. J. Brown, *J. Am. Chem. Soc.*, **50**, 9 (1928).

[5] F. Ishikawa, S. Yamazaki and T. Murooka, *Science Rep. Tohoku Imp. Univ.*, **23**, 115 (1934).

TABLE 40
THERMODYNAMIC DATA ON COPPER[1]
(Heat and free energy of formation in kcal. Entropy of substance in cal./deg.)

Formula	Description	State	$\Delta H°$	$\Delta F°$	$S°$
Cu		g	*81.52*	*72.04*	*39.744*
Cu	metal	c	*0.0*	*0.0*	*7.96*
Cu^+		g	*260.828*		
Cu^+		aq	*12.4(?)*	*12.0*	*−6.3 (?)*
Cu^{++}		g	*730.118*		
Cu^{++}		aq	*15.39*	*15.53*	*−23.6*
CuO		g	*35.*		
CuO		c	*−37.1*	*−30.4*	*10.4*
$HCuO_2^-$		aq		−61.42	
CuO_2^{--}		aq		*−43.5*	
Cu_2O		c	*−39.84*	*−34.98*	*24.1*
CuH		g	*71.*	*64.*	*46.89*
$Cu(OH)_2$		c	*−106.1*	−85.3	(19.)
CuF		g	*44.*		
CuF_2		c	*−126.9*	−116.	(20.2)
$CuF_2·2H_2O$		c	*−274.5*	*−235.2*	*36.2*
CuCl		g	*32.*	*25.*	*56.50*
CuCl		c	*−32.5*	*−28.2*	*20.2*
$CuCl_2$		c	*−52.3*	−42.	(26.8)
$CuCl_2^-$		aq	*−66.1*	*−57.9*	*49.4*
CuBr		g	*38.*	*28.*	*59.22*
CuBr		c	*−25.1*	*−23.81*	*21.9*
$CuBr_2$		c	*−33.8*	−30.3	(22.6)
$CuBr_2·4H_2O$		c	*−317.0*	*−258.4*	(70.2)
$CuBr_2^-$		aq		*−45.2*	
CuI		g	*62.*	*50.*	*61.06*
CuI		c	*−16.2*	*−16.62*	*23.1*
CuI_2		c	*−5.1*	−5.7	(38.)
CuI_2^-		aq		−24.6	
CuS		c	*−11.6*	*−11.7*	*15.9*
Cu_2S		c	*−19.0*	*−20.6*	*28.9*
$CuSO_4$		c	*−184.00*	*−158.2*	*27.1*
$CuSO_4·H_2O$		c	*−259.00*	*−219.2*	*35.8*
$CuSO_4·3H_2O$		c	*−402.25*	*−334.6*	*53.8*
$CuSO_4·5H_2O$		c	*−544.45*	*−449.3*	*73.0*
Cu_2SO_4		c	*−179.2*	−156.	(43.6)
CuSe		c	*−6.6*	−7.9	(22.2)
CuN_3	Azide	c	*60.5*		
$Cu(NO_3)_2$		c	*−73.4*	−27.3	(46.2)
$Cu(NH_3)^+$		aq		−2.8	
$Cu(NH_3)_2^+$		aq	*−36.1*	*−15.6*	63.
$Cu(IO_3)_2$		c		−58.4	
$Cu(NH_3)_4^{++}$		aq	*−79.9 (?)*	−40.8	
CuP_2		c	*−28.9*		
$CuCO_3$		c	*−142.2*	*−123.8*	*21.*
$Cu(CHO_2)_2$		aq	*−178.6*		(39.)
$Cu(CN)_2^-$		aq		69.3	
CuCNS		c		*15.0*	
$Cu(MoO_4)$		c	*−226.6*		(33.8)
$Cu(WO_4)$		c	*−250.*		(35.8)
$Cu(C_2O_4)^{--}$		aq		−317.5	
$Cu_4(OH)_6C_2O_4$		c		−415.5	

[1] Bureau of Standards values in *italics;* estimated values in parentheses.

Noyes and Chow[1] investigated $CuCl_2^-$, and Bodlander and Storbeck,[2] $CuBr_2^-$ and CuI_2^-. Approximate free energies have been calculated from the work of Spitzer[3] on cuprous cyanide and Immerwahr[4] on cuprous thiocyanate.

Anderson[5] has given data on Cu_2S and CuS.

Bjerrum[6] has made an extensive study of the cuprous and cupric ammonia complex ions. Lewis and Randall[7] gave the free energy of cupric ion, Cu^{++}, as 15.91 kcal. The constants for CuO in alkaline solution have been given by McDowell and Johnston.[8] Haehnel[9] has reported the solubility product of cupric carbonate. Meites[10] has given the free energies of $Cu(C_2O_4)_2^{--}$, $Cu_4(OH)_6C_2O_4$, and $K_2Cu(HCO_3)_4$. An approximate figure for the solubility product of cupric iodate was given by Auerbach[11] and the hydrolysis of Cu^{++} by Hagesawa.[12]

Cuprous and cupric potentials. The free energies may be employed to calculate the potentials of a large number of couples. For the single ions, we find

$$Cu = Cu^{++} + 2e^-, \qquad E^\circ = -0.337;$$
$$Cu = Cu^+ + e^-, \qquad E^\circ = -0.521;$$
$$Cu^+ = Cu^{++} + e^-, \qquad E^\circ = -0.153.$$

The cuprous ion is unstable.

$$Cu^{++} + Cu = 2Cu^+, \qquad K = 6.3 \times 10^{-7}.$$

Fenwick[13] gave 1×10^{-6} for this constant and her value is doubtless more reliable. Indeed, the free energy of Cu^+ probably should be calculated from her constant and the free energy of Cu^{++}. Thus, the reduction of Cu^{++} in nitric or sulfuric acid goes to the metal, although the unstable Cu^+ may be formed as an intermediate. However, in the

[1] A. A. Noyes and M. Chow, *J. Am. Chem. Soc.*, **40**, 739 (1918).

[2] G. Bodlander and O. Storbeck, *Z. anorg. Chem.*, **31**, 458 (1902).

[3] F. Spitzer, *Z. Elektrochem.*, **11**, 345 (1905).

[4] C. Immerwahr, *Z. anorg. Chem.*, **24**, 269 (1900).

[5] C. T. Anderson, *J. Am. Chem. Soc.*, **54**, 107 (1932).

[6] J. Bjerrum, *Kgl. Danske Videnskab. Selskab. Math-fys.*, **12**, No. 15 (1934).

[7] G. N. Lewis and M. Randall, *Thermodynamics*, NewYork: McGraw-Hill Book Company, Inc., 1923, p. 433.

[8] L. A. McDowell and H. L. Johnston, *J. Am. Chem. Soc.*, **58**, 2009 (1936).

[9] O. Haehnel, *J. prakt. Chem.*, **108**, 189 (1924).

[10] L. Meites, *J. Am. Chem. Soc.*, **72**, 184 (1950).

[11] F. Auerbach, *Z. physik. Chem.*, **86**, 243 (1914).

[12] H. Hagesawa, *Bull. Inst. Phys. Chem. Research*, **18**, 275 (1939).

[13] F. Fenwick, *J. Am. Chem. Soc.*, **48**, 860 (1926).

presence of various ions or molecules, the $+1$ state is stabilized and the equilibrium shifted far to the right. The following summary gives the copper-cuprous and cuprous-cupric potentials for various compounds and complex ions. The values for the simple ions have been included for comparison.

```
                        -0.337
        ┌─────────────────────────────────────┐
        │      -0.521              -0.153      │
   Cu───────────────Cu+────────────────Cu++
                 0.358              0.080
   Cu + OH⁻───────────────Cu₂O───────────────Cu(OH)₂
                -0.137             -0.538
   Cu + Cl⁻───────────────CuCl───────────────Cu++ + Cl⁻
                -0.033             -0.640
   Cu + Br⁻───────────────CuBr───────────────Cu++ + Br⁻
                 0.185             -0.86
   Cu + I⁻────────────────CuI────────────────Cu++ + I⁻
                 0.12               0.01
   Cu + 2NH₃──────────────Cu(NH₃)₂⁺───────────Cu(NH₃)₄++
                 0.93               0.54
   Cu + S⁻⁻───────────────Cu₂S───────────────CuS
               ca 0.43            ca -1.12
   Cu + 2CN⁻──────────────Cu(CN)₂⁻────────────Cu++ + 2CN⁻
               ca 0.27            ca -0.96
   Cu + CNS⁻──────────────Cu(CNS)──────────────Cu++ + CNS⁻
```

Cuprous equilibrium constants. The following equilibria involving cuprous ion may be written:

$CuCl = Cu^+ + Cl^-$,	$K = 3.2 \times 10^{-7}$
$CuBr = Cu^+ + Br^-$,	$K = 5.9 \times 10^{-9}$
$CuI = Cu^+ + I$,	$K = 1.1 \times 10^{-12}$
$CuCl + Cl^- = CuCl_2^-$,	$K = 6.5 \times 10^{-2}$
$CuBr + Br^- = CuBr_2^-$,	$K = 4.6 \times 10^{-3}$
$CuI + I^- = CuI_2^-$,	$K = 6.3 \times 10^{-4}$
$Cu(CN)_2^- = Cu^+ + 2CN^-$,	$K = 1 \times 10^{-16}$
$CuCNS = Cu^+ + CNS^-$,	$K = 4 \times 10^{-14}$
$\frac{1}{2}Cu_2O + \frac{1}{2}H_2O = Cu^+ + OH^-$,	$K = 1.4 \times 10^{-15}$
$Cu(NH_3)^+ = Cu^+ + NH_3(aq)$,	$K = 6.6 \times 10^{-7}$

$$Cu(NH_3)_2^+ = Cu^+ + 2NH_3(aq), \qquad K = 1.35 \times 10^{-11}$$
$$Cu_2S = 2Cu^+ + S^{--}, \qquad K = 1.2 \times 10^{-49}.$$

Cupric-copper equilibria. The following constants involving cupric ion are given:

$$Cu(OH)_2 = Cu^{++} + 2OH^-, \qquad K = 1.6 \times 10^{-19}$$
$$CuO + OH^- = HCuO_2^-, \qquad K = 1.03 \times 10^{-5}$$
$$CuO + 2OH^- = CuO_2^-, \qquad K = 8.1 \times 10^{-5}$$
$$HCuO_2^- = H^+ + CuO_2^-, \qquad K = 7.9 \times 10^{-14}$$
$$Cu(OH)_2 + 2OH^- = 2H_2O + CuO_2^{--}, \qquad K = 1.2 \times 10^{-3}$$
$$2CU^{++} + 2H_2O = Cu_2(OH)_2^{++} + 2H^+, \qquad K = 1.38 \times 10^{-11}$$
$$CuS = Cu^{++} + S^{--}, \qquad K = 8 \times 10^{-37}$$
$$CuCO_3 = Cu^{++} + CO_3^{--}, \qquad K = 2.5 \times 10^{-10}$$
$$Cu(NH_3)_4^{++} = Cu^{++} + 4NH_3(aq), \qquad K = 4.7 \times 10^{-15}$$
$$Cu(NH_3)_5^{++} = Cu(NH_3)_4^{++} + NH_3(aq), \qquad K = 2.8$$
$$CuSe = Cu^{++} + Se^{--}, \qquad K = 10^{-49}$$
$$Cu(IO_3) = Cu^{++} + 2IO_3^-, \qquad K = ca\ 1.3 \times 10^{-7}$$
$$Cu(C_2O_4)_2^{--} = Cu^{++} + 2C_2O_4^{--}, \qquad K = 4.8 \times 10^{-11}$$
$$K_2Cu(HCO_3)_4 = Cu^{++} + 2K^+ + 4HCO_3^-, \qquad K = 3 \times 10^{-12}$$
$$Cu(CO_3)_3^{-4} + 2OH^- = Cu(OH)_2 + 3CO_3^{--}, \qquad K = 1.5 \times 10^7.$$

Jellinek and Gordon[1] give the concentration of Cu^{++} in equil brium with the complex tartrate ion ($10^{-3}M$) and $1M$ OH^- as 10^{-15}. They write

$$\frac{(Cu^{++})^2(Tart.)^2}{(complex)(H^+)^4} = K$$

but there appears to be some uncertainty regarding the formula of the complex ion.

Laitinen, Onstatt, Bailor, and Swann[2] concluded that cupric ion co-ordinated with two molecules of the following: ethylenediamine, propylenediamine, diethylenetriamine, and glycine, and gave the dissociation constants as 1.9×10^{-20}, 6.8×10^{-21}, 1.4×10^{-21}, and 7.9×10^{-16}, respectively.

[1] K. Jellinek and H. Gordon, *Z. physik. Chem.*, **112**, 207 (1924).

[2] H. A. Laitinen, E. I. Onstatt, J. C. Bailor, Jr., and S. Swann, Jr., *J. Am. Chem. Soc.*, **71**, 1530 (1950).

Copper in the +3 state. Hypochlorite in alkaline solution dissolves cupric hydroxide, apparently with the formation of CuO_2^-. The sesquioxide has not been prepared, but the slightly soluble calcium salt may be precipitated. In acid solution, oxygen is rapidly evolved. From these facts,

$$Cu(OH)_2 = CuO_2^- + H_2O + e^-, \qquad E_B^{\circ} > -0.8;$$
$$Cu^{++} = Cu^{+++} + e^-, \qquad E^{\circ} > -1.8.$$

SILVER

The oxidation states of silver. Although the ions of +2 and +3 silver are known, they are such powerful oxidizing agents that they are unstable in water solutions with respect to their reduction by water. The +1 silver ion forms many slightly soluble compounds and slightly ionized complex ions. For most of these, data are available for the evaluation of their free energies.

The free energies of Ag^+ compounds. The Bureau of Standards free energy values for Ag^+ and its compounds are in close agreement with those given in our *First Edition*. For convenience, the reference given for the original calculations will be repeated, together with a few new references.

Ag^+ [1]

Ag_2O [2]

$AgCl$, $AgBr$, AgI, $AgCN$, and $AgCNS$ [3]

$AgNO_2$, $AgBrO_3$, and $AgIO_3$ [4]

Ag_2S [5]

Ag_2CO_3 [6]

$Ag_2C_2O_4$ [7]

$AgCNO$ [8]

Ag_2CrO_4 [9]

$Ag_4Fe(CN)_6$ [10]

AgN_3 [11]

Ag_2SO_4 [12]

Ag_2MoO_4 and Ag_2WO_4 [13]

$AgC_2H_3O_2$ [14]

[1] G. N. Lewis and M. Randall, *Thermodynamics*, New York: McGraw-Hill Book Company, Inc., 1923.

[2] K. S. Pitzer and W. V. Smith, *J. Am. Chem. Soc.*, **59**, 2633 (1938).

[3] J. Randall and L. E. Young, *J. Am. Chem. Soc.*, **50**, 989 (1928); M. Randall and J. O. Halford, *J. Am. Chem. Soc.*, **52**, 178 (1930); H. S. Harned and R. W. Ehlers, *J. Am. Chem. Soc.*, **55**, 2179 (1933); H. S. Harned, A. S. Keston and J. G. Donelson, *J. Am. Chem. Soc.*, **58**, 989 (1936).

[4] M. Randall, *International Critical Tables*, **VII**, 267.

[5] A. A. Noyes and E. S. Freed, *J. Am. Chem. Soc.*, **42**, 476 (1920); K. K. Kelley, *Bul. Bureau Mines*, No. 477, p. 83 (1950).

[6] A. C. Walker, U. B. Bray, and J. Johnston, *J. Am. Chem. Soc.*, **49**, 1256 (1927).

Potentials of Ag⁺ and its compounds. Potentials for the various silver couples have been calculated from the free energies and are summarized in Table 42, together with the solubility product or dissociation constant.

The acid dissociation of silver oxide was studied by Laue[1] who reported

$$\tfrac{1}{2}Ag_2O + \tfrac{1}{2}H_2O = AgO^- + H^+, \qquad K = 1.98 \times 10^{-18}.$$

Vosburgh and McClure[2] gave 4.3×10^{-4} for the dissociation of $Ag(NH_3)+$ and 6.2×10^{-8} for the dissociation of $Ag(NH_3)_2^+$. Treadwell and Hepenstrick[3] postulated the formation of AgSH by the action of hydrogen ion on Ag_2S and wrote

$$AgSH(aq) = H^+ + AgS^-, \qquad K = 5 \times 10^{-6};$$
$$Ag^+ + H_2S = AgSH(aq) + H^+, \qquad K = 1.76 \times 10^9.$$

Silver in the +2 and +3 oxidation states. Noyes and his co-workers[4] studied the Ag^+—Ag^{++} couple in HNO_3 and $HClO_4$. With acid molalities of 4, they found $E = -1.927$ in HNO_3 and $E = -1.970$ in $HClO_4$. The difference obviously arises from complex nitrate formation. The $E°$ involves the extrapolation to zero ionic strength, which cannot be made at present. We shall write

$$Ag^+ = Ag^{++} + e^-, \qquad E° = -1.98.$$

These investigators, having prepared Ag^{++} solutions by the action of ozone upon Ag^+, present convincing evidence to show that the mech-

[7] D. T. Ferrill, I. Blackburn, and W. C. Vosburgh, *J. Am. Chem. Soc.*, **70**, 3812 (1948).

[8] L. Birckenbach and K. Huttner, *Z. anorg. allgem. Chem.*, **190**, 26 (1930).

[9] J. Y. Cann and G. B. Mueller, *J. Am. Chem. Soc.*, **57**, 2525 (1935).

[10] J. N. Pearce and L. D. Ough, *J. Am. Chem. Soc.*, **60**, 80 (1938).

[11] A. C. Taylor and L. F. Nims, *J. Am. Chem. Soc.*, **60**, 262 (1938).

[12] W. M. Latimer, J. F. G. Hicks, Jr., and P. W. Schutz, *J. Chem. Phys.*, **1**, 424 (1933).

[13] H. T. S. Britton and W. L. German, *J. Chem. Soc.*, 1159 (1934).

[14] F. H. McDougall and J. Rehner, *J. Am. Chem. Soc.*, **56**, 368 (1934).

[1] E. Laue, *Z. anorg. Chem.*, **165**, 315 (1927).

[2] W. C. Vosburgh and R. S. McClure, *J. Am. Chem. Soc.*, **65**, 1060 (1943).

[3] W. D. Treadwell and H. Hepenstrick, *Helv. chem. acta.*, **32**, 1872 (1949).

[4] A. A. Noyes, D. DeVault, C. D. Coryell, and T. J. Deahl, *J. Am. Chem. Soc.*, **59**, 1326 (1937). Corrected for new γ value of $HClO_4$ by DeVault (unpublished).

Table 41

THERMODYNAMIC DATA ON SILVER[1]

(Heat and free energy of formation in kcal. Entropy of substance in cal./deg.)

Formula	Description	State	$\Delta H°$	$\Delta F°$	$S°$
Ag		g	*69.12*	*59.84*	*41.3221*
Ag	metal	c	0.0	0.0	*10.206*
Ag^+		g	*245.274*		
Ag^+		aq	*25.31*	*18.430*	*17.67*
Ag^{++}		g	*742.05*		
Ag^{++}		aq		64.1	
Ag^{+++}		g	*1576.0*		
AgO^+		aq		53.9	
AgO^-		aq		−5.49	
Ag_2O		c	*−7.306*	*−2.586*	*29.09*
AgO		c	*−6.0*	2.6	
Ag_2O_3		c		20.8	
AgH		g	*67.7*	*60.8*	*48.86*
AgF		c	*−48.5*	*−44.2*	*20.*
$AgF·H_2O$		c	*−120.4*	−101.8	(27.4)
$AgF·2H_2O$		c	*−191.2*	*−159.0*	*38.*
$AgF·4H_2O$		c	*−331.5*	−268.6	(45.9)
AgCl		g	*23.23*	*16.79*	*58.5*
AgCl		c	*−30.362*	*−26.224*	*22.97*
$AgClO_2$		c	*0.0*	16.0	*32.16*
$AgClO_3$		c	*−5.73*	16.	(37.7)
$AgClO_4$		c	*−7.75*	21.	(38.8)
AgBr		c	*−23.78*	*−22.930*	*25.60*
$AgBrO_3$		c		17.6	
AgI		c	*−14.91*	*−15.85*	*27.3*
$AgIO_3$		c	*−41.7*	−24.080	*35.7*
$Ag_2H_3IO_6$		c			*59.44*
Ag_2S	rhombic α	c	*−7.60*	*−9.62*	*34.8*
Ag_2S	β	c	*−7.01*	*−9.36*	*35.9*
Ag_2SO_4		c	*−170.50*	*−147.17*	*47.8*
$Ag(S_2O_3)_2{}^{---}$		aq	−285.5	−247.6	
$Ag(SO_3)_2{}^{---}$		aq		−225.4	
Ag_2SeO_4		c	*−94.7*	*−68.5*	*48.3*
AgN_3		c	66.8	90.	
$AgNO_2$		c	*−10.605*	*4.744*	*30.62*
$AgNO_3$		c	*−29.43*	*−7.69*	*33.68*
$Ag_2N_2O_2$		c	14.	29.4	(42.)
$Ag(NH_3)_2{}^+$		aq	*−26.724*	−4.16	57.8
Ag_2CO_3		c	*−120.97*	*−104.48*	40.0
$Ag_2C_2O_4$		c	*−159.1*	−137.2	(48.)
$Ag(CH_3CO_2)$	acetate	c	*−93.41*	−74.2	(33.8)
Ag_2MoO_4		c		−196.4	
Ag_2WO_4		c		−206.0	
Ag_2CrO_4		c	−176.2	−154.7	51.8
$Ag_4Fe(CN)_6$		c		188.4	
AgCN		c	*34.94*	*39.20*	*20.0*
$Ag(CN)_2{}^-$		aq	*64.5*	*72.05*	*49.0*
Ag_2CN_2		c	*51.5*		
AgCNO		c	*−21.1*	−14.7	
AgONC		c	*43.2*		
AgCNS		c	*21.0*	23.3	

[1] Bureau of Standards values in *italics;* estimated values in parentheses.

TABLE 42

$E°$ VALUE FOR Ag—Ag COMPOUNDS AND SOLUBILITY
PRODUCTS OR DISSOCIATION K

Substance	$E°$	Solubility Product or Dissociation K
Ag^+	-0.7991	
Ag_2SO_4	-0.653	1.24×10^{-5}
$AgC_2H_3O_2$	-0.643	2.3×10^{-3}
$AgNO_2$	-0.564	1.2×10^{-4}
$AgBrO_3$	-0.55	5.4×10^{-5}
Ag_2MoO_4	-0.49	2.6×10^{-11}
$Ag_2C_2O_4$	-0.472	1.1×10^{-11}
Ag_2CO_3	-0.47	8.2×10^{-12}
Ag_2CrO_4	-0.446	1.9×10^{-12}
$Ag(SO_3)_2^{---}$	-0.43	3.0×10^{-9}
$AgCNO$	-0.41	2.3×10^{-7}
$Ag(NH_3)_2^+$	-0.373	5.9×10^{-8}
$AgIO_3$	-0.35	3.1×10^{-8}
Ag_2O	-0.344	2.0×10^{-8}
AgN_3	-0.292	2.5×10^{-9}
$AgCl$	-0.2222	1.7×10^{-10}
$Ag_4Fe(CN)_6$	-0.194	1.55×10^{-41}
$AgCNS$	-0.09	1.0×10^{-12}
$AgBr$	-0.03	5.0×10^{-13}
$Ag(S_2O_3)_2^{---}$	-0.01	6.0×10^{-14}
$AgCN$	0.017	1.6×10^{-14}
AgI	0.151	8.5×10^{-17}
$Ag(CN)_2^-$	0.31	1.8×10^{-19}
$Ag_2S\alpha$	0.69	5.5×10^{-51}

anism of the reaction involved the following steps:

$$Ag^+ + O_3 = AgO^+ + O_2,$$
$$AgO^+ + 2H^+ + Ag^+ = 2Ag^{++} + H_2O.$$

The last reaction reaches equilibrium with the ratio of Ag^{++}/AgO^+ quite large. Assuming that $\Delta F°$ for this second reaction is approximately -5000 cal.,

$$H_2O + Ag^{++} = AgO^+ + 2H^+ + e^-, \qquad E° = \text{ca } -2.1;$$
$$H_2O + Ag^+ = AgO^+ + 2H^+ + 2e^-, \qquad E° = \text{ca } -2.0.$$

The potential of the Ag^{++}—AgO^+ couple could hardly be much greater negatively than 2.2 and permit the formation of AgO^+ from ozone which has a potential of -2.07. This potential cannot be much less and still keep the ratio of Ag^{++}/AgO^+ high. The Ag^{++} ion appears to be a rapid oxidizing agent, and the catalytic action of silver ion upon the rate of oxidation by peroxysulfate is certainly connected with the formation of these higher oxidation states of silver. In agreement with the potentials the free energy of formation of Ag^{++} is 64.1 kcal.

Luther and Pokorny[1] measured the potential of AgO and Ag_2O_3 in alkaline solution and their results have been confirmed by a number of workers.[2]

$$2OH^- + Ag_2O = 2AgO + H_2O + 2e^-, \qquad E_B^\circ = -0.57;$$
$$2OH^- + 2AgO = Ag_2O_3 + H_2O + 2e^-, \qquad E_B^\circ = -0.74.$$

The corresponding free energies of formation are AgO, 2600 cal., and Ag_2O_3, 20,800 cal. However, it has not been definitely established that the Ag_2O_3 in the cell measurements is a pure substance.

GOLD

Oxidation states.   Although the aurous ion, Au^+, is unstable, it forms a number of stable complex ions. Auric ion, Au^{+++}, is a very powerful oxidizing agent. It also forms a number of very stable complex ions. The very insoluble $+2$ sulfide is stable, but all other compounds of this state are decomposed by water.

Free energy of auric compounds.   In agreement with the Bureau of Standards value for the free energy of auric hydroxide, we write

$$Au + 3H_2O = Au(OH)_3 + 3H^+, \qquad E^\circ = -1.45.$$

This E° differs considerably from the experimental potential -1.363 found by Gerke and Rourke[3] and by Buehrer and Roseveare.[4] The solubility of the hydroxide in nitric acid has been measured by Jirsa and Jelinek.[5] The reported solubility was 3×10^{-5} moles of gold in 0.45 molal nitric acid at 21° C. Using 0.73 as the activity coefficient of the acid,

$$Au(OH)_3 + 3H^+ = Au^{+++} + 3H_2O, \qquad \Delta F^\circ = 2.82 \text{ kcal.}$$
$$Au(OH)_3 = Au^{+++} + 3OH^-, \qquad K = 8.5 \times 10^{-45}.$$

[1] R. Luther and F. Pokorny, *Z. anorg. Chem.*, **57**, 291 (1908).
[2] F. Jirsa and J. Jelinek, *Z. anorg. allgem. Chem.*, **158**, 61 (1926).
[3] R. H. Gerke and M. D. Rourke, *J. Am. Chem. Soc.*, **49**, 1855 (1927).
[4] T. F. Buehrer and W. E. Roseveare, *J. Am. Chem. Soc.*, **49**, 1989 (1927).
[5] F. Jirsa and H. J. Jelinek, *Z. Elektrochem.*, **30**, 286 and 535 (1924).

TABLE 43

THERMODYNAMIC DATA ON GOLD[1]

(Heat and free energy of formation in kcal. Entropy of substance in cal./deg.)

Formula	Description	State	$\Delta H°$	$\Delta F°$	$S°$
Au		g	*82.29*	*72.83*	*43.12*
Au	metal	c	*0.0*	*0.0*	*11.4*
Au^+		g	*296.62*		
Au^+		aq		39.0	
Au^{++}		g	*296.62*		
Au^{+++}		aq		103.6	
Au_2O_3		c	*19.3*	*39.0*	*30.0*
$H_2AuO_3^-$				−45.8	
$HAuO_3^{--}$		aq		−27.6	
AuO_3^{---}		aq		−5.8	
$Au(OH)_3$		c	−100.0	−69.3	*29.0*
$Au(OH)_3$		aq		−61.8	
$AuCl$		c	−8.4	−4.2	(24.)
$AuCl_3$		c	−28.3	−11.6	(35.)
$AuCl_3 \cdot 2H_2O$		c	−167.7	−123.3	(54.)
$AuCl_4^-$		aq	−77.8	−56.2	61.
$AuBr$		c	−4.4	−3.7	(27.)
$AuBr_2^-$		aq		−27.1	
$AuBr_3$		c	−13.0	−5.9	(24.)
$AuBr_3$		aq	−9.2		
$AuBr_4^-$		aq	−45.5	−38.1	75.
$HAuBr_4 \cdot 5H_2O$		c	−398.5		
AuI		c	0.2	−0.76	(28.5)
Au_2P_3		c	−24.1		
$Au(CN)_2^-$		aq	*58.4*	64.4	29.5
$Au(CNS)_2^-$		aq		57.7	
$Au(CNS)_4^-$		aq		130.1	

[1] Bureau of Standards values in *italics;* estimated values in parentheses.

Then compute for the free energy of Au^{+++}, 103.6 kcal.

$$Au = Au^{+++} + 3e^-, \qquad E° = -1.50.$$

Johnston and Leland[1] found that when auric hydroxide is treated with sodium hydroxide, the solid phase changes from $Au(OH)_3$ to Na_2HAuO_3 if the OH^- concentration is greater than $0.4M$. The Bureau of Standards free energies of $H_2AuO_3^-$, $HAuO_3^{--}$, and AuO_3^{---} appear to be based upon the results of these authors.

$$Au(OH)_3(c) = H^+ + H_2AuO_3^-, \qquad K = 6 \times 10^{-13};$$
$$H_2AuO_3^- = H^+ + HAuO_3^{--}, \qquad K = 5 \times 10^{-14};$$
$$HAuO_3^{--} = H^+ + AuO_3^{---}, \qquad K = 10^{-16}.$$

[1] H. L. Johnston and H. L. Leland, *J. Am. Chem. Soc.,* **60**, 1439 (1938).

Bjerrum and Kirschner[1] have measured the potential of the gold-auric complex chloride and gold-auric complex thiocyanate couples at 18° C.

$$4Cl^- + Au = AuCl_4^- + 3e^-, \qquad E° = -1.00;$$
$$AuCl_4^- = Au^{+++} + 4Cl^-, \qquad K = 5 \times 10^{-22};$$
$$Au + 4CNS^- = Au(CNS)^- + 3e^-, \qquad E° = -0.66;$$
$$Au(CNS)_4^- = Au^{+++} + 4CNS^-, \qquad K = ca\ 10^{-42};$$
$$\Delta F° \text{ (formation) } AuCl_4^- = -56.2 \text{ kcal.} : Au(CNS)_4^- = 128.8 \text{ kcal.}$$

For the potential of the corresponding bromide complex, Grube and Morita[2] report, at 60° C.,

$$4Br^- + Au = AuBr_4^- + 3e^-, \qquad E° = -0.87.$$

The value at 25° C. probably does not differ by more than 0.02 volt.

Iodide reduces $AuCl_4^-$ to AuI and the cyanide complex ion $Au(CN)_4^-$ is unstable upon warming with respect to $Au(CN)_2^-$ and cyanogen.

The gold-aurous couples. Aurous ion is unstable with respect to its decomposition into gold and auric ion and the ratio Au^+/Au^{+++} is so small that no accurate measurement has been made of the concentration of aurous ion in any solution. For this reason no direct experimental value can be given for the Au—Au^+ couple. However, we may make some calculations which will give us an approximate figure for the potential.

The heat of formation of aurous iodide, as given by Fischer and Biltz,[3] 200 cal., agrees excellently with the older value by Thomsen of 300 cal. The entropy of aurous iodide is not known, but a value of 28.5 cal./deg. is probably accurate to at least one entropy unit. Hence $\Delta S°$ of formation is 3.2 and $\Delta F°$, -760 cal.

$$I^- + Au = AuI + e^-, \qquad E° = -0.50.$$

The error in this potential is probably not more than 0.02 volt. A knowledge of the solubility product of aurous iodide would permit a calculation of the Au—Au^+ couple. The solubility products for CuI and AgI are about 10^{-12} and 10^{-16}, respectively, and an extrapolation of these values, together with the general trend of halide solubilities

[1] N. Bjerrum and A. Kirschner, *Kgl. Danske Videnskab. Selskab. Math-fys.*, **V**, No. 1 (1918).

[2] G. Grube and T. Morita, *Z. Elektrochem.*, **38**, 117 (1932).

[3] W. Fischer and W. Biltz, *Z. anorg. allgem. Chem.*, **176**, 81 (1928).

in this region of the periodic system, would place the solubility product of AuI at about 10^{-20}. The use of this figure would give

$$Au = Au^+ + e^-, \qquad E^\circ = ca \ -1.68;$$
$$Au^+ = Au^{+++} + 2e^-, \qquad E^\circ = ca \ -1.41;$$
$$3Au^+ = Au^{+++} + 2Au, \qquad K = ca \ 1 \times 10^{10};$$
$$\Delta F^\circ \ (\text{formation}) \ Au^+ = ca \ 39.0 \ \text{kcal.}$$

This value may be checked by a similar calculation with $AuCl$.

$$Au + Cl^- = AuCl + e^-, \qquad E^\circ = -1.17.$$

Aurous oxide, Au_2O, is sufficiently soluble so that it is unstable, in contact with water, with respect to the decomposition into the metal and Au_2O_3.

Bodländer[1] gave
$$2CN^- + Au = Au(CN)_2^- + e^-, \qquad E^\circ = 0.60.$$

This potential is remarkably high and leads to a value of the dissociation constant of the complex ion,

$$Au(CN)_2^- = Au^+ + 2CN^-, \qquad K = ca \ 5 \times 10^{-39}.$$

The free energy of $Au(CN)_2^-$ is 64.4 kcal. This value and the ΔH° correspond to an entropy of 29.5 for $Au(CN)_2^-$ which seems quite reasonable. As indicated by the potential, gold, in the presence of cyanide, is a powerful reducing agent and is very readily oxidized by oxygen. This reaction is the basis of the cyanide process for the extraction of gold from low-grade ores.

Bjerrum and Kirschner[2] have studied the thiocyanate complex ions $Au(CNS)_2^-$ and $Au(CNS)_4^-$. At 18° C. they found

$$2CNS + Au = Au(CNS)_2^- + e^-, \qquad E^\circ = -0.69;$$
$$2CNS^- + Au(CNS)_2^- = Au(CNS)_4^- + 2e^-, \qquad E^\circ = -0.645.$$

From these potentials it is obvious that $Au(CNS)_2^-$ is unstable.

$$3Au(CNS)_2^- = 2Au + Au(CNS)_4^- + 2CNS^-, \qquad K = 33.$$

However, they also found

$$Au(CNS)_4^- = Au(CNS)_2^- + (CNS)_2, \qquad K = 0.49 \times 10^{-4}.$$

[1] G. Bodländer, *Ber.*, 36, 3933 (1903).
[2] N. Bjerrum and A. Kirschner, *Kgl. Danske Videnskab. Selskab Math-fys.*, V, No. 1 (1918).

Grube and Morita[1] gave for 60° C.

$$2Br^- + Au = AuBr_2^- + e^-, \qquad E° = -0.96$$

and, combining with their potential for Au—$AuBr_4^-$,

$$2Br^- + AuBr_2^- = AuBr_4^- + 2e^-, \qquad E° = -0.82.$$

It follows that $AuBr_2^-$ is unstable with respect to the decomposition into Au and $AuBr_4^-$.

Claims are made for the formation of aurous sulfide, Au_2S, and also the thioacid ion, AuS^-, but nothing is known regarding their free energies.

Gold in the +2 oxidation state. A number of compounds of +2 gold have been prepared, as for example $AuCl_2$, at high temperatures, but the only one which is stable in contact with water appears to be the sulfide. This is doubtless because of its very slight solubility, for although the solubility product is unknown, it can be judged from mercuric sulfide that it must be very small. The sulfide is formed by the action of hydrogen sulfide upon auric chloride and is soluble in polysulfide to form thioaurates, but no energy values can be given for those reactions. From our approximate value for the Au^+—Au^{+++} couple and the knowledge that Au^{++} must oxidize and reduce itself to give Au^+ and Au^{+++}, these limits can be set:

$$Au^{++} = Au^{+++} + e^-, \qquad E° > -1.29;$$
$$Au^+ = Au^{++} + e^-, \qquad E° < -1.29;$$

but no estimate can be given of the concentration of Au^{++} present in the Au^+—Au^{+++} equilibrium.

Summary of subgroup I potentials. For comparison, the potentials relating the oxidation states of the three elements of the group are summarized in the following diagram:

---

[1] G. Grube and T. Morita, *Z. Elektrochem.*, **38**, 117 (1932).

Acid Solution

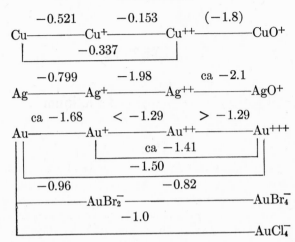

$$-0.521 \qquad -0.153 \qquad (-1.8)$$
$$\text{Cu}\text{---}\text{Cu}^+\text{---}\text{Cu}^{++}\text{---}\text{CuO}^+$$
$$-0.337$$

$$-0.799 \qquad -1.98 \qquad \text{ca } -2.1$$
$$\text{Ag}\text{---}\text{Ag}^+\text{---}\text{Ag}^{++}\text{---}\text{AgO}^+$$

$$\text{ca } -1.68 \qquad < -1.29 \qquad > -1.29$$
$$\text{Au}\text{---}\text{Au}^+\text{---}\text{Au}^{++}\text{---}\text{Au}^{+++}$$
$$\text{ca } -1.41$$
$$-1.50$$

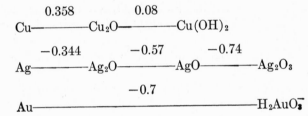

$$-0.96 \qquad\qquad -0.82$$
$$\text{---}\text{AuBr}_2^-\text{---}\text{AuBr}_4^-$$
$$-1.0$$
$$\text{---}\text{AuCl}_4^-$$

Basic Solution

$$0.358 \qquad\qquad 0.08$$
$$\text{Cu}\text{---}\text{Cu}_2\text{O}\text{---}\text{Cu(OH)}_2$$

$$-0.344 \qquad\qquad -0.57 \qquad\qquad -0.74$$
$$\text{Ag}\text{---}\text{Ag}_2\text{O}\text{---}\text{AgO}\text{---}\text{Ag}_2\text{O}_3$$

$$-0.7$$
$$\text{Au}\text{---}\text{H}_2\text{AuO}_3^-$$

CHAPTER 12

Nickel, Palladium, and Platinum

Each element of this group marks the end of a so-called "transition series" in which 10 d electrons have been added to the preceding noble gas. However, the groups of d electrons are not yet fully stabilized, and even in the monatomic gas molecules, the d^9s^1 state has roughly the same energy as the d^{10} state, that is, one of the electrons may be present in the next higher s level. Because of this instability, a number of electrons may be removed by chemical oxidation; hence the group has oxidation numbers ranging at least as high as $+6$. The more important oxidation states are $+2$ and $+4$, but there is considerable variation in the relative stabilities of the various states with the different elements. In the formation of complex ions, there is a strong tendency to share enough additional electrons to complete all of the nd, $(n + 1)s$, and $(n + 1)p$ orbitals.

Oxidation states. The zero oxidation state is represented by the compounds $Ni(CO)_4$ and $K_4Ni(CN)_4$. The eight additional electrons which are shared are sufficient to complete the $4s$-$4p$ orbitals, and since only the s and p are involved, the geometry is tetrahedral. The $+1$ cyanide NiCN and its complex salts are known. The $+2$ state is by far the most important and in water solution the chemistry of nickel is very largely that of the ion, Ni^{++}, and its compounds. Although the oxide, Ni_2O_3, may be prepared, it probably is not a true $+3$ compound, but a mixture of the $+2$ and $+4$ oxides. No other compounds of the $+3$ state exist. The $+4$ oxide, NiO_2, is a very powerful oxidizing agent, and compounds of the $+4$ state are not known in acid solution. There is some evidence of $+6$ and $+8$ oxides.

The nickel-nickelous couple. An accurate value for the potential of the Ni—Ni^{++} couple cannot be given, as a truly reversible equilibrium appears to be unattainable. Colombier[1] gives 0.227.

[1] L. Colombier, *Compt. rend.*, 199, 273 (1934).

TABLE 44

THERMODYNAMIC DATA ON NICKEL[1]

(Heat and free energy of formation in kcal. Entropy of substance in cal./deg.)

Formula	Description	State	$\Delta H°$	$\Delta F°$	$S°$
Ni		g	*101.61*	*90.77*	*43.502*
Ni		c	0.0	0.0	*7.20*
Ni$^+$		g	*279.11*		
Ni^{++}		g	*700.8*		
Ni^{++}		aq	-15.3 (?)	-11.53	(?)
NiO		g	*59.3*	*51.8*	*57.*
NiO$_2$		c		-47.5	
NiH		g	*93.*		
NiH		c	-2.7		
NiH$_2$		c	-6.2		
Ni(OH)$_2$		c	-128.6	-108.3	19.
Ni(OH)$_3$		c	-162.1	-129.5	(19.5)
NiF$_2$		c	-159.5	-148.8	(19.9)
NiCl		g	*15.*		
NiCl$_2$		c	-75.5	-65.1	*25.6*
NiBr$_2$		c	-54.2	-50.8	(32.8)
NiI$_2$		c	-20.5	-21.3	(37.7)
Ni(IO$_3$)$_2$		c	-124.5	-86.7	(54.5)
NiS	α	c		-17.7	
NiS	γ	c		-27.3	
NiO		c	-58.4	-51.7	*9.22*
NiSO$_4$		c	-213.0	-184.9	18.6
NiSO$_4$·6H$_2$O	green	c	-644.98		
NiSO$_4$·6H$_2$O	blue	c	-642.5	-531.0	*73.1*
Ni(NO$_3$)$_2$		c	-102.2	-56.4	(45.9)
Ni(NH$_3$)$_4$$^{++}$		aq		-46.9	
Ni(NH$_3$)$_6$$^{++}$		aq		-60.1	
NiCO$_3$		c	-158.7	-147.0	(21.9)
Ni(CO)$_4$		g			97.
Ni(CO)$_4$		liq			74.
Ni(CN)$_2$		c	*27.1*	37. (?)	(22.5)
Ni(CN)$_4$$^{--}$		aq	*86.9*	117.1	(33.)

[1] Bureau of Standards values in *italics;* estimated values in parentheses.

Haring and Bosche[1] report 0.231. Murata[2] found 0.248. The Bureau of Standards free energy corresponds to 0.241. However, their value for the entropy of Ni^{++} is -38.1 cal./deg., and we cannot accept such a low value in comparison to Fe^{++} and Cu^{++}, even though there may be considerable divergence because of the multiplicity of the ground

[1] M. M. Haring and E. G. Vanden Bosche, *J. Phys. Chem.*, **33**, 161 (1929).
[2] K. Murata, *Bull. Chem. Soc. Japan*, **3**, 57 (1928).

states. Therefore, we shall continue to use our previous arbitrary value and write

$$Ni = Ni^{++} + 2e^-, \qquad E^\circ = 0.250.$$

The corresponding free energy of formation of Ni^{++} is -11.5 kcal. From the free energy of nickel hydroxide we calculate

$$Ni + 2OH^- = Ni(OH)_2 + 2e^-, \qquad E_B^\circ = 0.72;$$
$$Ni(OH)_2 = Ni^{++} + 2OH^-, \qquad K = 1.6 \times 10^{-16}.$$

Gayer and Garret[1] report 6.5×10^{-18} for the basic constant and for the acid constant

$$Ni(OH)_2 = H^+ + HNiO_2^-, \qquad K = 6 \times 10^{-19}.$$

For the basic constant, Wijs[2] gave 1.6×10^{-14} from a study of the equilibrium with the ammonia complex ions. Nasanen[3] has found 6.2×10^{-16}. In view of the uncertainty with regard to the free energy of Ni^{++}, the experimental value for K base by Gayer and Garret is to be preferred to our value from thermal data.

Complex nickelous ions.   Bjerrum[4] in his review paper reported the following:

$$Ni(NH_3)_4^{++} = Ni^{++} + 4NH_3(aq), \qquad K = 1 \times 10^{-8};$$
$$Ni(NH_3)_6^{++} = Ni^{++} + 6NH_3(aq), \qquad K = 1.8 \times 10^{-9}.$$

Hence,

$$Ni + 6NH_3(aq) = Ni(NH_3)_6^{++} + 2e^-, \qquad E^\circ = 0.49.$$

Nickelous ion forms a complex with cyanide, $Ni(CN)_4^{--}$. Using a very approximate value for the entropy of the complex ion, we calculate

$$Ni(CN)_4^{--} = Ni^{++} + 4CN^-, \qquad K = 10^{-22}.$$

This value has been checked by Hume and Kolthoff.[5] These authors give the formula of $Ni(CN)_2$ as $Ni[Ni(CN)_4]$. The four $Ni—CN$ bonds are combination orbitals of one d, one s, and two p orbitals, and the geometry is square planar. The ammonia complex ion, $Ni(NH_3)_4^{++}$,

[1] K. H. Gayer and A. B. Garret, *J. Am. Chem. Soc.*, **71**, 2973 (1949).
[2] H. J. Wijs, *Rec. trav. chim.*, **44**, 663 (1925).
[3] R. Nasanen, *Ann. Acad. Fenni cal.*, **A59**, 3 (1943).
[4] J. Bjerrum, *Chem. Rev.*, **46**, 381 (1950).
[5] D. H. Hume and I. M. Kolthoff, *J. Am. Chem. Soc.*, **72**, 4423 (1950).

is tetrahedral, and one concludes that the bonds are largely dipolar attractions.

Powerful reducing agents reduce $Ni(CN)_4^{--}$ to the $+1$ complex ion $Ni(CN)_4^{---}$. Grube[1] has measured the potential,

$$Ni(CN)_4^{---} = Ni(CN)_4^{--} + e^-, \qquad E° = 0.82.$$

Nickel carbonate and sulfide. For the solubility product of the carbonate, Ageno and Valla[2] reported

$$NiCO_3 = Ni^{++} + CO_3^{--}, \qquad K = 1.36 \times 10^{-7}.$$

From this we compute, $\Delta F°$ of $NiCO_3$ is -147.0 kcal. and

$$Ni + CO_3^{--} = NiCO_3 + 2e^-, \qquad E° = 0.45.$$

Theil and Gessner[3] conclude that there are three forms of nickel sulfide with the following solubility products:

(α)	$NiS = Ni^{++}(\alpha) + S^{--}$,	$K = 3 \times 10^{-21}$;
(β)	$NiS = Ni^{++}(\beta) + S^{--}$,	$K = 1 \times 10^{-26}$;
(γ)	$NiS = Ni^{++}(\gamma) + S^{--}$,	$K = 2 \times 10^{-28}$.

The α-form, mixed with some β- and γ-, is precipitated in cold alkaline solution. This would agree with the solubility calculated above from the heat of precipitation of nickel with sodium sulfide. The conversion of α-nickel sulfide to the other forms is favored by acid, which explains the well-known fact that nickel and cobalt sulfides do not dissolve in hydrochloric acid but cannot be precipitated from acid solution by hydrogen sulfide. Based on the Theil and Gessner constants,

$$S^{--} + Ni = NiS(\alpha) + 2e^-, \qquad E° = 0.83;$$
$$S^{--} + Ni = NiS(\gamma) + 2e^-, \qquad E° = 1.04.$$

Nickelic oxide. The oxidation of nickelous hydroxide in alkaline solution appears to form either a solid solution or a series of compounds of NiO_2 and NiO with some water of hydration. With fairly high concentrations of hydroxide, it is probably possible to obtain pure NiO_2.[4] This oxide mixture is the oxidizing agent used in the Edison storage battery, and the electrode is often considered as the $Ni(OH)_2$—$Ni(OH)_3$ couple. Foerster[5] has studied the potential of the

[1] G. Grube, *Z. Elektrochem.*, **32**, 561 (1926).
[2] F. Ageno and E. Valla, *Atti. Accad. Lincei, Ser.*, **5**, *20:2*, 706 (1911).
[3] A. Theil and H. Gessner, *Z. anorg. Chem.*, **86**, 49 (1914).
[4] O. R. Howell, *J. Chem. Soc.*, **123**, 1772 (1923).
[5] F. Foerster, *Z. Elektrochem.*, **13**, 414 (1907).

electrode, and from his work we shall write

$$2OH^- + Ni(OH)_2 = NiO_2 + 2H_2O + 2e^-, \qquad E_B^o = -0.49.$$

The couple is readily reversible, as is indicated by its use in the nickel accumulator. For the Ni^{++}—NiO_2 couple in acid, we compute,

$$2H_2O + Ni^{++} = NiO_2 + 4H^+ + 2e^-, \qquad E^o = -1.68.$$

This potential is sufficient to cause the rapid oxidation of water, so the oxide is unstable in acid solutions.

Higher oxidation states of nickel. When nickelous hydroxide is fused with potassium nitrate and potassium hydroxide, the nickelate compound, K_2NiO_4, is formed. It is also unstable in acid solutions because of its high oxidizing power.

$$4H_2O + Ni^{++} = NiO_4^{--} + 8H^+ + 4e^-, \qquad E^o < -1.8.$$

Claims are also made for the formation by the same process of some pernickelate, K_2NiO_5, but the evidence is not conclusive.

PALLADIUM

Oxidation states. The most important oxidation state is the $+2$. Like Ni, the zero-state complex cyanide, $K_4Pd(CN)_4$, has been prepared. The $+4$ oxidation state is represented by the dioxide and complex chlorides, for example, K_2PdCl_6, and there is evidence of the $+6$ oxide, PdO_3.

The element absorbs hydrogen to a remarkable extent—600 to 900 volumes of the gas per volume of the metal, depending upon its physical condition. The hydrogen appears to be present as a solid solution of the compound Pd_2H. Gillespie and Hall[1] report for 30° C.

$$Pd_2H(\text{in sat. Pd}) = 2Pd(\text{in sat. } Pd_2H) + \tfrac{1}{2}H_2, \qquad P = 0.0246 \text{ atm.}$$

The solution is a very much faster reducing agent than hydrogen (cf. hydrogen overvoltage) and, for example, reduces ferric ion readily.

Palladium-palladous couples. Templeton, Watt, and Garner[2] have measured the Pd—Pd^{++} couple.

$$Pd = Pd^{++} + 2e^-, \qquad E^o = -0.987.$$

[1] L. J. Gillespie and F. P. Hall, *J. Am. Chem. Soc.*, **48**, 1207 (1926).
[2] D. H. Templeton, G. W. Watt, and C. S. Garner, *J. Am. Chem. Soc.*, **65**, 1608 (1943).

TABLE 45

THERMODYNAMIC DATA ON PALLADIUM[1]

(Heat and free energy of formation in kcal. Entropy of substance in cal./deg.)

Formula	Description	State	$\Delta H°$	$\Delta F°$	$S°$
Pd		g	*93.*	*84.*	*39.91*
Pd		c	0.0	0.0	*8.9*
Pd^+		g	*276.*		
Pd^{++}		g	*734.*		
Pd^{++}		aq		45.5	
PdO		c	*−20.4*	−14.4	(13.2)
Pd_2H		c	*−8.9*		
$Pd(OH)_2$		c	*−92.1*	−72.	(21.7)
$Pd(OH)_4$		c	*−169.4* (?)	−126.2 (?)	(24.7)
$PdCl_4^{--}$		aq	*−129.8*	−96.7	*36.*
$PdCl_6^{--}$		aq	*−156.7* (?)	−99.6	(52.)
$PdBr_2$		c	*−24.9*	−21.8	(34.5)
$PdBr_4^{--}$		aq	*−88.6*	−70.7	(44.)
$PdI_2 \cdot H_2O$		c	*−87.3*	−74.4	(49.3)

[1] Bureau of Standards values in *italics;* estimated values in parentheses.

From our calculated value for the free energy of the hydroxide we write

$$Pd + 2OH^- = Pd(OH)_2 + 2e^-, \qquad E° = -0.07;$$
$$Pd(OH)_2 = Pd^{++} + 2OH^-, \qquad K = 1 \times 10^{-31}.$$

The Pd—$PdCl_4^{--}$ couple was also studied by Templeton, Watt, and Garner.[1] The free energy of the ion as recalculated by the Bureau of Standards, leads to the following:

$$Pd + 4Cl^- = PdCl_4^{--} + 2e^-, \qquad E° = -0.62;$$
$$PdCl_4^{--} = Pd^{++} + 4Cl^-, \qquad K = 5 \times 10^{-13}.$$

For the corresponding complex bromide we calculate

$$Pd + 4Br^- = PdBr_4^{--} + 2e^-, \qquad E° = -0.6;$$
$$PdBr_4^{--} = Pd^{++} + 4Br^-, \qquad K = 8 \times 10^{-14}.$$

Palladium in the +4 and +6 states. Wellman[2] found by direct measurement

$$PdCl_4^{--} + 2Cl^- = PdCl_6^{--} + 2e^-, \qquad E° = -1.288.$$

---

[1] *Ibid.*
[2] H. B. Wellman, *J. Am. Chem. Soc.,* **52,** 985 (1930).

This $E°$ corresponds to a value of -99.6 kcal. for the free energy of $PdCl_6^{--}$. From the thermal data, we calculate -112 kcal. for this free energy. It appears that the heat of formation of $PdCl_6^{--}$ as listed is too negative. Wellman also measured the solubility product of the potassium salt

$$K_2PdCl_6 = 2K^+ + PdCl_6^{--}, \qquad K = 6.0 \times 10^{-6}.$$

Jirsa[1] gave -0.95 for the PdO—PdO_2 couple in alkali. From the thermal data, we calculate -0.46. As indicated above, the heats of formation of the $+4$ compounds may be too negative, and we will write, in agreement with the Wellman value for the complex chloride,

$$Pd(OH)_2 + 2OH^- = Pd(OH)_4 + 2e^-, \qquad E_B^° = \text{ca} -0.73.$$

Jirsa also reported,

$$PdO_2 + 2OH^- = PdO_3 + H_2O + 2e^-, \qquad E_B^° = -1.2.$$

The trioxide in acid solution is obviously a very powerful oxidizing agent and no compounds are known.

PLATINUM

Oxidation states. The principal oxidation states are the $+2$ and $+4$. The free ions corresponding to these states are present only at low concentrations in water solutions, but many halogeno-, nitro-, amido-, cyano-, and other complex platinites and platinates exist in solution. These compounds are, in general, much more stable and important than the oxides and their complexes. However, the free-energy data pertaining to the platinum complex acids are very limited, and only a few cases can be discussed. The $+1$ and $+3$ chlorides and a few other compounds of these states have been prepared, but their stability is not great.

$$2PtCl = Pt + PtCl_2, \qquad \Delta F° = 1.9 \text{ kcal.};$$
$$2PtCl_3 = PtCl_2 + PtCl_4, \qquad \Delta F = -1.4 \text{ kcal.}$$

The $+6$ oxide and a few salts, for example, K_2PtO_4, are known.

Platinum-platinous couples. Many investigators have been discouraged by the lack of reproducibility of platinum electrodes. Lorenz and Spielmann[2] discuss the problem for a number of couples.

[1] F. Jirsa, *Z. physik. Chem.*, **113**, 241 (1924).
[2] R. Lorenz and P. E. Spielmann, *Z. Elektrochem.*, **15**, 293 (1909).

However, although their potentials were not very constant, they do
agree in general with values which we may calculate from thermal

TABLE 46

THERMODYNAMIC DATA ON PLATINUM[1]

(Heat and free energy of formation in kcal. Entropy of substance in cal./deg.)

Formula	Description	State	$\Delta H°$	$\Delta F°$	$S°$
Pt		g	*121.6*	*110.9*	*45.96*
Pt		c	0.0	0.0	10.0
Pt$^+$		g	*328.*		
Pt^{++}		aq		(54.8)	
Pt(OH)$_2$		c	−87.2	−68.2	26.5
PtCl		c	−17.7	−14.1	(24.9)
PtCl$_2$		c	−35.5	−26.3	(31.4)
PtCl$_3$		c	−49.9	−33.6	(35.9)
PtCl$_4$		c	−62.9	−42.3	(47.6)
PtCl$_4$·5H$_2$O		c	−425.8	−336.4	(94.6)
PtCl$_4^{--}$		aq	−123.4	−91.9	42.
PtCl$_6^{--}$		aq	−167.4	−123.1	52.6
PtBr$_4$		c	−41.3	−33.1	(55.2)
PtBr$_4^{--}$		aq	−91.1	−71.5	(49.)
PtBr$_6^{--}$		aq	−117.1		
PtI$_4$		c	−21.1	−22.0	(67.2)
PtI$_6^{--}$		aq	−55.7		
PtS		c	−20.8 (?)	−21.6 (?)	(20.2)
PtS$_2$		c	−27.8	−25.6	(17.8)

[1] Bureau of Standards values in *italics;* estimated values in parentheses.

data. For the hydroxide, Pt(OH)$_2$, the free energy is −68.2 kcal.
Hence,

$$2OH^- + Pt = Pt(OH)_2 + 2e^-, \qquad E_B^o = -0.15.$$

The hydroxide is not appreciably soluble in 1 molal acid; hence we
may write

$$2H_2O + Pt = Pt(OH)_2 + 2H^+ + 2e^-, \qquad E° = -0.98.$$

Lorenz and Spielmann found −0.98 as an average of a number of
values for this couple.

However, the hydroxide dissolves somewhat in concentrated nitric
acid, and, as a rough estimate, the solubility product is

$$Pt(OH)_2 = Pt^{++} + 2OH^-, \qquad K = ca \ 10^{-35}.$$

This leads to the following potential for the ion:

$$Pt = Pt^{++} + 2e^-, \qquad E° = ca -1.2.$$

The corresponding free energy of the ion, Pt^{++}, is 54.8 kcal.

From the free energies we may write the following equations:

$$Pt + 4Cl^- = PtCl_4^{--} + 2e^-, \qquad E° = -0.73;$$
$$PtCl_4^{--} = Pt^{++} + 4Cl^-, \qquad K = ca\ 10^{-16};$$
$$Pt + 4Br^- = PtBr_4^{--} + 2e^-, \qquad E° = -0.58;$$
$$PtBr_4^{--} = Pt^{++} + 4Br^-, \qquad K = ca\ 3 \times 10^{-21}.$$

Lorenz and Spielmann found -0.726 for the Pt—$PtCl_4^{--}$ couple, and the Bureau of Standards data agree with this figure. The value is consistent with the fact that ferric chloride slowly oxidizes platinum.

The thermal data on PtS lead to the following:

$$Pt + H_2S(g) = PtS + 2H^+ + 2e^-, \qquad E° = 0.30;$$
$$Pt + S^{--} = PtS + 2e^-, \qquad E° = 0.95;$$
$$PtS = Pt^{++} + S^{--}, \qquad K = 8 \times 10^{-73}.$$

According to these potentials, platinum should tarnish with hydrogen sulfide

$$Pt + H_2S = PtS + H_2, \qquad \Delta F° = -13.7\ kcal.$$

This free energy seems to be too negative. Also, although the solubility product of PtS must be very small in order for it to be stable, the figure 10^{-73} for the solubility product seems a little excessive. A value of -12.0 kcal. for the heat of formation of the sulfide would appear to be more reasonable.

Free energies cannot be calculated for the numerous ammonia and nitrite complex salts. The iodoplatinite is unstable.

$$PtI_4^{--} = PtI_6^{--} + 2I^- + Pt.$$

Platinous-platinic couples. The potential of the $PtCl_4^{--}$—$PtCl_6^{--}$ couple has been measured by a number of investigators. Smith[1] found -0.792 for the couple in $0.1N$ Cl^-, and the Bureau of Standards free energy has apparently been calculated from this work.

$$PtCl_4^{--} + 2Cl^- = PtCl_6^{--} + 2e^-, \qquad E° = -0.68.$$

---

[1] E. R. Smith, *U. S. Bur. Standards J. Research*, **5**, 735 (1930).

This would make the $+2$ complex slightly unstable with respect to the decomposition,

$$2PtCl_4^{--} = PtCl_6^{--} + Pt + 2Cl^-.$$

The heat of the similar reaction (that is, with H_2—$2H^+$) for the bromoplatinites and platinates is 4100 cal. less, and assuming the entropy of the two reactions to be closely the same,

$$2Br^- + PtBr_4^{--} = PtBr_6^{--} + 2e^-, \qquad E^° = -0.59.$$

No data are available for the calculation of the dissociation constants of the chloro- or bromoplatinates. The acid dissociation constants of many of the nitro-, chloro-, and amido-complex ions have been studied by Grunberg and Faermann.[1] They give, for example,

$$Pt(NH_3)_6^{+4} = Pt(NH_3)_5(NH_2)^{+++} + H^+, \qquad K = 1.3 \times 10^{-9}.$$

However, we cannot at present calculate free energies for these complex ions.

Terrey[2] gave the following value for the cyanide couple in chloride solution:

$$2Cl^- + Pt(CN)_4^{--} = PtCl_2(CN)_4^{--} + 2e^-, \qquad E^° = -0.89.$$

From the solubility data, rough values may be obtained by the solubility products of many of the chloroplatinates, for example,

$$K_2PtCl_6 = 2K^+ + PtCl_6^{--}, \qquad K = 1 \times 10^{-5};$$
$$(NH_4)_2PtCl_6 = 2NH_4^+ + PtCl_6^{--}, \qquad K = 9 \times 10^{-6}.$$

The silver salt is but very slightly soluble.

The heats of formation of the dioxide, PtO_2, and the platinic acid, $H_2Pt(OH)_6$, have not been determined. Platinous hydroxide is readily oxidized in air to the dioxide or, in alkaline solution, to platinate.

$$4OH^- + Pt(OH)_2 = Pt(OH)_6^{--} + 2e^-, \qquad E_B^° = -0.1 \text{ to } -0.4.$$

Since platinum hydroxide does not decompose in acid into the metal and the dioxide, the potential of the $Pt(OH)_2$—PtO_2 couple must be less than that for the Pt—$Pt(OH)_2$ couple, that is, < -0.99. Lorenz and Spielmann found -1.01, and we shall write

$$Pt(OH)_2 = PtO_2 + 2H^+ + 2e^-, \qquad E^° = ca -1.1.$$

[1] A. A. Grunberg and G. P. Faermann, *Z. anorg. allgem. Chem.*, **193**, 193 (1930).
[2] H. Terrey, *J. Chem. Soc.*, 202 (1928).

The dioxide is soluble in concentrated sulfuric acid, apparently form-ing the ions $Pt(OH)_2^{++}$ or $Pt(OH)^{+++}$. No values can be given for their free energies.

The heat of formation of the disulfide, PtS_2, is given as -20.8 kcal. A value of 17.8 is probably fairly close for the entropy of the sulfide, so the free energy of formation is also -25.6 kcal. With this value we may calculate

$$H_2S(g) + PtS = PtS_2 + 2H^+ + 2e^-, \qquad E^\circ = -0.01;$$
$$S^{--} + PtS = PtS_2 + 2e^-, \qquad E_B^\circ = 0.64.$$

Since the free energy of the ion Pt^{+4} is not known, we cannot calculate the solubility product. The sulfide is soluble in excess sulfide to form the thioplatinate PtS_3^{--}, but no quantitative figures can be given.

Perplatinate. The anodic oxidation of a solution of platinate in potassium hydroxide results in the deposition of the potassium per-platinate, K_2PtO_4. The oxide, PtO_3, may be prepared from this com-pound. Since oxygen is not able to bring about this oxidation, it fol-lows that

$$2OH^- + Pt(OH)_6^{--} = PtO_4^- + 4H_2O + 2e^-, \qquad E_B^\circ < -0.4.$$

Summary of the group potentials. For comparison of the potentials of the three members of the group, the following summary is given:

Acid Solution

0	+2	+4	+6
	0.250	-1.78	< -1.8
Ni———————Ni^{++}————————NiO$_2$————————NiO$_4^{--}$			
	-0.987	-1.6	ca $-2.$
Pd———————Pd^{++}————————Pd^{+4}————————PdO$_3$			
ca -1.2			
Pt———————Pt^{++}			
	-0.98	ca -1.1	< -2.0
———————Pt(OH)$_2$————————PtO$_2$————————PtO$_3$			

Basic Solution

$$\overset{0.72}{Ni}\text{————}\overset{-0.49}{Ni(OH)_2}\text{————}\overset{<-0.4}{NiO_2}\text{————}NiO_4^{--}$$

$$\overset{-0.07}{Pd}\text{————}\overset{ca\ -0.73}{Pd(OH)_2}\text{————}Pd(OH)_4$$

$$\overset{-0.15}{Pt}\text{————}\overset{ca\ -0.2}{Pt(OH)_2}\text{————}\overset{<-0.4}{Pt(OH)_6^{--}}\text{————}PtO_4^{--}$$

CHAPTER 13

Cobalt, Rhodium, and Iridium

Each element of this group has nine electrons more than the preceding noble gas. In the monatomic gas atoms the lowest electronic states are s^1d^8 and s^2d^7, the two levels lying close together. The important oxidation states are $+2$, $+3$, $+4$, and $+6$; the lower states becoming less stable and the higher states more stable with increasing atomic weight, but compounds of the $+6$ state are always very powerful oxidizing agents.

Oxidation states. Like the neighboring elements of the first transition series, cobalt forms compounds of the $+2$ ion. Unlike nickel but like iron, compounds of the $+3$ ion exist in solution. The ion, Co^{+++}, is such a powerful oxidizing agent that it decomposes water, but many of its complex ions are more stable than the corresponding cobaltous complex ions. There are, indeed, hundreds of these complex cobaltic ions, and the description of their properties constitutes some of the most interesting pages in chemical literature. The co-ordination number of $+3$ cobalt is 6, and ions or molecules in the coordination position are held with remarkable firmness. For example, chloride in such a position is not precipitated by silver ion. However, quantitative data are to be found for only a few ions, and our discussion will be confined to these cases.

There is evidence for the $+4$ oxide, CoO_2, but the oxide is very unstable in water and the chemistry of this state is therefore limited.

Cobalt-cobaltous couples. Like the nickel electrode, it appears to be impossible to obtain a satisfactory reversible cobalt-cobaltous potential. The following $E°$ values have been calculated from the work of a number of investigators: 0.253, Neuman;[1] 0.298, Labendzinski;[2] 0.292, Coffetti and Foerster;[3] 0.283, Schildbach;[4] 0.246, Lamb

---

[1] B. Neumann, Z. physik. Chem., 14, 215 (1894).
[2] S. Labendzinski, Z. Elektrochem., 10, 77 (1904).
[3] G. Coffetti and F. Foerster, Ber., 38, 2936 (1905).
[4] R. Schildbach, Z. Elektrochem., 16, 967 (1910).

TABLE 47

THERMODYNAMIC DATA ON COBALT[1]

(Heat and free energy of formation in kcal. Entropy of substance in cal./deg.)

Formula	Description	State	$\Delta H°$	$\Delta F°$	$S°$
Co		g	*105.*	*94.*	*42.881*
Co	metal	c	*0.0*	*0.0*	*6.8*
Co^+		g	*287.27*		
Co^{++}		g	*687.7*		
Co^{++}		aq	(−14.2)	−12.8	(−27.)
Co^{+++}		aq		28.9	
CoO		c	−55.2	−49.0	10.5
Co_3O_4		c	−204.	−179.4	(35.8)
CoH		c	*−4.1*		
CoH_2		c	*−10.2*		
$Co(OH)_2$		c	−129.3	−109.0	(19.6)
$Co(OH)_3$		c	−174.6	−142.6	(20.)
CoF_2		c	−157.	−146.45	(20.)
CoF_3		c	−185.	−168.	(22.6)
$CoCl_2$		c	−75.8	−65.5	*25.4*
$CoBr_2$		c	−53.5	−50.3	(32.4)
CoI_2		c	−22.2	−23.3	(37.8)
CoS	α precipitated	c	−19.3	−19.8	(16.1)
Co_2S_3		c	*−47.(?)*		
$CoSO_4$		c	−205.5	−180.1	*27.1*
$Co(NO_3)_2$		c	−100.9	−55.1	(46.)
$Co(NH_3)_6^{++}$		aq		−57.7	
$Co(NH_3)_6^{+++}$		aq		−55.2	
$[CO(NH_3)_5H_2O]^{+++}$		aq	*−192.9*	*−106.2*	*73.4*
$[Co(NH_3)_5NO_3]^{++}$		aq	*−173.0*		
$[Co(NH_3)_4Cl_2]^+$	cis	aq	*−171.4*		
$[Co(NH_3)_4Cl_2]^{++}$	trans	aq	*−173.4*		
$[Co(NH_3)_5Cl]^{++}$		aq	*−162.1*	−86.2	96.1
$[Co(NH_3)_5Br]^{++}$		aq	*−152.7*		
Co_3C		c	*9.5*	*7.1*	29.5
$CoCO_3$		c		−155.57	

[1] Bureau of Standards values in *italics;* estimated values in parentheses.

and Larson;[1] and 0.278, Haring and Westfall.[2] In addition, Heymann and Jellinek[3] studied the equilibrium between cobalt and nickel and their ions and report $Ni^{++}/Co^{++} = 0.125$. This leads to a difference of 0.027 volt between the $E°$ values of the two elements; and, having chosen 0.250 for nickel, we shall take

$$Co = Co^{++} + 2e^-, \qquad E° = 0.277.$$

[1] A. B. Lamb and A. T. Larson, *J. Am. Chem. Soc.*, **42**, 2038 (1920).

[2] M. M. Haring and B. B. Westfall, *Trans. Electrochem. Soc.*, **65**, 235 (1934).

[3] T. Heymann and K. Jellinek, *Z. physik. Chem.*, **160**, 34 (1932).

This value is a fairly good average of the various e.m.f. measurements. Assuming 27 cal./deg. for the entropy of cobaltous ion and using this potential, we calculate roughly $-13,500$ cal. for the heat of formation of the ion. This is 3000 cal. less (negatively) than the Bureau of Standards value. All their heats which depend upon the ion will be corrected by this amount when used in later calculations. The free energy of Co^{++} in agreement with the $E°$ is $-12,800$ cal.

For the solubility product of the hydroxide we shall use

$$Co(OH)_2 = Co^{++} + 2OH^-, \qquad K = 2.5 \times 10^{-16},$$

which is the value given by Gayer and Garret.[1] These authors also report

$$Co(OH)_2(c) = H^+ + HCoO_2^-, \qquad K = 8 \times 10^{-20}.$$

The calculated free energy of $Co(OH)_2$ is 109.0 kcal., and the corresponding potential of the couple in alkaline solution is

$$2OH^- + Co = Co(OH)_2 + 2e^-, \qquad E_B° = 0.73.$$

The hydroxide is said to be appreciably soluble in $8M$ KOH, forming CoO_2^-.

Lamb and Larson also studied the cobaltous ammonia complex and found

$$Co(NH_3)_6^{++} = Co^{++} + 6NH_3(aq), \qquad K = 1.25 \times 10^{-5}.$$

Combining this with our value for the $Co-Co^{++}$ couple, we find

$$6NH_3(aq) + Co = Co(NH_3)_6^{++} + 2e^-, \qquad E° = 0.42.$$

Cobalt sulfide, like nickel sulfide, has at least two modifications, differing considerably in their solubilities. See, for example, the work of Mickwitz.[2] Taking the entropy of CoS as 16.1, the same as FeS, and using $-19,300$ cal. as the heat of formation, we compute for the free energy of formation $-19,800$ cal. Since this heat was obtained by precipitating the sulfide, this calculation should give the value for the more soluble α form. Hence,

$$CoS(\alpha) = Co^{++} + S^{--}, \qquad K = 5 \times 10^{-22};$$
$$S^{--} + Co = CoS(\alpha) + 2e^-, \qquad E_B° = 0.90.$$

[1] K. H. Gayer and A. B. Garret, J. Am. Chem. Soc., 71, 3923 (1950).
[2] A. Mickwitz, Z. anorg. allgem. Chem., 196, 116 (1931).

Mellor[1] quotes 1.9×10^{-27} for K and this would appear to apply to the less soluble β form. Hence,

$$CoS(\beta) = Co^{++} + S^{--}, \qquad K = 1.9 \times 10^{-27};$$
$$S^{--} + Co = CoS(\beta) + 2e^{-}, \qquad E_B^{\circ} = 1.07.$$

Kelley and Anderson[2] compute $-155,570$ cal. for the free energy of formation of cobalt carbonate. Combining with our value for the free energy of cobalt ion, we find

$$CoCO_3 = Co^{++} + CO_3^{--}, \qquad K = 8 \times 10^{-13};$$
$$CO_3^{--} + Co = CoCO_3 + 2e^{-}, \qquad E_B^{\circ} = 0.64.$$

Cobaltous-cobaltic couples. Noyes and Deahl[3] from potential measurement found in $3M$ HNO_3,

$$Co^{++} = Co^{+++} + e^{-}, \qquad E = -1.842.$$

It is difficult to calculate an accurate E° but we shall use as an approximate value for the free energy of Co^{+++}, 28.9 kcal. As this potential indicates, the free ion at high concentrations rapidly oxidizes water to oxygen.

Taking -174.6 kcal. for the heat of formation of cobaltic hydroxide and 20 as the estimated entropy of the hydroxide, the entropy of formation is found to be -103.2 cal./deg. and the free energy to be -142.6 kcal.

$$Co(OH)_3 = Co^{+++} + 3OH^{-}, \qquad K = 1 \times 10^{-43};$$
$$OH^{-} + Co(OH)_2 = Co(OH)_3 + e^{-}, \qquad E_B^{\circ} = -0.17.$$

Lamb and Larson also studied the dissociation of a number of the cobaltammines. The following constants, which have been calculated from concentrations and not activities, are of special interest:

$$Co(NH_3)_6^{+++} = Co^{+++} + 6NH_3(aq), \qquad K = 2.2 \times 10^{-34};$$
$$Co(NH_3)_5 \cdot H_2O^{+++} = Co^{+++} + 5NH_3(aq) + H_2O,$$
$$K = 1.6 \times 10^{-35}.$$

The aquopentamminecobalti ion is thus slightly more stable than the hexammine. The $Co(NH_3)_5NO_2^{+++}$ and $Co(NH_3)_4(NO_2)_2^{+++}$ ions

[1] J. W. Mellor, *Treatise Inorganic and Theoretical Chemistry*, 14, p. 753.
[2] K. K. Kelley and C. T. Anderson, *U. S. Bur. Mines Bull.*, 384 (1935).
[3] A. A. Noyes and T. J. Deahl, *J. Am. Chem. Soc.*, 59, 1337 (1937). See also A. B. Lamb and A. T. Larson, *J. Am. Chem. Soc.*, 42, 2024 (1920).

have stability constants of the same order of magnitude. For the free energies of formation we calculate $Co(NH_3)_6^{+++}$, -55.2 kcal. and $Co(NH_3)_5H_2O^{+++}$, -106.2 kcal.

$$Co(NH_3)_6^{++} = Co(NH_3)_6^{+++} + e^-, \qquad E^\circ = -0.1.$$

For the potential of the complex cyanide couple, Grube and Schächterle[1] report 0.814 at 2° C. However, Hume and Kolthoff[2] have concluded that Grube and Schächterle measured only the OH^-—H_2 couple and that the cyanide couple is not readily reversible. According to Hume and Kolthoff, the addition of cyanide to a $+2$ cobalt solution results in the formation of the aquapentacyano-cobaltIIate ion which may be oxidized to the aquapentacyano-cobaltIIIate or reduced to cobalt I complex. It seems that no values can be given for these potentials.

From the free energy of the ion,

$$Co(NH_3)_5Cl^{++} = Co^{+++} + 5NH_3 + Cl^-, \qquad K = 10^{-38}.$$

The free energy of the cobaltinitrite is not known. Galsimiskii and Pankova[3] report -157.9 kcal. as the heat of formation. This value would make the dissociation constant around 10^{-18}, which is certainly too large. The cobalto-complex decomposes to the cobalti-complex and nitric oxide. The solubility of the sodium potassium salt, $NaK_2Co(NO_2)_6 \cdot H_2O$, is given as 0.7 gram per liter; hence, the solubility product is about

$$NaK_2(CoNO_2)_6 \cdot H_2O = Na^+ + 2K^+ + Co(NO_2)_6^{---} + H_2O,$$
$$K = ca\ 2.2 \times 10^{-11}.$$

Cobalt dioxide. Powerful oxidizing agents in alkaline solution appear to form the dioxide CoO_2 or a solution of CoO_2 in Co_2O_3. From the curves obtained by Grube[4] for the anodic oxidation of cobalt in hydroxide,

$$OH^- + Co(OH)_3 = CoO_2 + 2H_2O + e^-,$$

the potential at 90° C. would appear to be about -0.7. However, this would lead to a value of -1.5 for the Co^{+++}—CoO_2 couple in acid which is certainly too high by at least 0.3 volts.

[1] G. Grube and P. Schächterle, Z. Elektrochem., **32**, 565 (1926).
[2] D. N. Hume and I. M. Kolthoff, J. Am. Chem. Soc., **71**, 867 (1949).
[3] K. B. Galsimiskii and L. L. Pankova, J. Gen. Chem. U.S.S.R., **19**, 617 (1949).
[4] G. Grube, Z. Elektrochem., **33**, 394 (1927).

RHODIUM

Oxidation states. Wohler and Muller[1] have definitely established the existence of Rh_2O and $RhCl$, and of RhO and $RhCl_2$. The most important oxidation state is the $+3$ and, like cobalt, the ion forms many complexes with ammonia, the halogens, cyanide, and nitrite. The dioxide, RhO_2, and trioxide, RhO_3, and their salts in alkaline solution have been prepared, but they are too powerful oxidizing agents to exist in acid.

The free energies of some rhodium compounds. Our only source of data regarding the energies of the various oxidation states are a few heats of formation. From these, we have calculated approximate values for the free energies by estimating the entropies. Using these free energies we may write

$$Rh + 3H_2O = Rh_2O_3(c) + 6H^+ + 6e^-, \qquad E^\circ = -0.87;$$
$$Rh + 6Cl^- = RhCl_6^{---} + 3e^-, \qquad E^\circ = -0.44.$$

The sesquioxide is obviously readily soluble in HCl with the formation

TABLE 48

THERMODYNAMIC DATA ON RHODIUM[1]

(Heat and free energy of formation in kcal. Entropy of substance in cal./deg.)

Formula	Description	State	ΔH°	ΔF°	S°
Rh		g	*138.*	*127.*	*44.39*
Rh		c	0.0	0.0	*7.6*
Rh^+		g	*306.*		
Rh^{+++}		aq		(55.3)	
RhO		c	*−21.7*	−16.0	(13.)
Rh_2O		c	*−22.7*	−19.1	(27.4)
Rh_2O_3		c	*−68.3*	−50.0	(26.5)
RhCl		c	*−16.*	−12.4	(22.2)
$RhCl_2$		c	*−36.*	−26.4	(29.)
$RhCl_3$		c	*−56.*	−39.6	(33.)
$RhCl_6^{---}$		aq	*−207.8*	−158.3	(50.)

[1] Bureau of Standards values in *italics;* estimated values in parentheses.

of the complex chloride. The oxide is probably fairly soluble in $HClO_4$, hence as a rough approximation

$$Rh = Rh^{+++} + 3e^-, \qquad E^\circ = ca -0.8.$$

[1] L. Wohler and S. Muller, *Z. anorg. allgem. Chem.*, **149**, 125 (1925).

This would correspond to a dissociation constant of $RhCl_6^{---}$ equal to about 10^{-19}, which would seem to be a reasonable value.

Dwyer, Nyholm, and Rodgers[1] report the oxidation of the $+3$ complex chloride to the $+4$ complex with ceric ion in dilute nitric acid This would seem to indicate the following approximate potential:

$$RhCl_6^{---} = RhCl_6^{--} + e^-, \qquad E^\circ = ca\ -1.2.$$

For the solid oxides Rh_2O and RhO, we calculate

$$2Rh + H_2O = Rh_2O(c) + 2H^+ + 2e^-, \qquad E^\circ = -0.8;$$
$$Rh_2O(c) + H_2O = 2RhO(c) + 2H^+ + 2e^-, \qquad E^\circ = -0.95.$$

These oxides are probably quite soluble in $1M\ H^+$, and the above equations have little chemical significance. In addition, we have no great confidence in the reliability of the thermal data. However, using these values as a guide, we estimate

$$Rh = Rh^+ + e^-, \qquad E^\circ = ca\ -0.6;$$
$$Rh^+ = Rh^{++} + e^-, \qquad E^\circ = ca\ -0.6.$$

No values can be given for the many complex ammines formed by Rh^{+++} or for the sulfide, Rh_2S_3, and the thioacid. The compound $K_3Rh(NO_2)_6$ has a very small solubility, but there are no quantitative data.

Rhodium in the $+4$ and $+6$ states. Chlorine in alkaline solution oxidizes Rh_2O_3 to RhO_2 and forms some RhO_4^{--} in solution. The dioxide has acid properties and forms salts when fused with $NaOH$. Both RhO_2 and RhO_4^{--} liberate chlorine when treated with hydrochloric acid.

$$2OH^- + Rh_2O_3 = 2RhO_2 + H_2O + 2e^-, \qquad E_B^\circ > -0.9;$$
$$4OH^- + RhO_2 = RhO_4^{--} + 2H_2O + 2e^-, \qquad E_B^\circ > -0.9;$$
$$2H_2O + RhCl_6^{---} = RhO_2 + 4H^+ + 6Cl^- + e^-, \qquad E^\circ < -1.4;$$
$$4H_2O + RhCl_6^{---} = RhO_4^{--} + 8H^+ + 6Cl^- + 3e^-, \qquad E^\circ < -1.4.$$

Grube and Gu[2] have studied the oxidation of $+3$ rhodium in nitric and perchloric acid solutions. Although the form of the $+4$ ion is not known, we shall give their potentials as

$$H_2O + Rh^{+++} = RhO^{++} + 2H^+ + e^-, \qquad E^\circ = -1.40;$$
$$3H_2O + RhO^{++} = RhO_4^{--} + 6H^+ + 2e^-, \qquad E^\circ = -1.46.$$

[1] F. P. Dwyer, R. S. Nyholm, and M. Rodgers, *J. Proc. Roy. Soc. N.S. Wales*, **81**, 267 (1947).
[2] G. Grube and B. Gu, *Z. Elektrochem.*, **43**, 397 (1937).

IRIDIUM

Oxidation states.   The $+1$ and $+2$ chlorides have been prepared by the decomposition of $IrCl_3$ at high temperatures. The $+3$ and $+4$ states exist in solution in the form of hundreds of complex ions of the same general nature as the cobalt and rhodium complex ions with the exception that the $+4$ compounds of iridium are much more stable

TABLE 49

THERMODYNAMIC DATA ON IRIDIUM[1]

(Heat and free energy of formation in kcal. Entropy of substance in cal./deg.)

Formula	Description	State	$\Delta H°$	$\Delta F°$	$S°$
Ir		g	*165.*	*154.*	*46.25*
Ir		c	0.0	0.0	*8.7*
Ir^+		g	*378.*		
Ir^{+++}		aq		(69.2)	
IrO_2		c	*−40.1*	−28.0	(17.2)
Ir_2O_3		c		(−42.0)	
IrF_6		c	*−130.*		
IrCl		c	*−22.3*	−19.8	(26.9)
$IrCl_2$		c	*−42.8*	−33.7	(31.4)
$IrCl_3$		c	*−61.5*	−45.6	(35.9)
$IrCl_6^{--}$		aq	*−155.0*	−111.2	(53.)
$IrCl_6^{---}$		aq	−186.4	−134.7	(43.)
IrS_2		c	*−30.0*	−30.4	(25.2)
Ir_2S_3		c	*−51.*	−49.8	34.3

[1] Bureau of Standards values in *italics;* estimated values in parentheses.

than are those of the lighter elements of the group. The $+6$ oxide and its salts in alkaline solution are known, but they cannot exist in acid solution.

Iridium potentials in HCl.   From the heat of formation of $IrCl_6^{--}$, we calculate -111.2 kcal. for the free energy.

$$Ir + 6Cl^- = IrCl_6^{--} + 4e^-, \qquad E° = -0.835.$$

Dwyer, McKenzie, and Nyholm[1] have reported

$$IrCl_6^{---} = IrCl_6^{--} + e^-, \qquad E° = -1.017;$$
$$IrBr_6^{---} = IrBr_6^{--} + e^-, \qquad E° = -0.99.$$

[1] F. P. Dwyer, H. A. McKenzie, and R. S. Nyholm, *J. Proc. Roy. Soc. N.S. Wales,* **81,** 216 (1947).

The heat of formation of $IrCl_6^{--}$, -249.8 kcal., given by the Bureau of Standards, is an obvious misprint.

For the $+1$ and $+2$ solid chlorides,

$$3IrCl = IrCl_3 + 2Ir, \qquad \Delta F^\circ = 8.1 \text{ kcal.};$$
$$3IrCl_2 = 2IrCl_3 + Ir, \qquad \Delta F^\circ = 7.8 \text{ kcal.}$$

These values indicate that the $+1$ and $+2$ chlorides in the solid state are stable with respect to the decomposition. However, in contact with water, the greater solubility and slight dissociation of the $+3$ chloride will doubtless cause the reactions to occur.

Iridium oxides and their ions. The potential of the Ir—IrO_2 couple is obtained from the free energy of the dioxide

$$Ir + 2H_2O = IrO_2 + 4H^+ + 4e^-, \qquad E^\circ = -0.93;$$
$$Ir + 4OH^- = IrO_2 + 2H_2O + 4e^-, \qquad E_B^\circ = -0.1.$$

There are no data for the sesquioxide Ir_2O_3. However, upon gentle heating, it decomposes.

$$2Ir_2O_3 = 2IrO_2 + Ir.$$

ΔF° for the reaction must be small and the free energy of Ir_2O_3 close to -42.0 kcal.

$$2Ir + 6OH^- = Ir_2O_3 + 3H_2O + 6e^-, \qquad E_B^\circ = -0.1.$$

The free energy of solution of the Ir_2O_3 in H^+ is unknown. However, the dissociation constant of $IrCl_6^{--}$ can hardly be less than 10^{-20}. Such a value would correspond to a ΔF° of formation of Ir^{+++} of 80.0 kcal.

$$Ir = Ir^{+++} + 3e^-, \qquad E^\circ = ca -1.15.$$

The uncomplexed Ir^{+++} by these calculations is unstable with respect to its disproportionation.

When the dioxide is fused with potassium nitrate and potassium hydroxide, the salt K_2IrO_4 is formed.

$$IrO_2 + 4OH^- = IrO_4^{--} + 2H_2O + 2e^-, \qquad E_B^\circ > -0.4.$$

Summary of group potentials. The following diagrams summarize the potentials of the group.

Acid Solution

	+2	+3	+4	+6

0.277
Co——————————Co++————————Co+++——————CoO₂
-1.82 < -1.8

(-0.6) (-0.6) (-1.2) (-1.4) (-1.5)
Rh————Rh+————Rh++ ————Rh+++——————RhO++————RhO₄⁻⁻
| | (-0.8) |
| -0.44 |
| ca -1.2
|_____RhCl₆⁻⁻⁻————— RhCl₆⁻⁻

< -1.1 > -1.1
┌————————Ir++————————┐
| ~ (-1.15) | (-0.7) > -1.3
Ir————————————————Ir+++————————IrO₂————————IrO₄⁻⁻
| | -0.93
| |_____|
| |
| | -0.77 -1.017
| |_____IrCl₆⁻⁻⁻ ————————IrCl₆⁻⁻
| -0.99
|_____IrBr₆⁻⁻⁻⁻ ——IrBr₆⁻⁻⁻

Basic Solution.

0.72 -0.14 $-0.7(?)$
Co————————————Co(OH)₂————————Co(OH)₃————————CoO₂

-0.04 > -0.9 > -0.9
Rh ————————————————————Rh₂O₃ ————————RhO₂————————RhO₄⁻⁻

-0.1 -0.1 > -0.4
Ir ————————————————————Ir₂O₃ ————————IrO₂————————IrO₄⁻⁻

CHAPTER 14

Iron, Ruthenium, and Osmium

The elements of this group have eight electrons more than the preceding noble gas, and these electrons in the gas atoms have the configuration s^2d^6, although the s^1d^7 state also lies very close. The important oxidation numbers are $+2$, $+3$, $+4$, $+6$, and $+8$. The latter state is shown in ruthenium and osmium in the tetroxides, RuO_4 and OsO_4, but the maximum oxidation number of iron is $+6$.

Oxidation states. The ions Fe^{++}, ferrous, and Fe^{+++}, ferric, exist in acid solution. These ions form the familiar series of ferrous and ferric salts and, in alkaline solution, the corresponding hydroxides. The perferrite ion, FeO_3^{--}, and the ferrate ion, FeO_4^{--}, of the $+4$ and $+6$ states, are known in alkaline solutions, but they rapidly evolve oxygen when acidified. There is evidence for low concentrations of the ferryl ion, FeO^{++}, in ferric solutions. Magnetite, Fe_3O_4, or $FeO \cdot Fe_2O_3$, is important in the high-temperature chemistry of iron but is not involved in equilibria in water solutions. Claims are made for the $+1$ state in the compound $(NO)_2FeSK$, but it is obviously difficult to say how the electrons are divided between the nitrogen, iron, and sulfur.

Iron-ferrous couples. Iron electrodes are readily polarized and, in common with other hard metals, usually show surface strains which are capable of producing very large variations in potential measurements with different samples of the metal. Richards and Behr[1] were the first to get reproducible results using finely divided iron. Randall and Frandsen[2] gave for the free energy of Fe^{++}, $-20,310$ cal.

$$Fe = Fe^{++} + 2e^-, \qquad E° = 0.440.$$

The Bureau of Standards value for the free energy of Fe^{++} is in agreement.

---

[1] T. W. Richards and G. E. Behr, Z. physik. Chem., **58**, 301 (1907).
[2] M. Randall and M. Frandsen, J. Am. Chem. Soc., **54**, 40, 47 (1932).

TABLE 50
THERMODYNAMIC DATA ON IRON[1]

(Heat and free energy of formation in kcal. Entropy of substance in cal./deg.)

Formula	Description	State	$\Delta H°$	$\Delta F°$	$S°$
Fe		g	*96.68*	*85.76*	*43.11*
Fe		c	0.0	0.0	*6.49*
Fe+		g	*277.9*		
Fe++		g	*650.7*		
Fe++		aq	*−21.0*	*−20.30*	*−27.1*
Fe+++		g	*1354.*		
Fe+++		aq	*−11.4*	*−2.53*	*−70.1*
Fe₁.₉₅°	wustite	c	*−63.7*	*−58.4*	*12.9*
Fe₂O₃	hematite	c	*−196.5*	*−177.1*	*21.5*
Fe₃O₄	magnetite	c	*−267.9*	*−242.4*	*35.0*
Fe(OH)++		aq	*−67.4*	*−55.91*	*−23.2*
Fe(OH)₂		c	*−135.8*	*−115.57*	*19.*
Fe(OH)₂+		aq		*−106.2*	
Fe(OH)₃		c	*−197.0*	*−166.0*	*(23.)*
FeCl++		aq	*−42.9*	*−35.9*	*−22.*
FeCl₂		c	*−81.5*	*−72.2*	*28.6*
FeCl₂		aq	*−101.0*		
FeCl₃		c	*−96.8*	*−80.4*	*(31.1)*
FeCl₃		aq	*−127.9*		
FeBr++		aq	*−34.2*	*−27.9*	*−28.(?)*
FeBr₂		c	*−60.02*	*−56.8*	*(32.2)*
FeBr₂		aq	*−79.1*		
FeI₂		c	*−29.98*	*−30.9*	*(37.6)*
FeI₂		aq	*−49.03*		
FeS	α	c	*−22.72*	*−23.32*	*16.1*
FeS	β	c	*−21.35*		
FeS₂	pyrites	c	*−42.52*	*−39.84*	*12.7*
Fe₂S₃		c		*−59.*	
FeSO₄		c	*−220.5*	*−198.3*	*(27.6)*
FeSO₄·7H₂O		c	*−718.7*	*−597.*	*(93.4)*
Fe₂N		c	*−0.9*	*2.6*	*24.2*
Fe₄N		c	*−2.55*	*0.89*	*37.3*
FeNO++		aq	*−9.7*	*1.5*	*−10.6*
FePO₄		c	*−299.6*	*−272.*	*(22.4)*
Fe₃C	cementite	c	*5.0*	*3.5*	*25.7*
FeCO₃	siderite	c	*−178.0*	*−161.06*	*22.2*
Fe(CO)₅		liq	*−187.8*		
Fe(CO)₄Br₂		c	*−195.7*		
Fe-(CN)₆‾‾‾‾		aq	*126.7*	170.4	*(68.) (?)*
FeCO-(CN)₅‾‾‾		aq	*47.2*		
Fe₄-(Fe(CN)₆)₃		c	*338.6*		
FeSe	precipitated	c	*−13.9*	−13.9	*(16.5)*

[1] Bureau of Standards values in *italics;* estimated values in parentheses.

TABLE 50—(*Continued*)

THERMODYNAMIC DATA ON IRON[1]

Formula	Description	State	$\Delta H°$	$\Delta F°$	$S°$
$H_4Fe(CN)_6$		c	*127.8*		
$H_4Fe(CN)_6$		aq	*127.4*		
$FeSiO_3$		c	*−276.*	257.	(20.9)
Fe_2SiO_4		c	*−343.7*	*−319.8*	*35.4*
$Zn_2Fe(CN)_6$		c	*49.4*		
$Fe(CrO_2)_2$		c	*−314.9*	*−317.7*	*34.9*
$FeMoO_4$		c	*−257.5*	−234.8	(33.4)
$FeWO_4$		c	*−274.1*	−250.4	(35.4)

[1] Bureau of Standards values in *italics;* estimated values in parentheses.

From the free energy of ferrous hydroxide, −115.57 kcal., we write

$$Fe + 2OH^- = Fe(OH)_2 + 2e^-, \qquad E_B° = 0.877;$$
$$Fe(OH)_2 = Fe^{++} + 2OH^-, \qquad K = 1.8 \times 10^{-15}.$$

The potential for the oxidation of iron by hydrogen ion is 0.440 volt while the potential for the oxidation by water in alkaline solution is only 0.05 volt. This is doubtless the reason for the more rapid rusting of iron in an acid environment, as the first step of the process appears to involve the reduction of hydrogen. The second step, the formation of ferric oxide, arises from the action of oxygen (see Fe^{++}—Fe^{+++} couple).

Reference should be made to Darken and Gurry[1] for thermodynamic data on FeO and other iron oxides.

The free-energy data permit the following calculations:

$$FeCO_3 = Fe^{++} + CO_3^{--}, \qquad K = 2.11 \times 10^{-11};$$
$$Fe + CO_3^{--} = FeCO_3 + 2e^-, \qquad E° = 0.756;$$
$$FeS(\alpha) = Fe^{++} + S^{--}, \qquad K = 4 \times 10^{-19};$$
$$Fe + S^{--} = FeS(\alpha) + 2e^-, \qquad E° = 0.97;$$
$$FeSe = Fe^{++} + Se^{--}, \qquad K = 10^{-26}.$$

The data on the carbonate are in agreement with the work of Kelley and Anderson.[2] Bruner and Zawadzki[3] gave 3.7×10^{-19} for the solubility product of ferrous sulfide.

---

[1] L. S. Darken and R. W. Gurry, *J. Am. Chem. Soc.*, **68**, 798(1946).
[2] K. K. Kelley and C. T. Anderson, *U. S. Bur. Mines Bull.*, 384 (1935).
[3] L. Bruner and J. Zawadzki, *Z. anorg. Chem.*, **67**, 454 (1910).

Several values have been reported for the $Fe—Fe(CN)_6^{---}$ couple, but the electrode does not appear to be reproducible. From the heat of formation of the ion and a very approximate value for its entropy, we calculate

$$Fe + 6CN^- = Fe(CN)_6^{-4} + 2e^-, \qquad E° = \text{ca } 1.5;$$

$$Fe(CN)_6^{-4} = Fe^{++} + 6CN^-, \qquad K = \text{ca } 10^{-35}.$$

The oxalate complex ion, $Fe(C_2O_4)_2^{--}$, has been studied by Schafer[1] but it is difficult to give a value for its dissociation constant.

Manchot and Haunschild[2] measured the partial pressure of nitric oxide in equilibrium with $FeNO^{++}$ and gave for equal concentration of the ions

$$FeNO^{++} = Fe^{++} + NO, \qquad K = 1150 \text{ mm.}$$

The corresponding free energy of $FeNO^{++}$, is 1.5 kcal.

Ferrous-ferric couples. The potential of the ferrous-ferric couple has been measured in many cells, but accurate corrections for the hydrolysis of ferric ion and for the activities have not been made in the earlier work. Bray and Hershey[3] reviewed the literature and calculated -0.772 for the $E°$. Schumb, Sherrill, and Sweetser[4] report -0.770. We shall take

$$Fe^{++} = Fe^{+++} + e^-, \qquad E° = -0.771.$$

The free energy of ferric ion then is -2530 cal. We compute from this and the free energy of ferrous ion

$$Fe = Fe^{+++} + 3e^-, \qquad E° = 0.036.$$

This potential has little significance since the mechanism always functions through the ferrous state. For the reduction of ferric ion by iron,

$$2Fe^{+++} + Fe = 3Fe^{++}, \qquad \Delta F° = -55,860 \text{ cal.},$$
$$K = 1 \times 10^{41},$$

and the concentration of ferric ion at equilibrium with iron and $1M$ Fe^{++} is very small.

---

[1] C. Schafer, Z. physik. Chem., **72**, 315 (1910).

[2] W. Manchot and H. Haunschild, Z. anorg. allgem. Chem., **40**, 22 (1924).

[3] W. C. Bray and A. V. Hershey, J. Am. Chem. Soc., **56**, 1889 (1934).

[4] W. C. Schumb, M. S. Sherrill, and S. B. Sweetser, J. Am. Chem. Soc., **59**, 2360 (1937).

From our value of the free energy of ferric hydroxide we calculate

$$Fe(OH)_3 = Fe^{+++} + 3OH^-, \qquad K = 6 \times 10^{-38}.$$

This value is in agreement with the calculation of Elder[1] and also checks approximately the work of Jellinek and Gordon[2] who reported 1×10^{-38}.

For the potential of the ferrous-ferric couple in alkaline solution, we then find,

$$OH^- + Fe(OH)_2 = Fe(OH)_3 + e^-, \qquad E_B^\circ = 0.56.$$

Ferrous hydroxide is thus a very much better reducing agent than ferrous ion. This fact is important in connection with the oxidation of iron by oxygen. From the equation

$$2Fe^{++} + \tfrac{1}{2}O_2 + 2H^+ = 2Fe^{+++} + H_2O,$$

it would appear that high hydrogen ion would favor the oxidation of ferrous ion as the energy of the reaction obviously increases. Experimentally the rate of the reaction decreases and hydrogen ion tends to stabilize ferrous solutions against oxidation. It is generally assumed that this slow rate in acid arises from the initial reduction of the O_2 molecule to hydrogen peroxide, which has a potential of only -0.68 volt, and that the equilibrium concentration of hydrogen peroxide does not rapidly oxidize ferrous ion. At low acid the hydrolysis of ferric ion and the slight solubility of ferric hydroxide reduces the potential of the Fe^{++}—Fe^{+++} couple sufficiently so that the reaction with oxygen proceeds rapidly. This explanation is doubtless approximately correct although the actual mechanism may be somewhat more complicated.

From the free energies which are in approximate agreement with the work of Rabinowitch and Stockmayer,[3]

$$FeCl^{++} + Cl^- = FeCl_2^+, \qquad\qquad K = 4.5;$$

$$Fe^{+++} + Cl^- = FeCl^{++}, \qquad\qquad K = 33;$$

$$FeCl_2^+ + Cl^- = FeCl_3(aq), \qquad\quad K = 0.1;$$

$$Fe^{+++} + Br^- = FeBr^{++}, \qquad\qquad K = 4;$$

$$Fe^{+++} + H_2O = Fe(OH)^{++} + H^+, \qquad K = 4.0 \times 10^{-3}.$$

[1] L. W. Elder, *Trans. Am. Electrochem. Soc.*, **57**, 383 (1930).

[2] K. Jellinek and H. Gordon, *Z. physik. Chem.*, **112**, 236 (1924).

[3] E. Rabinowitch and W. H. Stockmayer, *J. Am. Chem. Soc.*, **64**, 335 (1942).

For the last reaction Arden[1] gave $K = 1.2 \times 10^{-3}$. He also gave 4.2×10^{-4} for the second hydrolysis constant.

Ferric hydroxide is quite soluble in concentrated alkali with the formation of ferrite ion, FeO_2^-. In 40 per cent sodium hydroxide, ferrous hydroxide forms some hypoferrite, FeO_2^{--}. Grube and Gmelin[2] report in such a solution at 80° C.,

$$FeO_2^{--} = FeO_2^- + e^-, \qquad E = 0.68.$$

This value would appear to be consistent with the potential of $Fe(OH)_2$—$Fe(OH)_3$ couple.

The ferrocyanide-ferricyanide couple reaches a rapid reversible equilibrium, and many concordant values have been obtained for cells employing this couple in the form of the potassium salts. However, the potential is a function of the potassium ion concentration and the correction to give an accurate $E°$ value becomes very large. With equal concentrations of the two negative ions, the observed potential is around -0.48. Kolthoff and Tomsicek[3] have made a calculation of the $E°$ value:

$$Fe(CN)_6^{----} = Fe(CN)_6^{---} + e^-, \qquad E° = -0.36.$$

From this potential and our approximate K for ferrocyanide, we find

$$Fe(CN)_6^{---} = Fe^{+++} + 6CN^-, \qquad K = \text{ca } 10^{-42}.$$

This value seems reasonable in view of the stability of ferricyanide in alkaline solutions with respect to the formation of ferric hydroxide.

Under conditions in which the above couple had a potential of -0.480, Davidson[4] gave for the potentials of the following couples

$$Fe(CN)_5(NH_3)^{---} = Fe(CN)_5(NH_3)^{--} + e^-, \qquad E = -0.374;$$
$$Fe(CN)_5(H_2O)^{---} = Fe(CN)_5(H_2O)^{--} + e^-, \qquad E = -0.491;$$
$$Fe(CN)_5(NO_2)^{---} = Fe(CN)_5(NO_2)^{--} + e^-, \qquad E = -0.516$$

Schaper[5] reported,

$$C_2O_4^- + Fe(C_2O_4)_2^{--} = Fe(C_2O_4)_3^{---} + e^-, \qquad E° = -0.02.$$

[1] T. V. Arden, *J. Chem. Soc.*, 350 (1951).
[2] G. Grube and H. Gmelin, *Z. Elektrochem.*, **26**, 466 (1920).
[3] I. M. Kolthoff and W. J. Tomsicek, *J. Phys. Chem* **39**, 945 (1935).
[4] D. Davidson, *J. Am. Chem. Soc.*, **50**, 2622 (1928).
[5] C. Schaper, *Z. physik. Chem.*, **72**, 315 (1910).

From this work we gave as an approximate value

$$Fe(C_2O_4)_3^{---} = Fe^{+++} + 3C_2O_4^{--}, \qquad K = ca\ 10^{-20}.$$

Babko and Kleiner[1] have reported the first five associations for ferric ion and fluoride

$$FeF_5^{--} = Fe^{+++} + 5F^-, \qquad K = 5 \times 10^{-16}.$$

The constant for FeF_6^{---} has approximately the same value.

For the deep red thiocyanate ferric complex, Rabinowitch and Stockmayer,[2] in their excellent review, list

$$FeCNS^{++} = Fe^{+++} + CNS^-, \qquad K = 1.04 \times 10^{-3}.$$

Golzschmidt[3] reported

$$Fe(CNS)_3 = Fe^{+++} + CNS^-, \qquad K = 26 \times 10^{-6};$$
$$Fe(CNS)_6^{-3} = Fe^{+++} + 6CNS^-, \qquad K = 8.0 \times 10^{-10}.$$

Ferrous and ferric ions form complexes with orthophenanthroline. Hume and Kolthoff[4] found

$$Fe(C_{12}H_8N_2)_3^{++} = Fe(C_{12}H_8N_2)_3^{+++} + e^- \qquad E^\circ = -1.06.$$

This couple has been widely used as an indicator in dichromate and ceric sulfate titrations because of the brilliant color change from the red ferrous to the blue ferric complex. For the nitro-derivative of phenanthroline, the E° is -1.25.

Jellinek and Gordon[5] gave,

$$Fe_2S_3 = 2Fe^{+++} + 3S^{--}, \qquad K = 10^{-88}.$$

This would make the free energy of formation of ferric sulfide about $-59{,}000$ cal. and leads to the following potential:

$$S^{--} + 2FeS = Fe_2S_3 + 2e^-, \qquad E_B^\circ = 0.7.$$

From this value it appears that ferric sulfide should not oxidize sulfide to sulfur in alkaline solution, but the two potentials are quite close.

The same authors studied the complex ferric tartrate and report for the reaction

$$Fe_2(C_4H_4O_6)_3(aq) = 2Fe^{+++} + 3C_4H_4O_6^{--}$$

[1] A. K. Babko and F. Kleiner, *J. Gen. Chem.* (*U.S.S.R.*), **17**, 59 (1947).
[2] E. Rabinowitch and W. H. Stockmayer, *J. Am. Chem. Soc.*, **64**, 335 (1942).
[3] B. A. Golzschmidt, *Izvest. Ivanovo-Voznesensk.*, **7**, 51 (1928).
[4] D. N. Hume and I. M. Kolthoff, *J. Am. Chem. Soc.*, **65**, 1895 (1943).
[5] K. Jellinek and H. Gordon, *Z. physik. Chem.*, **112**, 241 (1924).

that (Fe^{+++}) was 10^{-39} in a solution in which tartrate was 1, ferric tartrate was 10^{-3} and hydrogen ion 10^{-14}.

Sandell and Spindler[1] studied the green complex ion of ferric and 8-hydroxyquinoline.

$$Fe(H-Q)^{+++} = Fe^{+++} + H-Q, \qquad K = 3 \times 10^{-15}.$$

From our value for the free energy of ferric phosphate we calculate

$$FePO_4 = Fe^{+++} + PO_4^{---}, \qquad K = 1.5 \times 10^{-18}.$$

Iron in the $+4$ and $+6$ states.   In highly alkaline solutions an iron anode may be oxidized to ferrate, FeO_4^{--}. This ion resembles permanganate in color and in acid solution evolves oxygen very rapidly. Grube and Gmelin[2] studied the FeO_2^{-}—FeO_4^{--} couple at $80°$ in 40 per cent sodium hydroxide and gave a value $E = -0.55$. Under these conditions they found no formation of perferrite, FeO_3^{--}. Hypochlorite in concentrated alkaline solution oxidizes iron to ferrate; hence we shall write

$$4OH^- + FeO_2^- = FeO_4^{--} + 2H_2O + 3e^-, \qquad E_B^\circ < -0.9;$$
$$4H_2O + Fe^{+++} = FeO_4^{--} + 8H^+ + 3e^-, \qquad E_B^\circ < -1.9.$$

Under certain limited conditions it is probably possible to form perferrite, and if the free ion is unstable with respect to the decomposition into the $+3$ and $+6$ states, the FeO_2^-—FeO_3^{--} couple must have a lower potential than the FeO_2^-—FeO_4^{--} couple. Slightly soluble perferrites have been prepared.

Bray and Gorin[3] have discussed the evidence regarding the formation of ferryl ion, FeO^{++}, in ferric solutions by the reaction

$$2Fe^{+++} + H_2O = Fe^{++} + FeO^{++} + 2H^+.$$

A study of the kinetics of a number of ferric reactions at low acid indicates the existence of this equilibrium, but no quantitative data can be given.

Summary of iron potentials.   The following diagrams are given as a summary of the iron potentials.

---

[1] E. B. Sandell and D. C. Spindler, *J. Am. Chem. Soc.*, **71**, 3806 (1949).
[2] G. Grube and H. Gmelin, *Z. Elektrochem.*, **26**, 466 (1920).
[3] W. C. Bray and M. H. Gorin, *J. Am. Chem. Soc.*, **54**, 2124 (1932).

Acid Solution

$$
\begin{array}{cccc}
0.440 & -0.771 & < -1.9 \\
\text{Fe}\underline{\hspace{1.5cm}}\text{Fe}^{++}\underline{\hspace{1.5cm}}\text{Fe}^{+++}\underline{\hspace{1.5cm}}\text{FeO}_4^- \\
\text{ca } 1.5 & -0.36 \\
\underline{\hspace{1cm}}\text{Fe(CN)}_6^{-4}\underline{\hspace{1cm}}\text{Fe(CN)}_6^{-3}
\end{array}
$$

Basic Solution

$$
\begin{array}{cccc}
0.887 & 0.56 & < -0.9 \\
\text{Fe}\underline{\hspace{1.5cm}}\text{Fe(OH)}_2\underline{\hspace{1.5cm}}\text{Fe(OH)}_3\underline{\hspace{1.5cm}}\text{FeO}_4^-
\end{array}
$$

RUTHENIUM

Oxidation states. The controversy over the $+1$ state seems definitely to be settled by the work of Crowell and Yost.[1] The blue solution formed by reduction of the $+3$ complex chloride is Ru^{++} and the lower state does not exist. In acid solutions the important oxidation states are the $+3$ and $+4$ which exist in the form of many complex ions. Oxidation of $+4$ ruthenium by powerful oxidizing agents forms the volatile $+8$ oxide, RuO_4, with unstable $+6$ and $+7$ compounds as intermediates. These latter compounds in the form of RuO_4^- and RuO_4^- are much more stable in alkaline solution. In addition to the tetroxide, the oxides, Ru_2O_3 and RuO_2, or their hydroxides, may be precipitated from solution.

Ruthenium potentials. The only quantitative data we have for ruthenium are the heats of formation of the trichloride, $-63,000$ cal., and of the dioxide, $-52,500$ cal. Estimating the entropy of the former as 33.5 and the latter as 16.5, the free energies of formation are: $RuCl_3$, $-49,200$ cal.; and RuO_2, -40.7 kcal. Hence, we compute

$$3Cl^- + Ru = RuCl_3(c) + 3e^-, \qquad E^\circ = -0.68;$$
$$2H_2O + Ru = RuO_2(c) + 4H^+ + 4e^-, \qquad E^\circ = -0.79;$$
$$4OH^- + Ru = RuO_2(c) + 2H_2O + 4e^-, \qquad E_B^\circ = 0.04.$$

These couples do not have much chemical significance, since the solids cannot exist in equilibrium with one-molal solutions of the ions. However, they do aid in the estimation of the couples which we wish to write. Thus, in hydrochloric acid, $RuCl_3$ forms $RuCl_5^-$, and RuO_2 forms $RuCl_5OH^{--}$. We do not know the free energies of these reac-

[1] W. R. Crowell and D. M. Yost, *J. Am. Chem. Soc.*, **50**, 374 (1928).

TABLE 51

THERMODYNAMIC DATA ON RUTHENIUM[1]

(Heat and free energy of formation in kcal. Entropy of substance in cal./deg.)

Formula	Description	State	$\Delta H°$	$\Delta F°$	$S°$
Ru		g	*160.*	*149.*	*44.57*
Ru		c	*0.0*	*0.0*	*6.9*
RuO_2		c	*−52.5*	−40.7	(16.5)
$RuCl_3$		c	*−63.*	−46.9	(33.5)
RuO_4		g		(−33.)	
$RuCl_5^{--}$		aq		(−129.)	
$RuCl_5OH^{--}$		aq		(−158.)	
RuS_2		c	*−48.1*	−46.7	(17.5)

[1] Bureau of Standards values in *italics;* estimated values in parentheses.

tions, but in neither case does the complex ion appear to be unusually stable. As approximate values, the following will be used:

$$5Cl^- + Ru = RuCl_5^{--} + 3e^-, \qquad\qquad E° = \text{ca } -0.4;$$
$$5Cl^- + H_2O + Ru = RuCl_5OH^{--} + H^+ + 4e^-, \qquad E° = \text{ca } -0.6.$$

In choosing these potentials the following facts were considered: the $RuCl_5^{--}$—$RuCl_5OH^{--}$ potential must be a little more positive than the Cl^-—Cl_2 potential, that is, about -1.2 or -1.3, since chloride ion will partially reduce the $+4$ complex; and the Ru—$RuCl_5^{--}$ potential must be greater than -0.55 as it is not reduced by iodide. It is, however, reduced by titanous.

Hot nitric acid will not oxidize the $+4$ complex to the tetroxide, but hot perchloric acid does; hence for the $RuCl_5OH^{--}$—RuO_4 potential, -1.5 will be used. On these values the following has been constructed:

```
0        +2        +3            +4            +6          +7          +8
(−0.45)  (−0.3)      (−1.3)       (−1.75)      (−1.6)      (−0.9)
Ru——Ru⁺⁺——RuCl₅⁻⁻——RuCl₅OH⁻⁻——RuO₄⁼——RuO₄⁻——RuO₄
|  (−0.4)  |                    |          (−1.25)
|      (−0.6)                   |      (−1.5)
```

The ruthenate ion, RuO_4^{--}, is stable in $1M$ OH^-, even if the solution is boiled, but if the pH is lowered to about 12, the following disproportionation occurs:

$$3RuO_4^{--} + 2H_2O = 2\ RuO_4^- + RuO_2 + 4OH^-.$$

The perruthenate ion exists in this equilibrium at pH12, but at higher acid it decomposes to RuO_2 and RuO_4, probably through the intermediate step.

$$2RuO_4^- = RuO_4^{--} + RuO_4.$$

The RuO_4 (or $HRuO_5$) appears to oxidize water slowly.

Connick and Hurley[1] found by direct cell measurement

$$RuO_4^{--} = RuO_4^- + e^-, \qquad E_B^\circ = -0.6.$$

The following potential diagram has been constructed to conform with the chemical behavior.

Values in these potential schemes are to be considered as purely tentative, but the author believes that they permit a coherent interpretation of the chemistry of ruthenium in hydrochloric acid and alkaline solutions. A similar scheme might be presented for hydrobromic acid, but the principal difference would be a somewhat greater stability of the complex bromides.

The tetraoxide forms perperruthenic acid, but the decomposition pressure of the oxide is high. Silverman and Levy[2] reported

$$H_2RuO_5 = H^+ + HRuO_5^-, \qquad K = 1.3 \times 10^{-12}.$$

OSMIUM

Oxidation states.   In hydrochloric acid, osmium may be present as chlorosmite, $OsCl_6^{---}$, chlorosmate, $OsCl_6^{--}$, and perperosmic acid, H_2OsO_5. These compounds may be classified as belonging to the +3, +4, and +8 states. The +2 ion is unstable in acid and only a few slightly soluble compounds of this state, for example, OsI_2, are known. Complex ions of the +3 and +4 states are formed by Br^-, NO_2^-, $C_2O_4^{--}$, NO, NH_3, and many other groups, but potentials will be considered

---

[1] R. E. Connick and C. R. Hurley, private communication.

[2] M. D. Silverman and H. A. Levy, Am. Chem. Soc. Meeting, Chicago, Sept. 1950.

only in the case of the chlorides. Crowell and Kirschman[1] have presented evidence for the existence, in acid, of unstable halogen derivatives of perosmic acid, $HOsO_4(+7)$, but it is not certain that they were not dealing with osmyl, OsO_2^{++}, derivatives. In alkaline solution the oxides Os_2O_3 and OsO_2 or their hydrates are precipitated from compounds of the $+3$ and $+4$ states. The tetroxide forms perperosmates and although the trioxide of the $+6$ state has not been isolated, many osmates, for example, K_2OsO_4, are known. A large number of

TABLE 52

THERMODYNAMIC DATA ON OSMIUM[1]

(Heat and free energy of formation in kcal. Entropy of substance in cal./deg.)

Formula	Description	State	$\Delta H°$	$\Delta F°$	$S°$
Os		g	*174.*	*163.*	*45.97*
Os		c	0.0	0.0	*7.8*
OsO_4		g	*−79.9*	*−67.9*	*65.6*
OsO_4	white	c, I	*−91.7*	*−70.5*	*34.7*
OsO_4	yellow	c, II	*−93.4*	*−70.7*	*29.7*
OsO_4		aq		*−68.59*	
OsO_2		c		(−50.)	
$HOsO_5^-$		aq		*−108.8*	
H_2OsO_5		aq		*−125.28*	
$OsCl_6^{--}$		aq		(−119.)	
$OsCl_6^{---}$		aq		(−139.)	
OsS_2		c	*−35.*	−34.4	(20.1)
OsP_2		c	*−40.*		

[1] Bureau of Standards values in *italics;* estimated values in parentheses.

osmyl compounds have been described, but they appear to decompose in acid solutions. There is no evidence of any salts of perosmic acid in alkaline solutions.

Osmium tetroxide. From the free energy of the solid yellow tetroxide we calculate

$$Os + 4H_2O = OsO_4(c) + 8H^+ + 8e^-, \qquad E° = -0.85;$$
$$OsO_4(c) + H_2O = H_2OsO_5(aq), \qquad \Delta F° = 2.1 \text{ kcal.}$$

Yost and White[2] report

$$H_2OsO_5 = H^+ + HOsO_5^-, \qquad K = 8 \times 10^{-13}.$$

[1] W. R. Crowell and H. D. Kirschman, *J. Am. Chem. Soc.*, **51**, 1695 (1929); *ibid.*, **54**, 1324 (1932).

[2] D. Yost and R. J. White, *J. Am. Chem. Soc.*, **50**, 81 (1928).

This gives -108.8 kcal. for the free energy of $HOsO_5$.

$$Os + 9OH^- = HOsO_5^- + 4H_2O + 8e^-, \qquad E_B^\circ = -0.02.$$

Potentials of other osmium couples. Although there are no quantitative data, the potentials involving the intermediate oxidation states of osmium are roughly fixed by known reactions of the compounds involved. In making these estimates, the potential of the Os—OsO_4 couple is a valuable aid, as the sum of the potentials of the reduction in steps is determined by this figure. The following diagram summarizes these estimated potentials in $1M$ acid solution:

0		+2		+3		+4		+8
Os	(-0.85)	Os^{++}	(-0.4)	$OsCl_6^{---}$	-0.85	$OsCl_6^{--}$	-1.0	$OsO_4(s)$

Os—$OsCl_6^{---}$: (-0.71); $OsCl_6^{---}$—$OsO_4(s)$: (-0.97); Os—$OsO_4(s)$: -0.85

A saturated solution of the tetroxide or perperosmic acid is almost as strong an oxidizing agent as is bromine. The $OsCl_6^{--}$ is less powerful, and there is some indication that the reduction to $OsCl_6^{---}$ is slow with certain reducing agents. Since Os^{++} is unstable, the Os—Os^{++} couple must be more negative than the Os^{++}—$OsCl_6^{---}$ couple. Iodide, however, reduces $OsCl_6^{---}$ to form OsI_2, the slight solubility of the latter compound increasing the energy of the reaction.

The reaction

$$3OH^- + HOsO_5^- + OsO_2 = 2OsO_4^{--} + 2H_2O$$

goes as written in $1M$ OH^- but is largely reversed at $10^{-7}M$ OH^-. Upon heating, the dioxide decomposes,

$$2OsO_2 = OsO_4 + Os,$$

and the pressure of OsO_4 is said to reach 1 atmosphere at 650° C. From the free energy of OsO_4, we calculate as an approximate value for the free energy of formation of OsO_2, $-50{,}000$ cal.

$$5OH^- + OsO_2 = HOsO_5 + 2H_2O + 4e^-, \qquad E_B^\circ = -0.2.$$

With these reactions as a basis, the following diagram of potentials is given for the oxidation states of osmium in alkaline solution:

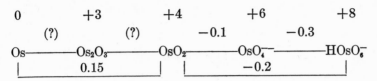

$$0 \qquad\qquad +3 \qquad\qquad +4 \qquad\qquad +6 \qquad\qquad +8$$

Dwyer, McKenzie, and Nyholm[1] studied the couples $OsBr_6^{--}$—$OsBr_6^{---}$ in HBr and $OsCl_6^{--}$—$OsCl_6^{---}$ in HCl. At zero acid strength both couples extrapolated to the same value, -0.45 volt. These authors suggested that at low H^+ the complex halides hydrolyzed to form OsO^+ and OsO^{++}.

[1] F. P. Dwyer, H. A. McKenzie, and R. S. Nyholm, *J. Proc. Roy. Soc. N.S. Wales*, **80**. 183, 242 (1947).

CHAPTER 15

Manganese, Technetium, and Rhenium

The elements of this group have seven valence electrons, and their electronic configuration in the monatomic gas atoms is s^2d^5 to give a $^6S_{5/2}$ state. Technetium does not occur in nature and the only known isotopes are made by nuclear reactions. The isotope Tc^{99} is formed by the action of neutrons on Mo^{98} and has a half-life of 10^6 years. The oxidation states of manganese range from $+1$ to $+7$, and of rhenium, from -1 to $+7$. Rhenium in the -1 state is the only example of an element in the transition series which is capable of adding an electron.

MANGANESE

Oxidation state. Manganese forms compounds of the manganous ion, Mn^{++}, and the manganic ion, Mn^{+++}. The corresponding oxides are basic. The $+4$ oxide MnO_2 is amphoteric but, like so many metal dioxides, is comparatively inert toward both hydrogen and hydroxide ions. An ion of the $+5$ state, hypomanganate, probably MnO_3^-, has been recently observed, but it is highly unstable in both acidic and basic solutions. The $+6$ oxidation state is represented by the manganate ion, MnO_4^{--}, which is stable only in alkaline solutions; the $+7$ state is represented by permanganate MnO_4^-. The $+1$ complex cyanide has been prepared.

Manganous ion and its compounds. There have been several recent investigations[1] of the free energy of Mn^{++}. We will give considerable weight to the work of Walkley and take for the free energy of formation, -54.4 kcal., which is 1 kcal. more negative than the Bureau of Standards value.

$$Mn = Mn^{++} + 2e^-, \qquad E° = 1.18.$$

---

[1] A. Walkley, *J. Electrochem.*, **93**, 316 (1948); A. F. Kapustinskii, *Acta Phys. Chem.* **14**, 503 (1941); J. C. Southard and C. H. Shomate, *J. Am. Chem. Soc.*, **64**, 1770 (1947).

TABLE 53

THERMODYNAMIC DATA ON MANGANESE[1]

(Heat and free energy of formation in kcal. Entropy of substance in cal./deg.)

Formula	Description	State	$\Delta H°$	$\Delta F°$	$S°$
Mn		g	*68.34*	*58.23*	*41.493*
Mn	α	c	0.0	0.0	*7.59*
Mn	γ	c	*0.37*	*0.33*	*7.72*
Mn^+		g	*240.863*		
Mn^{++}		g	*601.45*		
Mn^{++}		aq	−53.3	−54.4	−20.
Mn^{+++}		aq	(−27.)	(−19.6)	
MnO		g	*34.6*		
MnO		c	*−92.0*	−86.8	*14.4*
$HMnO_2^-$		aq		−120.9	
MnO_2	pyrolusite	c	−124.2	−111.1	12.7
MnO_4^-		aq	−129.7	−107.4	*45.4*
MnO_4^{--}		aq		−120.4	
Mn_2O_3		c	*−232.1*	−212.3	(22.1)
Mn_3O_4	c, I	c	*−331.4*	*−306.0*	*35.5*
$Mn(OH)_2$	precipitated	c	−166.8	−146.9	*21.1*
$Mn(OH)_3$		c	*−212.*	−181.	(23.8)
MnF_2		c	*−189.*	*−179.*	*22.2*
$MnCl_2$		c	*−115.3*	*−105.5*	*28.0*
$MnCl_2·H_2O$		c	*−188.5*	−164.5	(35.9)
$MnBr_2$		c	*−90.7*	−87.4	(32.1)
$MnBr_2·4H_2O$		c	*−367.5*	−308.9	(69.7)
MnI_2		c	*−59.3*	−59.9	(37.5)
MnS	green	c	*−48.8*	*−49.9*	*18.7*
MnS	red	c	*−47.6*		
MnS	precipitated	c		−53.3	
$MnSO_4$		c	*−254.24*	*−228.48*	*26.8*
$Mn_2(SO_4)_3$		c	*−666.9*	−580.9	(61.7)
$Mn(N_3)_2$		c	*92.2*	122.8	44.3
Mn_5N_2		c	*−57.8*		
$Mn(NO_3)_2$		c	*−166.32*	−118.6	(40.3)
$Mn_3(PO_4)_2$	precipitated	c	*−771.*	−683.	(71.6)
Mn_3C		c	*−1.*	−1.	*23.6*
$MnCO_3$		c	*−213.9*	*−195.4*	*20.5*
$MnCO_3$	precipitated	c	−212.	−194.3	23.8
MnC_2O_4		c	*−258.2*	−234.2	(28.)
$Mn(HCO_2)_2$	formate	c	*−242.2*	−212.0	(38.3)
$Mn(CH_3CO_2)_2$	acetate	c	*−273.0*	−222.6	(48.3)
$MnSiO_3$		c	*−302.5*	*−283.3*	*21.3*

[1] Bureau of Standards values in *italics;* estimated values in parentheses.

Likewise, we will make a similar correction to the Bureau of Standards value for $Mn(OH)_2$ and use ΔF -146.9 kcal.

$$Mn + 2OH^- = Mn(OH)_2 + 2e^-, \qquad E_B^0 = 1.55;$$
$$Mn(OH)_2 = Mn^{++} + 2OH^-, \qquad K = 2 \times 10^{-13}.$$

Fox, Swinehart, and Garrett[1] give two values, 1.6×10^{-13} and 2.8×10^{-13}, for the solubility product. The agreement with our free energies is very satisfactory. Tarbutton, Egan, and Frary, in the reference quoted, also found

$$Mn(OH)_2 = H^+ + HMnO_2^-, \qquad K = 1 \times 10^{-19}.$$

From this value the free energy of $HMnO_2^-$ is -120.9 kcal.

Manganese may be precipitated by cathodic reduction. Allmand and Campbell[2] employed a concentrated manganous sulfate and ammonium sulfate electrolyte. It appears to be necessary to keep the acid concentration low, but if it becomes less than pH6, considerable oxide forms on the metal surface.

For the solubility product of precipitated manganous carbonate, Agena and Valla[3] gave

$$MnCO_3 = Mn^{++} + CO_3^{--}, \qquad K = 8.8 \times 10^{-11}.$$

The free energy values are in agreement.

$$Mn + CO_3^{--} = MnCO_3 + 2e^-, \qquad E^0 = 1.48.$$

The free energy of precipitated MnS has been taken in agreement with the solubility product reported by Kolthoff:[4]

$$MnS = Mn^{++} + S^{--}, \qquad K = 7 \times 10^{-16}.$$

The following solubility products may be calculated from the free energies:

$$Mn_3(PO_4)_2 = 3Mn^{++} + 2PO_4^{---}, \qquad K = 10^{-22};$$
$$MnC_2O_4 = Mn^{++} + C_2O_4^{--}, \qquad K = 1.1 \times 10^{-15}.$$

[1] P. K. Fox, D. F. Swinehart, and A. B. Garrett, *J. Am. Chem. Soc.*, **63**, 1779 (1941).

[2] A. J. Allmand and A. N. Campbell, *Trans. Faraday Soc.*, **20**, 379 (1924).

[3] See J. W. Mellor, *Inorganic and Theoretical Chemistry*, New York: Longmans, 1932, Vol. 12, p. 437.

[4] I. M. Kolthoff, *J. Phys. Chem.*, **35**, 2720 (1931).

Manganic potentials. We will use the value of Grube and Metzger[1] for the potential of the Mn^{++}—Mn^{+++} couple, although the couple was measured in concentrated sulfuric acid, and obviously there is a large unknown correction for the activities.

$$Mn^{++} = Mn^{+++} + e^-, \qquad E^\circ = ca\ 1.5.$$

Using an estimated value for the entropy, we calculate for the free energy of $Mn(OH)_3$ $-181.$ kcal.

$$Mn(OH)_2 + OH^- = Mn(OH)_3 + e^-, \qquad E_B^\circ = -0.1;$$
$$Mn(OH)_3 = Mn^{+++} + 3OH^-, \qquad K = 10^{-36}.$$

The calculated solubility product appears to be reasonable. These free energies make Mn^{+++} highly unstable in acid solution and $Mn(OH)_3$ slightly unstable.

$$2Mn^{+++} + H_2O = MnO_2 + Mn^{++} + 4H^+, \qquad \Delta F^\circ = -26.\ kcal.;$$
$$2Mn(OH)_3 = Mn(OH)_2 + MnO_2 + 2H_2O, \quad \Delta F^\circ = -10.\ kcal.$$

The instability of Mn^{+++} is well known but there is some uncertainty with regard to $Mn(OH)_3$. However, the actual equilibria in alkaline solution may involve solid solutions of the hydrous oxides or complex manganous manganites, such as $H_2Mn_2O_4$.

Taube[2] has reported the following manganic constants

$$MnCl^{++} = Mn^{+++} + Cl^-, \qquad K = 1.1 \times 10^{-1};$$
$$MnF^{++} + H^+ = Mn^{+++} + HF, \qquad K = 3.3 \times 10^{-3};$$
$$Mn(C_2O_4)^+ = Mn^{+++} + C_2O_4^{--}, \qquad K = 10^{-10};$$
$$Mn(C_2O_4)_2^- = Mn^{+++} + 2C_2O_4^{--}, \qquad K = 2.5 \times 10^{-17};$$
$$Mn(C_2O_4)_3 = Mn^{+++} + 3C_2O_4^{--}, \qquad K = 7.1 \times 10^{-20}.$$

Complex manganese cyanides. From the work of Grube and Brause[3]

$$Mn(CN)_6^{-4} = Mn(CN)_6^{---} + e^-, \qquad E^\circ = 0.22.$$

The stability of the $+3$ complex thus greatly reduces the potential of the $+2$ to $+3$ couple. The authors also report the formation of a $+1$

[1] G. Grube and H. Metzger, *Z. Elektrochem.*, **29**, 17 (1923).
[2] H. J. Taube, *J. Am. Chem. Soc.*, **70**, 3928 (1948).
[3] G. Grube and W. Brause, *Ber.*, **60**, 2273 (1927).

complex with very powerful reducing agents.

$$2CN^- + Mn(CN)_4^{---} = Mn(CN)_6^{-4} + e^-, \qquad E° = 0.7.$$

Meyer[1] reported

$$Mn(OH)_3 + 3CN^- + 3HCN = Mn(CN)_6^{---} + 2H_2O,$$
$$K = 2.5 \times 10^{-6}(0° C.).$$

Manganese dioxide, manganate, and permanganate. Cells involving manganese dioxide appear to be reversible, but considerable variations in measured potentials have been observed, which is apparently the result of the variation of the thermodynamic properties of the dioxide with different samples. However, the values obtained with pyrolusite, which is made by heating manganous nitrate, are quite consistent and we will limit our discussion to this form of the dioxide. From the work of Hutchison[2] we will take

$$Mn^{++} + 2H_2O = MnO_2 \text{ (pyrolusite)} + 4H^+ + 2e^-, \qquad E° = -1.23,$$

and the free energy of MnO_2 (pyrolusite) as -111.1 kcal. This gives

$$Mn(OH)_2 + 2OH^- = MnO_2 \text{ (pyrolusite)} + 2H_2O + 2e^-,$$
$$E_B° = 0.05.$$

Andrews and Brown[3] found from direct cell measurements,

$$MnO_2(\text{pyrolusite}) + 4OH^- = MnO_4^- + 2H_2O + 3e^-,$$
$$E_B° = -0.588.$$

The corresponding value for the free energy of MnO_4^- is -107.4 kcal. This free energy is in agreement with the heat of formation of MnO_4^-, determined by Hugus and Latimer,[4] and the entropy of MnO_4^- as given by Brown, Smith, and Latimer.[5] We may then write for the couple in acid solution

$$MnO_2 \text{ (pyrolusite)} + 2H_2O = MnO_4^- + 4H^+ + 3e^-, \qquad E° = -1.695.$$

---

[1] J. Meyer, *Z. anorg. Chem.*, **81**, 385 (1913).

[2] A. W. Hutchison, *J. Am. Chem. Soc.*, **69**, 3051 (1947). See also A. D. Wadsley and A. Walkley, *J. Electrochem. Soc.*, **95**, 11, (1949), and D. J. Brown and H. A. Liebhafsky, *J. Am. Chem. Soc.*, **52**, 2595 (1930).

[3] L. V. Andrews and D. J. Brown, *J. Am. Chem. Soc.*, **57**, 254 (1935).

[4] Z. Z. Hugus and W. M. Latimer, *J. Electrochem. Soc.*, **98**, 296 (1951).

[5] O. L. I. Brown, W. V. Smith, and W. M. Latimer, *J. Am. Chem. Soc.*, **58**, 2144 (1936).

The free energy of manganate ion, MnO_4^{--}, is obtained from the following equilibrium:

$$3MnO_4^{--} + 2H_2O = MnO_2 + 2MnO_4^- + 4OH^-,$$
$$\Delta F^\circ = -1.64 \text{ kcal.}$$

which was studied by Schlesinger and Siems.[1] This gives for the free energy of MnO_4^{--}, -120.42 kcal., and we may write the following half-reactions:

$$MnO_4^{--} = MnO_4^- + e^-, \qquad\qquad E^\circ = -0.564;$$
$$MnO_2 + 2H_2O = MnO_4^{--} + 4H^+ + 2e^-, \qquad E^\circ = -2.26;$$
$$MnO_2 + 4OH^- = MnO_4^{--} + 2H_2O + 2e^-, \qquad E_B^\circ = -0.60.$$

In the author's opinion the stability of MnO_4^{--} in alkaline solution is somewhat greater than indicated by the work of Schlesinger and Siems quoted above, that is, the free energy of MnO_4^{--} should be slightly more negative than the value taken.

The blue hypomanganate,[2] which may be observed on the reduction of manganate, is highly unstable in both acid and alkaline solution. As a rough estimate of the instability toward disproportionation, we give 0.5 volt.

The Mn^{++}—MnO_4^- couple in acid solution is one of the most important in analytical chemistry. We compute for the over-all potential:

$$4H_2O + Mn^{++} = MnO_4^- + 8H^+ + 5e^-, \qquad E^\circ = -1.51.$$

The mechanism of a change involving five electrons must obviously be quite complicated. In the important case of the reduction by oxalic acid, the formation of complex oxalate ions of $+3$ and $+5$ manganese is probably involved. From the potentials of the various steps it appears that the $+4$ to $+3$ reduction has a low energy, and the formation of a stable $+3$ complex may have an important bearing on the rate. If the reduction of permanganate in acid solution has to go through the manganate state, the low potential of this step would also constitute a barrier. In this connection it is interesting to note that iodide with an oxidation potential approximately equal to the MnO_4^{--}—MnO_4^- couple reacts instantly with permanganate. Several aspects of the problem have been discussed by Polissar.[3]

[1] H. I. Schlesinger and H. B. Siems, *J. Am. Chem. Soc.*, **46**, 1965 (1924).

[2] H. H. Miller and L. B. Rodgers, *Science*, **109**, 61 (1949).

[3] M. J. Polissar, *J. Phys. Chem.*, **39**, 1057 (1935); *J. Am. Chem. Soc.*, **58**, 1372 (1936).

From the potential values it may be seen that permanganate will oxidize manganous ion to the dioxide in acid solution; hence reduction of permanganate to manganous ion occurs only with excess of reducing agent. In neutral or alkaline solution the reduction generally stops at the dioxide.

Permanganate is unstable with respect to its reduction by water, and at moderately high acid, oxygen is slowly evolved. The reaction in neutral or slightly alkaline solution is not appreciable in several months in the dark, but is accelerated by light.

In agreement with the potentials, oxygen will not oxidize manganese dioxide to manganate in aqueous alkaline solution, but the reaction does occur in fused potassium hydroxide. Under these conditions the reaction stops at manganate.

No value can be given for the solubility of the dioxide in acid. The reduction of permanganate to manganous in acid solution may occur without the separation of the dioxide, and an appreciable concentration of $+4$ manganese doubtless is present, possibly as MnO^{++}. A number of complex ions of the $+4$ state are known. Manganites are readily formed by fusion of the dioxide with alkalies, but the solubility of the oxide in aqueous hydroxide is very low.

Manganese dioxide electrode in dry cells. It is of interest to discuss the manganese dioxide electrode, used so extensively in dry cells. Inasmuch as the electrolyte is ammonium chloride, it is difficult to write a single net reaction, but the most probable equation (written backward for conformity of $E°$ values) for the electrode reaction appears to be

$$NH_4OH + Mn(OH)_3 = MnO_2 + NH_4^+ + 2H_2O + e^-,$$
$$E° = ca\ -0.5.$$

Instead of manganic hydroxide, the product may be a mixed $+2$ and $+4$ oxide or some solid solution of these oxides. The reaction certainly does not involve the formation of molecular hydrogen on the electrode and its oxidation by the manganese dioxide, as is frequently postulated. The electrode does polarize readily but it is doubtless because of the slow rate of diffusion of the ammonium ion.

For the reaction at the zinc electrode, we may write

$$2Cl^- + Zn = ZnCl_2(s) + 2e^-, \qquad E° = ca\ 0.7.$$

By the diffusion of the ammonia, some zinc hydroxide may also be formed. The sum of these half-reaction potentials gives 1.2 volts for the cell potential instead of 1.5, the actual value. The agreement is satisfactory in view of the low activity of the NH_4OH.

Summary of manganese potentials. The following diagram is given as a summary of the manganese potentials

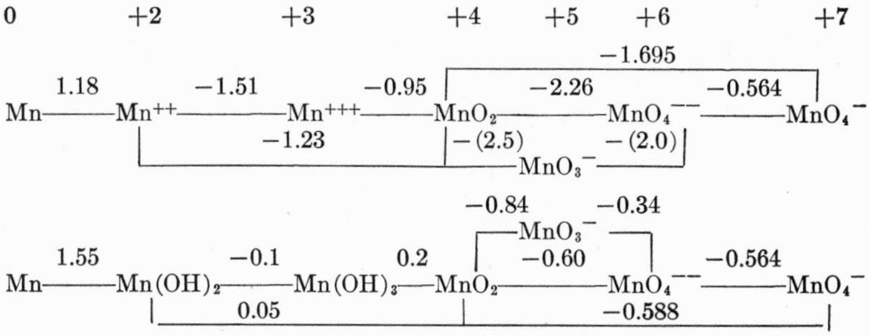

TECHNETIUM

Oxidation states. Technetium, like manganese, appears to have as its most important oxidation states[1] the $+2, +4,$ and $+7$. The metal is not nearly as electropositive as manganese and TcO_4^- and TcO_2 are much less powerful oxidizing agents than MnO_4^- and MnO_2.

The literature on the chemistry of technetium is very limited, but since the isotope Tc^{99} has a half-life of about 10^6 years, it appears probable that in the near future sufficient quantities of the element will be made, so that the chemistry may be studied in detail.

Potential diagram. The following approximate potential diagram gives the very meager data available on the chemical behavior of technetium.

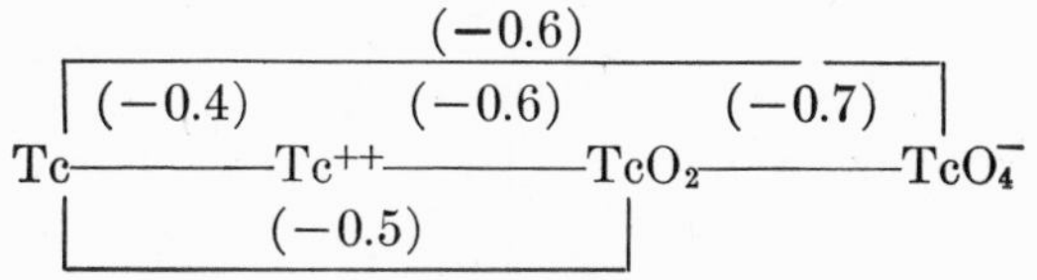

RHENIUM

Oxidation states. Compounds of rhenium corresponding to all of the oxidation states from -1 to $+7$ have been reported. The metal

---

[1] J. F. Flagg and W. E. Bleidner, *J. Chem. Phys.*, **13**, 269 (1945).

burns in oxygen with the formation of the oxides, Re_2O_7 and ReO_3. The former is soluble in water to form the strong perrhenic acid, $HReO_4$, and the perrhenates are stable in both acid and alkaline solution. The ReO_3 is slowly soluble in alkaline solution but the rhenate ion, ReO_4^-, is unstable with respect to its decomposition into perrhenate and the dioxide, ReO_2. The latter is amphoteric, but comparatively inert. However, it is more soluble in acids than is manganese dioxide. The sesquioxide, Re_2O_3, is precipitated from solutions which contain Re^{+++} in the form of complex ions, and the $+1$ oxide,

TABLE 54

THERMODYNAMIC DATA ON RHENIUM[1]

(Heat and free energy of formation in kcal. Entropy of substance in cal./deg.)

Formula	Description	State	$\Delta H°$	$\Delta F°$	$S°$
Re		g	*189.*	*179.*	*45.13*
Re	metal	c	0.0	0.0	10.
Re^-				(9.2)	
ReO_2				−90.2	
ReO_4^-		aq	*−190.3*	−168.3	(50.)
Re_2O_7		c	*−297.5*		
$HReO_4$		aq	*−189.4*		
ReF_6		g	*−273.*		
ReS_2		c	*−44.3*	*−45.8*	(20.)

[1] Bureau of Standards values in *italics;* estimated values in parentheses.

Re_2O, is said to be precipitated by the reduction of perrhenate by zinc. The chlorides $ReCl_5$ and $ReCl_3$ may be prepared at high temperatures and the chloroacids, H_2ReCl_6 and $HReCl_4$, are stable in acid solutions. The pentachloride is instable in both acid and alkaline solutions, giving perrhenate and the dioxide.

The sulfide, Re_2S_7, may be precipitated from perrhenate solutions by hydrogen sulfide. The sulfide appears to be soluble in excess of sulfide ion, forming thioperrhenate, ReS_4^-. The disulfide, ReS_2, is precipated by the action of hydrogen sulfide upon $ReCl_6^-$.

Zinc in dilute sulfuric acid reduces perrhenate to hydrorhenic acid, HRe.

Rhenium potentials. From the heat of formation of perrhenate ion ReO_4^-, -190.3 kcal., and an estimation of 50 cal./deg. for the entropy by comparison with MnO_4^-, we calculate -168.3 kcal. as the free energy of the ion.

$$Re + 4H_2O = ReO_4^- + 8H^+ + 7e^-, \qquad E^\circ = -0.363;$$
$$Re + 8OH^- = ReO_4^- + 4H_2O + 7e^-, \qquad E_B^\circ = 0.584.$$

By direct cell measurements, Hugus[1] found

$$ReO_2 + 2H_2O = ReO_4^- + 4H^+ + 3e^-, \qquad E^\circ = -0.51;$$
$$ReO_2 + 4OH^- = ReO_4^- + 2H_2O + 3e^-, \qquad E_B^\circ = 0.594.$$

The free energy of ReO_2 is -90.2 kcal. and, from these couples and the Re—ReO_4^- couple,

$$Re + 2H_2O = ReO_2 + 2H^+ + 4e^-, \qquad E^\circ = -0.252;$$
$$Re + 4OH^- = ReO_2 + H_2O + 4e^-, \qquad E_B^\circ = 0.576.$$

From these values ReO_2 is stable in acid and low hydroxide concentrations, but unstable in high OH^-. The hydroxide $Re(OH)_3$ may be precipitated from solutions containing $ReCl_4^-$ and appears to be stable in alkaline solutions.

$$Re + 3OH^- = Re(OH)_3 + 3e^-, \qquad E_B^\circ > 0.58.$$

The ions Re^{+++}, Re^{++}, and Re^+ are probably unstable in acid solutions but some of the evidence is conflicting.

$$Re = Re^{+++} + 3e^-, \qquad E^\circ < -0.25.$$

Rhenium trioxide does not dissolve readily in either acids or bases and the solutions appear to disproportionate.

In fairly concentrated hydrochloric acid, iodide reduces perrhenate to chlororhenate $ReCl_6^{--}$, with $ReCl_6^-$ probably formed as an intermediate. Further reduction forms $ReCl_4^-$, which is stable with respect to disproportionation.

Lundell and Knowles[2] have prepared rhenide, Re^-, in solution by reduction of perrhenate with zinc in dilute sulfuric acid. Rhenide is readily oxidized and the following E° value is probably reasonably close:

$$Re^- = Re + e^-, \qquad E^\circ = ca\ 0.4.$$

Summary of rhenium potentials. The following potential diagrams summarize the rhenium potentials.

[1] Z. Z. Hugus, University of California, private communication.
[2] G. E. F. Lundell and H. B. Knowles, *U. S. Bur. Standards J. Research* **18**, 629 (1937)

Acid Solution

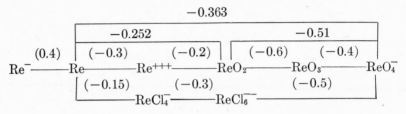

Basic Solution

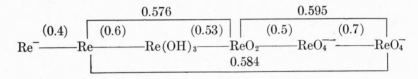

CHAPTER 16

Chromium, Molybdenum, and Tungsten (or Wolfram)

The elements of this group have six valence electrons. In the gas atoms both the $s^1d_5(^7S_3)$ and the $s^2d^4(^5D_0)$ states are close together, the lowest energy being in the former state for the two lighter elements and in the latter for the heavier members of the group. The oxidation states range from $+2$ to $+6$. With each element the highest state is important, but the lower ones vary considerably in their stabilities with the different elements.

Uranium resembles the elements of this group in many of its properties, but since it contains $5f$ electrons in the valence shell, it will be considered as a member of the actinide series.

CHROMIUM

Oxidation states. Chromium forms compounds having the oxidation numbers $+2$, $+3$, and $+6$. The $+2$ state is basic. The chromous ion is such a powerful reducing agent that it is not very stable in water solutions even at low hydrogen ion concentrations. The $+3$ state is amphoteric, forming compounds of the chromic ion with acids and chromites with bases. Chromium trioxide, CrO_3, is soluble in water. One of the principal characteristics of the trioxides of this group is the formation of polyacids; hence in addition to the chromate ion, CrO_4^{--}, dichromate, $Cr_2O_7^{--}$, and even the tri- and tetrachromates, $Cr_3O_{10}^{--}$ and $Cr_4O_{13}^{--}$, are known. The latter two, however, are not important. A few derivatives of the chromyl ion, CrO_2^{++}, may also be prepared. The blue peroxychromic acid is well known, but there are no data on its reduction potential.

The free energy of chromic ion. Grube and Schlecht[1] and other investigators have sought to measure the potential of the Cr—Cr^{+++}

---

[1] G. Grube and L. Schlecht, *Z. Elektrochem.*, **32,** 178 (1926); *ibid.*, **33,** 112 (1927).

TABLE 55

THERMODYNAMIC DATA ON CHROMIUM[1]

(Heat and free energy of formation in kcal. Entropy of substance in cal./deg.)

Formula	Description	State	$\Delta H°$	$\Delta F°$	$S°$
Cr		g	80.5	69.8	41.637
Cr	metal	c	0.0	0.0	5.68
Cr^+		g	237.39		
Cr^{++}		g	621.7		
Cr^{++}		aq	−33.2 (?)	−42.1	
Cr^{+++}		g	1310.		
Cr^{+++}	$[Cr(6H_2O)]^{+++}$	aq	−61.2 (?)	−51.5	−73.5
CrO		g	65.		
CrO_3		c	−145.8		
Cr_2O_3		c	−269.7	−250.2	19.4
$Cr_2O_7^{--}$		aq	−364.0	−315.4	51.1
$Cr(OH)^{++}$	$[Cr(5H_2O)OH]^{++}$	aq	−113.5	−103.0	−16.4
$HCrO_4^-$		aq	−220.2	−184.9	16.5
CrO_4^{--}		aq	−213.75	−176.1	9.2
CrO_2^-		aq		−125.	
$Cr(OH)_2$		c		−140.5	
$Cr(OH)_3$		c	−247.1	−215.3	(19.2)
$Cr(OH)_3$	hydrous, probably $[Cr(5H_2O)(OH)](OH)_2$	c	−236.6	−205.5	19.6
CrF_3		c	−265.2	−248.3	(22.2)
CrF_2		c	−181.0	−170.7	(19.6)
$CrCl^{++}$	$[Cr(5H_2O)Cl]^{++}$	aq	−134.5		
$CrCl_2^+$	$[Cr(4H_2O)Cl_2]^+$	aq	−130.0	−115.2	(30.)(?)
$CrCl_2$		c	−94.56	−85.15	27.4
$CrCl_3$		c	−134.6	−118.0	30.0
CrO_2Cl_2		liq	−143.1	−125.4	(50.)
$CrBr_2^+$	$[Cr(4H_2O)Br_2]^-$	aq	−37.4		
CrI_2		c	−54.2	−55.3	(37.4)
CrN		c	−29.8		
Cr_2N		c	−23.4		
$(NH_4)_2CrO_4$		c	−282.6	−238.0	(40.1)
$(NH_4)_2Cr_2O_7$		c	−440.8		
Cr_3C_2		c	−21.0	−21.2	20.4
Cr_7C_3		c	−42.5	−43.8	48.0
Cr_4C		c	−16.4	−16.8	25.3

[1] Bureau of Standards values in *italics;* estimated values in parentheses.

couple through the intermediate chromous ion. The $E°$ values obtained for the metal-chromic couple are near 0.51. However this value is not in agreement with the thermal data. Choosing the most favorable data, the lowest value that can be calculated is 0.67. It seems advisable to assume that the chromium electrode is not reversible and to rely entirely upon the third-law calculations, even though these are at best rather sketchy, and a number of our calculated potentials may be in error by 0.1 volt.

Two important chromic ions will be considered. One is the so-called "violet ion," which is generally considered to be $Cr(H_2O)_6^{+++}$ and will be written simply as Cr^{+++}, and the other is the green ion, stable in chloride solutions, $CrCl_2(H_2O)_4^+$, which will be written $CrCl_2^+$. Lamb and Fonda[1] studied the hydrolysis of these ions and reported

$$Cr^{+++} + H_2O = CrOH^{++} + H^+, \qquad K = 1.5 \times 10^{-4};$$
$$CrCl_2^+ + H_2O = CrOH^{++} + H^+ + 2Cl^-, \qquad K = 1.9 \times 10^{-6};$$

from which we compute,

$$CrCl_2^+ = Cr^{+++} + 2Cl^-, \qquad K = 1.26 \times 10^{-2};$$
$$\Delta F^\circ = 2600 \text{ cal.}$$

We have two possible calculations to obtain the free energy of Cr^{+++}. First the Bureau of Standards value for the heat of formation, -61.2 kcal., may be used with an estimated value for the entropy of the ion to calculate the free energy. Using -67 ± 5 cal./deg. for the entropy, we find ΔF° to be -53.5 ± 1.5 kcal. Second, we estimate the entropy of $CrCl_2^-$ to be 25. ± 5 cal./deg. and this with the ΔH° of formation gives -115.2 ± 1.5 kcal. as the free energy of formation. Combining this value with the free energy of dissociation of $CrCl_2^-$, given above, we obtain for the free energy of Cr^{+++}, -49.9 ± 1.5 kcal. The value selected from these two calculations is -51.5 kcal.

$$Cr = Cr^{+++} + 3e^-, \qquad E^\circ = 0.74.$$

Calculations might be made for the green sulfate and bromide complex ions. Guiter[2] reported

$$Cr^{+++} + SO_4^{--} + H_2O = CrOHSO_4 + H^+, \qquad K = 0.4.$$

Hundreds of complex chromic ions with the halogens, ammonia, cyanide, and nitrite are known, but the data are largely qualitative. Stability constants for successive additions of thiocyanate to chromic ion have been given by Bjerrum[3] and from these we calculate

$$Cr(CNS)_3 = Cr^{+++} + 3CNS^-, \qquad K = 1.6 \times 10^{-6}.$$

[1] A. B. Lamb and G. R. Fonda, *J. Am. Chem. Soc.*, **43**, 1155 (1921).
[2] H. Guiter, *Compt. rend.*, **222**, 1002 (1948).
[3] J. Bjerrum, *Chem. Rev.*, **46**, 381 (1950).

Chromic hydroxide. Bjerrum[1] found for the precipitated chromic hydroxide, probably $[Cr(5H_2O)OH](OH)_2$.

$$Cr(OH)_3 + 2H^+ = Cr(OH)^{++} + 2H_2O, \qquad K = 1 \times 10^8.$$

This with the constant for the hydrolysis of the ion gives

$$Cr(OH)_3 = Cr^{+++} + 3OH^-, \qquad K = 6.7 \times 10^{-31},$$

and we calculate for the free energy of the hydroxide -205.5 kcal· The $\Delta H°$ and $\Delta F°$ values give an entropy for the hydroxide which is reasonable.

$$Cr + 3OH^- = Cr(OH)_3 + 3e^-, \qquad E_B^0 = 1.3.$$

An approximate value for the free energy of chromite may be obtained from the work of Fricke and Windhausen.[2] These authors found that in dilute hydroxide, the ion CrO_2^-, presumably is formed, while at concentrations above $10M$ NaOH, the principal ion is CrO_3^{--}, but at high concentration of hydroxide the total solubility is low, since the sodium salt is not very soluble. From their solubility data,

$$Cr(OH)_3 + OH^- = 2H_2O + CrO_2^-, \qquad K = 9 \times 10^{-3};$$
$$Cr(OH)_3 = CrO_2^- + H^+ + H_2O, \qquad K = 9 \times 10^{-17}.$$

We compute for the free energy of the ion, CrO_2^-, -125.5 cal.

$$4OH^- + Cr = CrO_2^- + 2H_2O + 3e^-, \qquad E_B^0 = 1.2.$$

Chromous ion. Grube and Breitinger[3] by direct cell measurement found

$$Cr^{++} = Cr^{+++} + e^-, \qquad E° = 0.41.$$

The free energy of chromous ion then is -42.1 kcal.

$$Cr = Cr^{++} + 2e^-, \qquad E° = 0.91.$$

Hume and Stone[4] reported for the solubility product of chromous hydroxide

$$Cr(OH)_2 = Cr^{++} + 2OH^-, \qquad K = 1.0 \times 10^{-17}.$$

[1] N. Bjerrum, *Z. physik. Chem.*, **73**, 740 (1910).
[2] R. Fricke and O. Windhausen, *Z. anorg. allgem. Chem.*, **132**, 273 (1924).
[3] G. Grube and G. Breitinger, *Z. Elektrochem.*, **33**, 112 (1927).
[4] D. N. Hume and W. H. Stone, *J. Am. Chem. Soc.*, **63**, 1199 (1941).

This makes the free energy of formation of the hydroxide -140.5 kcal.

$$Cr + 2OH^- = Cr(OH)_2 + 2e^-, \qquad E_B^o = 1.41.$$

Chromate and dichromate. In the first edition, the free energy of CrO_4^{--} was calculated from the entropy of the ion determined by Smith, Pitzer and Latimer[1] and the heat of formation as given by Bichowsky and Rossini.[2] This value was combined with the following data by Neuss and Rieman[3] to give the free energy of $Cr_2O_7^{--}$.

$$HCrO_4^- = H^+ + CrO_4^{--}, \qquad \begin{aligned} K &= 3.2 \times 10^{-7}, \\ \Delta F^\circ &= 8850 \text{ cal.}; \end{aligned}$$

$$Cr_2O_7^{--} + H_2O = 2HCrO_4^-, \qquad \begin{aligned} K &= 2.3 \times 10^{-2}, \\ \Delta F^\circ &= 2230 \text{ cal.} \end{aligned}$$

The values of ΔH° and ΔF° for $Cr_2O_7^{--}$ chosen by the Bureau of Standards are -349.1 and -300.5 kcal., and the potential of the Cr^{+++}—$Cr_2O_7^{--}$ couple would be -1.44 volts, which, from the chemical evidence, appears to be too negative. Therefore, we have used the work of Evans,[4] which gives ΔH for $2Cr^{+++}$—$Cr_2O_7^{--}$ as 241.6 kcal., to recalculate the $+6$ chromium values. From our figure for the free energy of dichromate, -315.4 kcal., and chromate, -176.25 kcal.

$$2Cr^{+++} + 7H_2O = Cr_2O_7^{--} + 14H^+ + 6e^-, \qquad E^\circ = -1.33;$$
$$Cr(OH)_3(\text{hydr.}) + 5OH^- = CrO_4^{--} + 4H_2O + 3e^-, \qquad E_B^o = 0.13.$$

Values in the literature are near -1.3 and 0.1, in agreement with these calculations. In $1M$ H^+, dichromate is not a very rapid oxidizing agent and it is difficult to measure the Cr^{+++}—$Cr_2O_7^{--}$ couple directly. Potential measurements in alkaline solution are fairly reproducible, but the reduction probably forms basic chromic chromate, $CrOHCrO_4$, or some other intermediate compound; hence it is not to be expected that the experimental values will be in close accord with our calculated potentials for the alkaline solution. We are unable to give a value for the free energy of the basic chromic chromate. It will be observed that hydrogen ion enters into the equations for the e.m.f. at a high power,

[1] W. V. Smith, K. S. Pitzer and W. M. Latimer, *J. Am. Chem. Soc.*, **59**, 2642 (1937).

[2] R. R. Bichowsky and F. D. Rossini, *Thermochemistry*, New York: Reinhold Publishing Corp., 1936.

[3] J. D. Neuss and W. Rieman, *J. Am. Chem. Soc.*, **56**, 2238 (1934).

[4] M. Evans, *Nat. Nuclear Energy Series*, **1413**, 282 (1949).

and chromic acid in concentrated solutions becomes a very strong oxidizing agent.

Metallic chromium may be plated by cathodic reduction from concentrated solutions of chromic acid containing sulfuric acid or chromic sulfate. The reduction process uses up hydrogen ions and a film of the basic chromic chromate appears to be formed on the cathode. In pure chromic acid solutions but little chromium is deposited and hydrogen is liberated. The explanation has been offered[1] that only hydrogen ion can penetrate the chromic chromate diaphragm, but if sulfate is present, it in some way acts to break the continuity of the film and the reduction of the chromium proceeds. The sulfate is thought to aid in stabilizing a layer of chromous ions on the metal surface, which is important as the reduction doubtless goes through this state.

Orlemann and Lewis[2] have studied the mechanism of the electrolytic reduction of chromic, and concluded that the Cr^{+++} to Cr^{++} step is a simple electron transfer and that the slow step in the reduction of Cr^{++} is the formation of Cr^+, which either disproportionates or is rapidly reduced to the metal.

It is difficult to oxidize chromic ion to chromate at a platinum electrode. However, at a lead anode, or if some lead salt is added to the electrolyte, the oxidation is highly efficient. It seems probable that the Pb^{++}—PbO_2 couple is involved in the mechanism of the reaction.

Chromyl chloride. The heat of formation of liquid chromyl chloride is given as $-134,600$ cal. A rough estimate of 50 cal./deg. for the entropy would make the free energy $-117,000$ cal. We then calculate for the hydrolysis of the liquid

$$2CrO_2Cl_2 + 3H_2O = Cr_2O_7^- + 6H^+ + 4Cl^-, \qquad \Delta F° = -20.0 \text{ kcal.}$$

MOLYBDENUM

Oxidation states. The most important oxidation state is the $+6$, and the chemistry of this state is largely that of the oxide, MoO_3, and its compounds. Some idea of the complexity of the polymolybdic acids is gained by the following series of ions, reported by Jander, Jahr, and Heukeshoven,[3] as formed by the addition of hydrogen ion to

[1] E. Miller, Z. Elektrochem., 32, 399 (1926); ibid., 40, 326 (1934).

[2] E. Orlemann and M. Lewis, Ph. D. Thesis, University of California, 1950.

[3] J. Jander, K. F. Jahr, and W. Heukeshoven, Z. anorg. allgem. Chem., 194, 413 (1930).

TABLE 56

THERMODYNAMIC DATA ON MOLYBDENUM[1]

(Heat and free energy of formation in kcal. Entropy of substance in cal./deg.)

Formula	Description	State	$\Delta H°$	$\Delta F°$	$S°$
Mo		g	*155.5*	*144.2*	*43.462*
Mo	metal	c	0.0	0.0	*6.83*
Mo^+		g	*327.23*		
Mo^{+++}		aq		(−13.8)	
MoO_2		c	*−130.*	−117.3	(13.3)
MoO_3		c	*−180.3*	−161.95	*18.68*
MoO_3		aq	*−188.1*		
MoO_4		aq	*−173.5*	−154.	(40.)
MoO_4^{--}		aq	*−254.3*	−218.8	(14.)
H_2MoO_4	white	c	*−256.9*		
H_2MoO_4	(probably complex)	aq	*−256.4*	(−227.)	(36.)
$H_2MoO_4 \cdot H_2O$	yellow	c	*−331.4*		
$MoCl_2$		c	*−44.*	−34.6	(28.5)
$MoCl_3$		c	*−65.*	−48.8	(33.0)
$MoCl_4$		c	*−79.*	−58.5	(44.7)
$MoCl_5$		c	*−90.8*	−64.6	(53.)
$MoCl_6$		c	*−90.*	−58.	(61.)
$MoBr_2$		c	*−29.*	−26.3	(34.1)
$MoBr_3$		c	*−41.*	−34.4	(39.3)
$MoBr_4$		c	*−45.*	−36.9	(52.3)
$MoBr_5$		c	*−51.*	−40.7	(63.)
MoI_2		c	*−12.*	−13.4	(39.5)
MoI_3		c	*−15.*	−15.4	(49.8)
MoI_4		c	*−18.*	−18.5	(64.3)
MoI_5		c	*−18.*	−18.7	(78.)
MoS_2		c	*−55.5*	*−53.8*	*15.1*
MoS_3		c	*−61.2*	−57.6	(18.)
Mo_2C		c	*4.3*	*2.9*	*19.7*

[1] Bureau of Standards values in *italics;* estimated values in parentheses.

an alkaline molybdate solution:

$$MoO_4^{--} \rightarrow Mo_3O_{11}^{-4} \rightarrow H(Mo_3O_{11})^{-3} \rightarrow HMo_6O_{21}^{-5} \rightarrow H_2Mo_6O_{21}^{-4}$$
$$\rightarrow H_3Mo_6O_{21}^{-3} \rightarrow H_7Mo_{12}O_{41}^{-3} \rightarrow H_7Mo_{24}O_{78}^{-5}$$
$$\rightarrow H_9Mo_{24}O_{78}^{-3} \rightarrow H_{12}Mo_{24}O_{78}.$$

The dioxide, +4 state, is formed at high temperatures, but it is unstable in water solution. The reduction of molybdic acid at low hydrogen-ion concentrations forms the blue oxide, $Mo_3O_8 \cdot 5H_2O$, which is probably $(MoO_2)_2MoO_4$. At high acid, the ions of the +5 state are probably MoO_2^+ or even MoO^{+++}. Further reduction gives the +3 state. The ion Mo^{+++} or MoO^+ appears to be present in the olive-green solutions, and at high concentrations of hydrochloric acid the solution turns red, probably with the formation of $MoCl_6^{--}$. However, Wardlow and Wormell[1] claim that the green and red substances are cis-trans isomers of the formula $MoOCl\cdot4H_2O$. Although the halogen complex ions of $+4$ molybdenum do not appear to be stable, the cyanide, $Mo(CN)_8^{-4}$, is known. The solid tetrachloride, $MoCl_4$, has been prepared, but it is decomposed in water to give the $+3$ and the $+5$ states. The dichloride $MoCl_2$ or Mo_3Cl_6 may be formed at high temperatures. It does not react readily with water but is probably slowly decomposed.

The trisulfide is acidic and dissolves in excess sulfide ion. The solution may be reduced by zinc to the $+5$ sulfide, Mo_2S_5. The disulfide, MoS_2, exists in nature and the sesquisulfide has been prepared.

The free energy of molybdate and molybdic acid. The heat of formation of molybdate is given as 254.3 kcal. By comparison with chromate, the estimated entropy of the ion is 14 entropy units. The free energy of formation is then calculated to be -218.8 kcal.

$$8OH^- + Mo = MoO_4^{--} + 4H_2O + 6e^-, \qquad E_B^\circ = 1.05.$$

From the free energy of molybdic oxide and acid, we write

$$MoO_4 + H_2O = H_2MoO_4(aq), \qquad\qquad \Delta F^\circ = -8.0 \text{ kcal.}$$
$$Mo + 4H_2O = H_2MoO_4(aq) + 6H^+ + 6e^-, \qquad E^\circ = 0.0.$$

Although the formula, H_2MoO_4, is used, the acid present is doubtless one of the polyforms. The metal may be electro-deposited from the aqueous solution, if high concentrations of salts, such as sodium formate, fluoride, or phosphate are present. The optimum pH range is 5.5 to 6.8.

The reduction of molybdic acid to the $+5$ and $+3$ states. At $1M$ H^+ the reduction of molybdic acid yields molybdenum blue. As a rough estimate,

$$4H_2O + (MoO_2)_2MoO_4 = 3H_2MoO_4(aq) + 2H^+ + 2e^-,$$
$$E^\circ = \text{ca } -0.6.$$

$$2H_2O + MoO_2^+ = H_2MoO_4(aq) + 2H^+ + e^-,$$
$$E^\circ = \text{ca } -0.4.$$

A powerful reducing agent is required to carry the reduction to the

---

[1] W. Wardlow and R. L. Wormell, *J. Chem. Soc.*, 130 (1927).

olive-green $+3$ ion. The $+3$ state is stable with respect to its own oxidation and reduction; and, in keeping with this fact and the over-all potential, we estimate

$$2H_2O + Mo^{+++} = MoO_2^+ + 4H^+ + 2e^-, \qquad E^\circ = ca\ 0.0;$$
$$Mo = Mo^{+++} + 3e^-, \qquad E^\circ = ca\ 0.2.$$

Foerster, Fricke, and Hausswald[1] have studied the potentials in hydrochloric acid. Their values for the $2N$ acid may be summarized in the following diagram:

$$
\begin{array}{c}
\overset{0.25}{\phantom{Mo^{+3}(g)}\text{———}}\qquad \overset{-0.53}{\phantom{Mo^{+5}}\text{———}} \\
Mo^{+3}(g)\text{———}Mo^{+5}\text{———}Mo^{+6} \\
\underset{-0.11}{}\ \big| \\
Mo^{+3}(r)\text{———}\big|
\end{array}
$$

We are unable to assign formulae to the molybdenum chloride complexes in these various oxidation states. The red and green ions of the $+3$ state have been discussed above. A number of $+5$ chloride ions are known, for example, $MoOCl_5^-$ and $MoOCl_4^-$, and salts of the $+6$ state, such as $Na(MoO_2Cl_3)$ and $Na_2(MoO_2Cl_4)$, have been prepared. The reduction of molybdic acid to Mo^{+++} by passing the acid solution through a Jones reductor (Zn) is a standard quantitative procedure in analytical chemistry.

The hydroxide $Mo(OH)_3$ does not appear to be stable in alkaline solutions.

Molybdenum cyanides. A large number of complex cyanide ions have been reported. Kolthoff and Tomsicek[2] have given the following potential:

$$Mo(CN)_6^{-4} = Mo(CN)_6^{-3} + e^-, \qquad E^\circ = -0.73.$$

However, as in the case of the ferro-ferric cyanide couple, the activities of the ions are difficult to obtain and the E° value cannot be accurately calculated from the measured potential

Molybdenum dioxide. It is evident from the free energy of the dioxide that it is unstable in both alkaline and acid solutions.

$$6MoO_2 + 8OH^- = 4MoO_4^{--} + 2Mo + 4H_2O, \qquad \Delta F^\circ = -85.0\ kcal.,$$
$$3MoO_2 + 6H^+ = 2Mo^{+++} + H_2MoO_4(aq) + 2H_2O,$$
$$\Delta F^\circ = -14.0\ kcal.$$

---

[1] F. Foerster, E. Fricke, and R. Hausswald, *Z. physik. Chem.*, **146**, 177 (1930).

[2] I. M. Kolthoff and W. J. Tomsicek, *J. Phys. Chem.*, **40**, 247 (1936).

Molybdenum peroxide. From the heat of formation of the peroxide MoO_4 in aqueous solution and an estimated entropy, we give as an approximate value

$$H_2MoO_4 = MoO_4(aq) + 2H^+ + 2e^-, \qquad E^\circ = ca\ -1.6.$$

TUNGSTEN (WOLFRAM)

Oxidation states. The oxides, WO_2, W_2O_5, and WO_3 are well known, although the $+5$ oxide may be a complex compound containing some WO_3 as its composition approaches the formula W_4O_{11}. Complex ions of the $+3$ state, such as WCl_5^{--}, may be prepared, but the simple $+3$ ion is probably unstable. Likewise complex halogen and cyanide ions of the $+4$ and $+5$ states exist in water solutions, but there are no simple oxygen ions. None of the lower oxidation states appear to be stable in alkaline solution. Tungstic oxide, like molybdic oxide, forms innumerable complex acids. The normal salts, for ex-

TABLE 57

THERMODYNAMIC DATA ON TUNGSTEN[1]

(Heat and free energy of formation in kcal. Entropy of substance in cal./deg.)

Formula	Description	State	ΔH°	ΔF°	S°
W		g	*201.6*	*191.6*	*41.552*
W		c	0.0	0.0	*8.0*
W$^+$		g	*387.2*		
WO$_2$		c	*-136.3*	-124.4	(17.)
WO$_3$	yellow	c	*-200.84*	*-182.47*	*19.90*
W$_2$O$_5$		c	*-337.9*	-306.9	(34.)
H$_2$WO$_4$		c	*-279.6*		
WO$_4^{--}$		aq	*-266.6*	-220.	(15.)
WCl$_2$		c	*-38.*	-27.	(31.2)
WCl$_4$		c	*-71.*	-51.	(47.4)
WCl$_5$		c	*-84.*	-59.	(58.)
WCl$_6$		c	*-98.7*	-70.	(69.)
WBr$_2$		c	*-19.*	-16.7	(36.8)
WBr$_4$		c	*-35.*	-27.4	(55.)
WBr$_5$		c	*-42.*		
WBr$_6$		c	*-44.*		
WI$_2$		c	*-1.*	-2.7	(41.9)
WI$_4$		c	*0.*	-1.	(67.)
WI$_5$		c	*27.*		
WS$_2$		c	*-46.3*	-46.2	*23.*
WC		c	*-9.09*		

[1] Bureau of Standards values in *italics;* estimated values in parentheses.

ample, Na_2WO_4, are readily prepared, but the paratungstates, for example, $Na_{10}W_{12}O_{41}$, are more common. Monotungstic acid, H_2WO_4, does not dissolve appreciably in water, but the paratungstic acid is readily soluble. The trisulfide is acidic, forming thiotungstates, WS_4^{--}, but no quantitative data are available.

Potentials of the oxides. From the free energies, the potentials relating the oxides in acid solution may be calculated.

$$W + 2H_2O = WO_2 + 4H^+ + 4e^-, \qquad E° = 0.12;$$
$$2WO_2 + H_2O = W_2O_5 + 2H^+ + 2e^-, \qquad E° = 0.043;$$
$$W_2O_5 + H_2O = 2WO_3 + 2H^+ + 2e^-, \qquad E° = 0.03.$$

The $E°$ values are very similar and should lead to equilibria involving the metal and the other oxides in the presence of H^+. However, the formation of solid solutions of the oxides would probably make it difficult to interpret the results even if the reaction rates were fast enough to attain the equilibria.

The free energy of tungstate. From the heat of formation and an estimated value for the entropy, we calculate for the free energy of WO_4^{--}, -220 kcal.

$$W + 8OH^- = WO_4^{--} + 4H_2O + 6e^-, \qquad E_B° = 1.05.$$

The heat of formation of $H_2WO_4(aq)$ is not known, and we do not know the actual formula of the aqueous molecule. For the potential of the metal to the $+6$ state in acid, we shall write the equation for the oxide.

$$W + 3H_2O = WO_3(c) + 6H^+ + 6e^-, \qquad E° = 0.09.$$

The reduction of tungstate in hydrochloric acid. Collenberg and Guthe[1] and Lingane and Small[2] have studied the reduction of tungstate in $12N$ HCl. The two investigations are in approximate agreement. Lingane and Small state that $+6$ tungsten, possibly $WO_2Cl_3^-$, is reduced to the $+5$ state, possibly $WOHCl_5^{--}$ at a potential of -0.26 volt. The $+5$ state is reduced at about 0.2 volt to the red $+3$ ion, probably WCl_5^{--}, without the formation of a $+4$ state. The red $+3$ ion changes spontaneously to a colorless or yellow form and then to the green ion, probably $W_2Cl_9^{-3}$. Oxidation of the colorless $+3$ ion

---

[1] O. Collenberg and A. Guthe, *Z. anorg. allgem. Chem.* **136**, 252 (1924).

[2] J. J. Lingane and L. A. Small, *J. Am. Chem. Soc.* **71**, 973 (1949).

gives a colorless +4 ion which disproportionates into the +5 ion and the red +3 ion. On continued oxidation the red ion is converted into a +4 ion, which forms a stable compound with the +5. (Average oxidation state of the tungsten is +4.5.) The green ion, $W_2Cl_9^{-3}$, is not easily oxidized at a mercury anode. The following diagram corresponds to the approximate potentials in the 12N HCl.

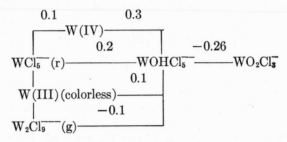

Cyanide complex ions. Collenberg[1] also measured the potential of the IV—V cyanide complex ion couple,

$$W(CN)_8^{-4} = W(CN)_8^{-3} + e^-, \qquad E^\circ = -0.57.$$

The ion $W(CN)_8^{-4}$ should have 18 electrons in the completed $s^2p^6d^{10}$ shell and should therefore have high stability in comparison with the $W(CN)_6^{-3}$ ion.

Summary of group potentials. The following are potential diagrams for the group.

---

[1] O. Collenberg, *Z. physik. Chem.*, **109**, 353 (1924).

Acid Solution

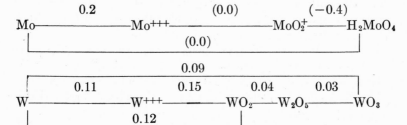

```
  0          +2           +3          +4          +5          +6

              0.74
  ┌─────────────────────────┐                    −1.33
  │ 0.91        0.41        │
Cr────────Cr⁺⁺────────Cr⁺⁺⁺───  ──────  ──────                Cr₂O₇⁻
         0.76
  │                 ┌────────CrCl₂⁺
  └─────────────────┘     −0.295
  └──────────────────────────────────────────────┘
```

```
          0.2                      (0.0)        (−0.4)
Mo────────────────────Mo⁺⁺⁺──── ──────────MoO₂⁺────────H₂MoO₄
  │                          (0.0)                   │
  └──────────────────────────────────────────────────┘
```

```
                        0.09
  ┌──────────────────────────────────────────────────┐
  │  0.11              0.15        0.04        0.03   │
W────────────────W⁺⁺⁺────  ──────WO₂────W₂O₅────────WO₃
  │                    0.12                 │
  └─────────────────────────────────────────┘
```

Basic Solution

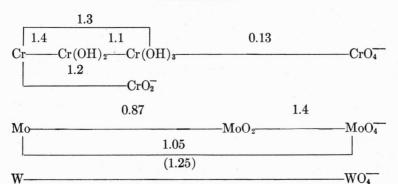

```
              1.3
  ┌──────────────────────────┐                       0.13
  │ 1.4          1.1         │
Cr────────Cr(OH)₂────Cr(OH)₃──────────────────────────CrO₄⁻
  │         1.2
  └─────────────────CrO₂⁻
```

```
              0.87                              1.4
Mo──────────────────────  ──────MoO₂────────────────MoO₄⁻
  │                        1.05                      │
  └──────────────────────────────────────────────────┘
                        (1.25)
W────────────────────────────────────────────────────WO₄⁻
```

CHAPTER 17

Vanadium, Niobium (Columbium), and Tantalum

The elements of this group have five valence electrons. In monatomic vanadium, the lowest electronic state is $d^3s^2(^4F_{3/2})$ and in niobium and tantalum, probably $d^4s^1(^6D_{1/2})$. The chemistry of protactinium is similar to that of these elements, but since its valence shell contains $5f$ electrons, it will be discussed with the elements of the actinide series. As the atomic weight increases in this group, the lower oxidation states become unstable and the chemistry is largely that of the inert $+5$ oxide.

Oxidation states. Vanadium forms the oxides VO, V_2O_3, VO_2, and V_2O_5. The two lower oxides are basic and give the ions V^{++} and V^{+++} in solution. The $+4$ oxide, often written V_2O_4, dissolves in acids with the formation of vanadyl ion, VO^{++}, and salts of this ion with most acid ions are well known. Although the oxide is not readily soluble in alkalies, vanadites may be prepared, for example, $(NH_4)_2V_2O_5$. The various ions present in solutions of the pentoxide in acids and bases are discussed below. The pentasulfide, V_2S_5, is acidic and dissolves in excess sulfide ion forming thiovanadates. Upon ignition the pentasulfide is reduced to the sesquisulfide, V_2S_3. The $+2$ sulfide, VS, appears to be formed at high temperatures. No quantitative data can be given for any of these sulfur compounds.

The $+5$ state. The solubility of vanadic oxide in water, as determined by Meyer and Aulich,[1] is $0.0043M$. The determination of the constitution of this solution has been a problem of singular difficulty. The earlier work of Düllberg[2] has been largely verified by the investigations of Bray and Tihenko.[3] The principal negative ion in the solution is $H_2V_6O_{17}^{--}$, that is, the first two steps in the ionization of the cor-

---

[1] J. Meyer and M. Aulich, *Z. anorg. allgem. Chem.*, **194**, 282 (1930).

[2] P. Düllberg, *Z. physik. Chem.*, **45**, 129 (1903).

[3] W. C. Bray and V. J. Tihenko, unpublished material, University of California.

TABLE 58

THERMODYNAMIC DATA ON VANADIUM[1]

(Heat and free energy of formation in kcal. Entropy of substance in cal./deg.)

Formula	Description	State	$\Delta H°$	$\Delta F°$	$S°$
V		g	*120.*	*109.*	*43.546*
V	metal	c	*0.0*	*0.0*	*7.05*
V+		g	*275.65*		
V++		g	*604.8*		
V++		aq		−54.7	
V+++		g	*1217.9*		
V+++		aq		−60.6	
VO		g	*52.*		
VO++		aq		−109.	
V(OH)₄+		aq		−256.	
VO₄⁻		aq	−210.9	−203.9	(48.)
VO₅⁻		aq	−195.5		
V₂O₂		c	−200.	−189.	(24.)
V₂O₃		c	−290.	−271.	*23.58*
V₂O₄		c	−344.	−318.	*24.65*
V₂O₅		c	−373.	−344.	*31.3*
V₃O₉‾‾‾		aq	−673.5		
HV₆O₁₇‾‾‾		aq		−1132.	
H₂V₆O₁₇‾‾		aq		−1135.	
VCl₂		c	−108.	−97.	*23.2*
VCl₃		c	−137.	−120.	*31.3*
VCl₄		liq	−138.		
VOCl₃		c	−172.		
VOSO₄		c	−312.5		
VN		c	−41.	−35.	*8.91*
NH₄VO₃		c	−251.2	−211.8	*33.6*
VC		c			*6.77*

[1] Bureau of Standards values in *italics;* estimated values in parentheses.

responding acids are complete. This is in agreement with the ratio of V/H^+ observed by Britton.[1]

For the third ionization, Bray and Tihenko found

$$H_2V_6O_{17}^{--} = HV_6O_{17}^{---} + H^+, \qquad K = 1.1 \times 10_{,}^{-2},$$

and they estimate ca 10^{-5} for the last step. From these data and the free energy of V_2O_5, we write

$$3V_2O_5 + 2H_2O = 2H^+ + H_2V_6O_{17}^{--}, \qquad K = 1.1 \times 10^{-8}$$

and the free energy of $H_2V_6O_{17}^{--}$ is -1135 kcal. and $HV_6O_{17}^{---}$, -1132.

[1] H. T. S. Britton, *J. Chem. Soc.*, 1842 (1934).

Metavanadates, for example, $NaVO_3$, give in solution the ion $V_3O_9^{---}$, the structure probably being a ring of three vanadium and three oxygen atoms alternating with two additional oxygens attached to each vanadium. The co-ordination number of the vanadium is thus four. With the addition of acid, two of the $V_3O_9^{---}$ ions combine to give $H_2V_6O_{17}^{-}$, but the equilibrium constant has not been obtained.

Orthovanadates, for example, Na_3VO_4, are formed by fusing the oxide with alkalies. In solution they appear to hydrolyze with the formation of the divanadate ion, $H_2V_2O_7^{--}$. In these ions the co-ordination number of four is again maintained. The divanadate ion is probably unstable with respect to the metavanadate complex, but this is not certain, and the rate of transformation is slow.

The addition of hydrogen ion to a vanadic acid solution forms pervanadyl ion, VO_2^+, or more probably $V(OH)_4^+$. From the solubility of vanadic oxide in nitric acid, determined also by Meyer and Aulich,

$$V_2O_5 + 2H^+ + 3H_2O = 2V(OH)_4^+, \qquad \Delta F^\circ = ca\ 2500\ cal.$$

The free energy of $V(OH)_4^+$ is -256 kcal. and we may write

$$V + 4H_2O = V(OH)_4^+ + 4H^+ + 5e^-, \qquad E^\circ = 0.253;$$
$$6V + 33OH^- = 16H_2O + HV_6O_{17}^{---} + 30e^-, \qquad E_B^\circ = 1.15.$$

Nothing is known regarding the mechanism of the formation of the hexavanadate by the addition of hydroxide to the pervanadyl.

The vanadyl-pervanadyl couple. From the work of Carpenter[1] and Coryell and Yost[2]

$$3H_2O + VO^{++} = V(OH)_4^+ + 2H^+ + e^-, \qquad E^\circ = -1.000.$$

Vanadic acid at $1M$ hydrogen ion is thus a fairly powerful oxidizing agent and is converted to vanadyl by moderately strong reducing agents.

The V^{+++}—VO^{++} and V^{++}—V^{+++} couples. Jones and Colvin[3] report

$$H_2O + V^{+++} = VO^{++} + 2H^+ + e^-, \qquad E^\circ = -0.361;$$
$$V^{++} = V^{+++} + e^-, \qquad E^\circ = 0.255.$$

The solubilities of the hydroxides, $VO(OH)_2$, $V(OH)_3$, and $V(OH)_2$, are

---

[1] J. E. Carpenter, *J. Am. Chem. Soc.*, **56**, 1847 (1934).
[2] C. D. Coryell and D. M. Yost, *J. Am. Chem. Soc.*, **55**, 1909 (1933).
[3] G. Jones and J. H. Colvin, *J. Am. Chem. Soc.* **66**, 1570 and 1579 (1944).

not known; hence no values can be given for any of the vanadium couples in alkaline solution. However, all these hydroxides appear to be stable with respect to their own oxidation and reduction. Vanadous ion is a powerful reducing agent and the vanadous hydroxide is extremely powerful. This seems to indicate that the vanadic hydroxide is much less soluble than the vanadous.

The metal—V^{++} couple. From the potentials of the three reduction steps given above, we obtain at least an approximate value for the free energy of V^{++} and the potential for its reduction to the metal.

$$V = V^{++} + 2e^-, \qquad E^\circ = \text{ca } 1.18.$$

Vanadium peroxides. Hydrogen peroxide forms both mono- and diperoxyacids with vanadium and, in high acid, at least one of the acids gives a positive peroxy ion. From the heat of formation and an estimated entropy, we calculate the free energy of VO_4^- to be -203.9 kcal.

$$V(OH)_4^+ = VO_4^- + 2e^- + 4H^+, \qquad E^\circ = -1.13.$$

NIOBIUM

Oxidation states. The $+5$ oxidation state, as represented by niobic oxide, Nb_2O_5, is similar to vanadium in the types of acid ions which are formed. The $+4$ oxide, NbO_2, is known but it is difficult to prepare. Solutions containing the ion, Nb^{+++}, or complexes of this ion are made by cathodic reduction or by reduction with zinc, of solutions of niobic oxide in sulfuric, hydrochloric, or hydrofluoric acids. The complex ammonium sulfate has been isolated. It is doubtful if the hydroxide, $Nb(OH)_3$, has been obtained in the pure state, as basic salts appear to be precipitated by alkalies. The oxidation state of the chloride formed by the reduction of the pentachloride by sodium at high temperature is still uncertain. The earlier formula, $(Nb_6Cl_{12})Cl_2 \cdot 7H_2O$, which was assigned to the substance extracted by water, is more likely $H(Nb_3Cl_7H_2O)3H_2O$, but there is some doubt about the niobium being present in the $+2$ state. The formula may be $(Nb_3Cl_7O)3H_2O$.

At least two peroxyniobic acids have been prepared. The formulas assigned are $HNbO_4$ and H_3NbO_8, but there are no data for their free energies. Hydrogen sulfide appears to have no action upon niobic acid or niobates.

Niobic oxide. The oxide is less soluble in water than is vanadic oxide; but, like the latter, it is much more soluble in concentrated acids. Kiehl and Hart[1] found that the solubility in $3M$ H_2SO_4 was about $0.038M$ Nb_2O_5. The solution may contain the ion $Nb(OH)_4^+$, but in more concentrated sulfuric acid probably forms a complex sulfate. The solution in hydrofluoric acid gives salts with the alkalies such as K_2NbOF_5 and $KNbF_6$.

TABLE 59

THERMODYNAMIC DATA ON NIOBIUM[1]

(Heat and free energy formation in kcal. Entropy of substance in cal./deg.)

Formula	Description	State	$\Delta H°$	$\Delta F°$	$S°$
Nb		g	*184.5*	*173.7*	*44.92*
Nb	metal	c	0.0	0.0	*8.3*
Nb_2O_4		c	*−387.8*	−362.4	(29.2)
Nb_2O_5		c	*−463.2*	−432.	(33.)
Nb^{+++}		aq		(−76.)	

[1] Bureau of Standards values in *italics;* estimated values in parentheses.

Ortho- and metamononiobates, and di- and hexaniobates similar to the corresponding vanadates, are known and it seems probable that the conclusions drawn concerning the relation between the meta- and hexavanadate ions in solution also holds true for these niobate ions. This is substantiated by the results of Süe,[2] who reports the precipitated hydrate, $3Nb_2O_5 \cdot 2H_2O$ or $H_4Nb_6O_{17}$. This is probably the formula of the acid in solution. There are no data on the ionization constants of the acid but it is doubtless somewhat weaker than vanadic acid. Süe gave some data for the hydrolysis of niobate solutions.

Niobium potentials. From the heat of formation and an estimated value for the entropy, we calculate −432. kcal. for the free energy of Nb_2O_5.

$$2Nb + 5H_2O = Nb_2O_5 + 10H^+ + 10e^-, \qquad E° = 0.65.$$

Kiehl and Hart[3] measured the e.m.f. of the Nb^{+3}—Nb^{+5} couple in various concentrations of sulfuric acid against a saturated potassium chloride calomel electrode. Using $3.14M$ H_2SO_4 and equal concentra-

[1] S. J. Kiehl and D. Hart, *J. Am. Chem. Soc.*, **50**, 2337 (1928).

[2] P. Süe, *Compt. rend.*, **194**, 1745 (1932).

[3] S. J. Kiehl and D. Hart, *J. Am. Chem. Soc.*, **50**, 2337 (1928).

tions of niobium in the two oxidation states, they found for the cell 0.373; and for 9.87M H_2SO_4, 0.426. It is difficult to account for the increase in potential at higher acid concentrations unless the $+5$ niobium forms a very stable complex with sulfate ion. The formula of this ion is not known but we will assume $NbO(SO_4)_2^-$ and write as an approximate value,

$$2SO_4^{--} + H_2O + Nb^{+++} = NbO(SO_4)_2^- + 2H^+ + 2e^-, \quad E^\circ = ca\ 0.1.$$

From the solubility data for niobic oxide in sulfuric acid by Kiehl and Hart, cited above, the free energy of solution of the oxide must be around 3000 cal. Hence, for the over-all potential for the Nb—NbO-$(SO_4)_2^-$ couple,

$$H_2O + 2SO_4^{--} + Nb = NbO(SO_4)_2^- + 2H^+ + 5e^-, \qquad E^\circ = 0.63,$$

and the potential for the Nb—$Nb(SO_4)_2^-$ couple is probably the same. This, then, gives

$$Nb = Nb^{+++} + 3e^-, \qquad E^\circ = ca\ 1.1.$$

However, in the $3M$ H_2SO_4 solution, the $+3$ niobium was probably not the simple ion Nb^{+++}.

Ott[1] reported the formation of the dioxide, NbO_2, by the reduction of solution of the complex fluoride, K_2NbOF_5; but Kiehl and Hart found no evidence for the $+4$ state. These authors stated that the $+3$ state was brown in concentrated acid solutions but became blue upon dilution, without change in the equivalents of reducing power.

No values can be given for the niobium potentials in alkaline solution. Isgarischew and Kaplan[2] reported the cathodic reduction of niobium in solutions of potassium hydroxide and oxalic acid with the formation of a mixture of the metal and intermediate solids which were not further reduced.

TANTALUM

Oxidation states. The only important compounds of tantalum are the oxide and halides of the $+5$ oxidation state and their derivatives. There is some evidence of the dioxide, TaO_2. When the pentachloride is heated with sodium and the resulting product extracted

[1] F. Ott, *Z. Elektrochem.*, **18**, 349 (1912).

[2] N. Isgarischew and G. E. Kaplan, *Z. Elektrochem.*, **40**, 33 (1934).

with water, a soluble complex is formed. Lindner[1] offers evidence in favor of the formula $H(Ta_3Cl_7H_2O)3H_2O$, which is a compound of the $+2$ oxidation state. However, Ruff and Thomas[2] believe the formula to be $(Ta_3Cl_7O)3H_2O$, that is, a compound of the $+3$ state.

The disulfide, TaS_2, is formed at high temperatures by direct union of the elements. When heated in water it forms the pentoxide, hydrogen, and hydrogen sulfide. There is no reaction between sulfide ion and tantalates in solution.

Hydrogen peroxide acts upon tantalates to form peroxytantalates. Salts of the acids $HTaO_4$ and H_3TaO_8 have been reported but no energy data can be given.

Tantalic oxide and fluoride. The oxide Ta_2O_5 is practically insoluble in perchloric or nitric acids. It dissolves slightly in sulfuric

TABLE 60

THERMODYNAMIC DATA ON TANTALUM[1]

(Heat and free energy of formation in kcal. Entropy of substance in cal./deg.)

Formula	Description	State	$\Delta H°$	$\Delta F°$	$S°$
Ta		g	*185.*	*175.*	*44.244*
Ta	metal	c	0.0	0.0	*9.9*
TaN		c	-58.2		
TaC		c			10.1
Ta₂O₅		c	-499.9	-470.6	*34.2*

[1] Bureau of Standards values in *italics*.

acid and more readily in oxalic acid, doubtless with the formation of complex sulfate and oxalate ions. No quantitative data have been obtained for any of these solubilities.

With alkalies, tantalates are formed, the most important being derivatives of hypothetical hexa-acids, for example, $(NH_4)_2Ta_6O_{16}\cdot5H_2O$ and $Na_8Ta_6O_{19}\cdot25H_2O$.

The pentafluoride TaF_5 forms by direct combination of the elements. It, and also the oxide, are soluble in hydrofluoric acid to give complex fluo-acids. Common potassium salts are $KTaF_6$, K_2TaF_7, and $KTaOF_4$.

[1] K. Lindner, *Z. anorg. allgem. Chem.*, **160**, 57 (1927).

[2] O. Ruff and F. Thomas, *Z. anorg. allgem. Chem.*, **148**, 19 (1925).

Tantalum potentials.   From the free energy of the pentoxide, we may write

$$2Ta + 5H_2O = Ta_2O_5 + 10H^+ + 10e^-, \qquad E° = 0.81.$$

Hevesy and Slade[1] studied the potential of the Ta—TaF$_5$ couple. They reported that tantalum in the passive state was more electronegative than silver and, when active, about like copper. From the potential calculated above and the solubility of the oxide in hydrofluoric acid it is obvious that their electrode, even in its active state, was far from the equilibrium potential.

No values can be given for the couple in alkaline solution. Except for the complex chloride, noted above, which was prepared by reduction at high temperature, there is no evidence of the existence of tantalum in lower oxidation states in water solutions.

Summary of group potentials.   For ease in comparison, the following summary of potential diagrams is given:

Acid Solution

```
    ca 1.2      0.25      −0.36           −1.0
V──────────V+2───────V+3────────VO++──────── V(OH)₄⁺
 |                        0.253                      |

         ca 1.1                    ca 0.1
Nb──────────────────Nb+3─────  ─────────Nb₂O₅
 |                     0.65                    |

                      0.81
Ta─────────────────────────────────────Ta₂O₅
```

[1] G. von Hevesy and R. E. Slade, *Z. Elektrochem.*, **18**, 1001 (1912).

CHAPTER 18

Titanium, Zirconium, and Hafnium

The elements of this group have four valence electrons, d^2s^2, and the lowest electronic state in the gaseous atoms is the $^3F_2$. The most important oxidation state is the $+4$. Cerium and thorium in their $+4$ states also resemble the elements of this group in many of their properties. However, since the evidence is definite that cerium has one $4f$ electron and thorium (probably) one $5f$ electron, these elements will be discussed with the lanthanide and actinide groups.

TITANIUM

Oxidation states. Titanium forms compounds of the $+2$, $+3$, and $+4$ oxidation states. The oxides of all three states are known but only the dioxide, TiO_2, is stable in contact with water. The spectrum of the monoxide is common in the light from certain types of stars. The two lower oxides are basic and the dioxide is amphoteric. The tetrafluoride is acidic and forms salts of the type K_2TiF_6; the trifluoride is also slightly acidic. The soluble peroxy-acid, H_2TiO_4, is well known.

Titanium dioxide. For the Ti—TiO_2 couple, we calculate from the free energies

$$Ti + 2H_2O = TiO_2(\text{hydrated}) + 4H^+ + 4e^-, \qquad E^\circ = 0.86.$$

The electrode is highly irreversible, and no direct measurements of the potential can be made. The unhydrated oxide does not dissolve appreciably in either acids or bases, but the hydrated forms are somewhat soluble in both. The two hydrates $TiO_2 \cdot H_2O$ and $TiO_2 \cdot 2H_2O$ are known. As a very rough approximation, we shall take the free energy of $TiO(OH)_2$ as equal to that of the hydrated oxide plus water, *i.e.*, to -196.3 kcal. plus -56.7 kcal., and write,

$$TiO(OH)_2 = TiO^{++} + 2OH^-, \qquad K = \text{ca } 10^{-29}.$$

TABLE 61

THERMODYNAMIC DATA ON TITANIUM[1]

(Heat and free energy of formation in kcal. Entropy of substance in cal./deg.)

Formula	Description	State	$\Delta H°$	$\Delta F°$	$S°$
Ti		g	95.	84.	43.069
Ti	metal	c	0.0	0.0	7.24
Ti$^+$		g	254.09		
Ti^{++}		g	570.0		
Ti^{++}		aq		(−75.1)	
Ti^{+++}		g	1208.0		
Ti^{+++}		aq		(−83.6)	
TiO		g	26.		
TiO		c			8.31
TiO$_2$	rutile III	c	−218.0	−203.8	12.01
TiO$_2$	hydrated	c	−207.	−196.3	
TiO(OH)$_2$		c		−253.	
TiO^{++}		aq		−138.	
Ti$_2$O$_3$		c	−367.	−346.	18.83
Ti$_3$O$_5$		c	−584.	−550.	30.92
TiF$_2$		c	−198.	187.1	(19.2)
TiF$_3$		c	−315.	−290.9	(21.8)
TiF$_4$		c	−370.	−346.3	(29.8)
TiF$_6$$^{--}$		aq	−555.1	−506.3	(20.)
TiCl		g	105.		
TiCl$_2$		c	−114.	−96.	(26.)
TiCl$_3$		c	−165.	−148.	(30.5)
TiCl$_4$		g			84.4
TiCl$_4$		liq	−179.3	−161.2	60.4
TiBr$_2$		c	−95.	−91.4	(31.6)
TiBr$_3$		c	−132.	−124.6	(36.8)
TiBr$_4$		c	−155.	−146.	(49.8)
TiI$_2$		c	−61.	−61.6	(37.)
TiI$_3$		c	−80.	−76.5	(47.3)
TiI$_4$		c	−102.	−102.	(61.8)
TiN		c	−73.0	−66.1	7.20
TiC		c	−54.	−53.	5.8
FeTiO$_3$		c	−288.5	−268.9	25.3

[1] Bureau of Standards values in *italics;* estimated values in parentheses.

We have no assurance that the principal ion is TiO^{++} in the saturated solution or in $1M$ acid, but an approximate value for the free energy of TiO^{++} consistent with the solubility product is -138 kcal., and we may write,

$$Ti + H_2O = TiO^{++} + 2H^+ + 4e^-, \qquad E° = ca\ 0.88.$$

Even the qualitative data on the solubility of the hydrated oxide in alkalies are conflicting, and no values will be given for the formation of the titanate ions. The common salts are derivatives of the meta-acid, for example, Na_2TiO_3, but di-, tri-, and pentatitanates are also known.

The Ti^{+3}—TiO^{++} couple. Diethelm and Foerster[1] studied the potential of solutions containing $+3$ and $+4$ titanium. For equal concentrations of the two ions in $4.1N$ H_2SO_4 they found $E° = -0.056$. Although they calculated their results for the ions, Ti^{+3} and Ti^{+4}, the potential was a function of the hydrogen ion, becoming more negative with higher acid concentration. Without attempting to recalculate their results in terms of activities, we shall write

$$H_2O + Ti^{+3} = TiO^{++} + 2H^+ + e^-, \qquad E° = ca\ -0.1.$$

From the free energies of Table 61,

$$2TiO_2 + H_2 = Ti_2O_3 + H_2O, \qquad \Delta F° = 4.9\ kcal.$$

Nasu[2] found 5.28 kcal. at 25°, calculated from equilibrium measurements at high temperature. We have no data on the hydration of Ti_2O_3 or the solubility of the hydroxide. In comparison with $Fe(OH)_3$ and $Cr(OH)_3$, a solubility product of about 10^{-30} would be expected, but a value of 10^{-40} would appear to be indicated by the free energy of Ti^{+++}.

$$Ti(OH)_3 = Ti^{+++} + 3OH^-, \qquad K = ca\ 10^{-40}.$$

The sesquioxide is unstable in water with respect to the evolution of hydrogen as shown in the equation written above. Experimentally this instability increases in alkali. The reduction of titanyl in acid solution is readily accomplished by zinc or by electrolysis.

The Ti^{++}—Ti^{+++} couple. Forbes and Hall[3] prepared a mixture of the chlorides, $TiCl_2$ and $TiCl_3$, by the action of hydrogen chloride upon finely divided titanium, and measured the potential of the couple at 0° C., using a mercury electrode. They gave for the $E°$ at 0° C., 0.37 volt. Although entropy of the reaction (with H_2—H^+ couple) is about 15 units, we shall not make the temperature correction but will give as an approximate value the same potential at 25° C.

$$Ti^{++} = Ti^{+++} + e^-, \qquad E° = ca\ 0.37.$$

[1] B. Diethelm and F. Foerster, *Z. physik. Chem.*, **62**, 129 (1908).
[2] N. Nasu, *J. Chem. Soc. Japan*, **56**, 659 (1935).
[3] G. S. Forbes and L. P. Hall, *J. Am. Chem. Soc.*, **46**, 385 (1924).

Considering the reactivity of the Ti^{++} ion, this potential appears to be lower than would be expected. However, it may be that the ion is simply a more rapid reducing agent. At any rate, it is impossible to have appreciable concentrations of $+2$ titanium in solutions which have an acidity greater than $0.1N$ H^+.

The $+2$ hydroxide, $Ti(OH)_2$, is less stable than the positive ion and readily evolves hydrogen. This is to be expected inasmuch as the solubility of the $+2$ hydroxide is doubtless much greater than that of the $+4$.

The Ti—Ti^{++} potential. From the potentials relating TiO^{++} to the metal and to the lower oxidation states, we may now calculate

$$Ti = Ti^{++} + 2e^-, \qquad E° = 1.63.$$

As this very positive value indicates, titanium cannot be precipitated by cathodic reduction in water solutions. However, the metal is very passive and is not readily oxidized by mild oxidizing agents.

Fluotitanate. Titanium dioxide dissolves in hydrofluoric acid with the formation of the fluotitanate, TiF_6^{--}. From the heat of formation, -555.1 cal., we may make a rough calculation of its free energy, using the estimated entropy of the ion as 20 cal./deg. The value is -506.3 cal. This gives for the metal-fluotitanate couple

$$6F^- + Ti = TiF_6^{--} + 4e^-, \qquad E° = 1.19.$$

Solid fluotitanites, such as $(NH_4)_2TiF_5$, have been prepared, but there is no evidence of their formation in solution by reduction of the $+4$ complex.

Summary of titanium potentials. The following diagram summarizes the titanium potentials:

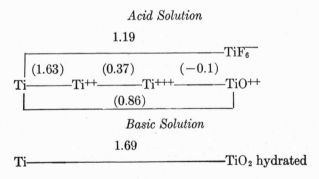

Acid Solution

1.19

Ti——Ti^{++}——Ti^{+++}——TiO^{++}——TiF$_6^{--}$
(1.63)   (0.37)   (−0.1)
(0.86)

Basic Solution

1.69

Ti————————————TiO$_2$ hydrated

ZIRCONIUM

Oxidation states. The only oxidation state stable in water solutions is the +4. The dioxide is somewhat more basic than titanium dioxide and, when hydrated, dissolves in concentrated acid. The solubility of the oxide in alkaline solution is slight and the zirconates are

TABLE 62

THERMODYNAMIC DATA ON ZIRCONIUM[1]

(Heat and free energy of formation in kcal. Entropy of substance in cal./deg.)

Formula	Description	State	$\Delta H°$	$\Delta F°$	$S°$
Zr		g	*125.*	*115.*	*43.313*
Zr	metal	c	0.0	0.0	*9.18*
Zr$^+$		g	*286.78*		
Zr^{++}		g	*611.84*		
Zr^{+++}		g	*1169.0*		
Zr^{+4}		aq		−141.	
ZrO^{++}		aq	−*223.1* (?)	−200.9 (?)	
ZrO$_2$		c	−*258.2*	−*244.4*	*12.03*
ZrO$_2$	hydrated	c	−*283.5* (?)		
ZrO(OH)$_2$		c	−*338.0*	−*311.5*	(22.)
Zr(OH)$_4$		c	−*411.2*	−*370.*	(31.)
HZrO$_3^-$				−287.7	
ZrF$_2$		c	−*230.*	−*219.2*	(21.5)
ZrF$_3$		c	−*350.*	−*332.8*	(24.1)
ZrF$_4$		c	−*445.*	−*424.3*	(32.1)
ZrCl$_2$		c	−*145.*	−134.8	(28.3)
ZrCl$_3$		c	−*208.*	−191.	(32.8)
ZrCl$_4$		c	−*230.*	−*209.*	*44.5*
ZrBr$_2$		c	−*120*	−116.5	(33.9)
ZrBr$_3$		c	−*174.*	−166.6	(39.1)
ZrBr$_4$		c	−*192.*	−183.1	(52.1)
ZrI$_2$		c	−*90.*	−90.7	(39.3)
ZrI$_3$		c	−*128.*	−128.	(49.6)
ZrI$_4$		c	−*130.*	−130.	(64.1)
Zr(SO$_4$)$_2$		c	−*597.4*	−538.9	(24.1)
ZrN		c	−*82.2*	−*75.4*	*9.23*
ZrC		c	−*45.*		

[1] Bureau of Standards values in *italics*; estimated values in parentheses.

much less stable than the titanates. The tetrafluoride forms numerous fluozirconates, for example, Na$_2$ZrF$_6$, but their thermodynamic properties have not been studied. Around 250° C. solid zirconium tetrachloride is reduced by powerful metallic reducing agents to the +3 and $+2$ chlorides. Hydrogen is evolved by the reaction of these chlorides with water.

Zirconium potentials. In agreement with the free energy of formation of the dioxide, -244.4 kcal.,

$$Zr + 2H_2O = ZrO_2 + 4H^+ + 4e^-, \qquad E^\circ = 1.43.$$

It has been generally assumed that the principal ion in acid solution is zirconyl ZrO^{++}, but recent experimental evidence casts considerable doubt on this assumption. Connick[1] has concluded that the ion in acid solution is Zr^{+4} and that the first step of the hydrolysis goes directly to a colloid. For a perchlorate solution with ionic strength of 2, he found

$$Zr^{+4} + 3H_2O + ClO_4^- = Zr(OH)_3ClO_4 \text{ (colloid)} + 3H^+,$$
$$K = 6 \times 10^2.$$

We will assume that the solubility of the hydroxide in acid gives approximately the same ratio of Zr^{+4} to H^+ and write

$$Zr(OH)_4 + 4H^+ = Zr^{+4} + 4H_2O, \qquad K = 6 \times 10^{-2}.$$

This would make the free energy of Zr^{+4}, $-141.$ kcal., and

$$Zr = Zr^{+4} + 4e^-, \qquad E^\circ = 1.53.$$

However, an additional uncertainty is the heat of formation of the hydroxide and other hydrated oxides of zirconium. From the Bureau of Standards values the heat of hydration of TiO_2 is $+11$ kcal., and that of ZrO_2, -25.3 kcal. Such a large difference appears unreasonable. From the constant above we can also write

$$Zr(OH)_4 = Zr^{+4} + 4OH^-, \qquad K = 6 \times 10^{-58}.$$

Larsen and Gammil[2] reported

$$ZrO(OH)_2 = ZrO^{++} + 2OH^-, \qquad K = 3 \times 10^{-26}.$$

We do not know which interpretation is correct.

The solubility of the hydrated oxide was reported by Venable and Clark[3] as 6×10^{-4} moles per liter of H_2ZrO_3 in 2.5M KOH. The

---

[1] R. E. Connick, private communication.

[2] E. M. Larsen and A. M. Gammil, *J. Am. Chem. Soc.* **72**, 3615 (1950).

[3] F. P. Venable and T. Clark, *J. Am. Chem. Soc.*, **18**, 434 (1896).

formula of the zirconate in solution is not known, but we shall use

$$H_2ZrO_3(c) + OH^- = HZrO_3^- + H_2O, \qquad\qquad K = ca\ 10^{-4};$$
$$4OH^- + Zr = H_2ZrO_3 + H_2O + 4e^-, \qquad\qquad E_B^o = 2.36.$$

Solid zirconates, such as Na_2ZrO_3, Na_4ZrO_4, and $Li_2Zr_2O_5$, have been prepared by fusion of the oxide with alkalies.

Zirconyl hydrogen phosphate, $ZrO(HPO_4)_2$, is very slightly soluble. Hevesy and Kimura[1] reported its solubility as 1.2×10^{-4} moles per liter in $6N$ HCl.

Zirconium disulfide, ZrS_2, and zirconyl sulfide, $ZrOS$, have been prepared at high temperatures, but neither of these sulfides can be precipitated from water solutions.

Zirconyl oxalate, $ZrOC_2O_4$, is precipitated from acid solutions by oxalic acid; the precipitate is soluble in excess oxalic acid and in ammonium oxalate with the formation of complex oxalate ions, but no quantitative data can be given.

Connick and McVey[2] have studied the complex ions of zirconium with sulfate and fluoride. They reported

$$H^+ + ZrSO_4^{++} = Zr^{+4} + HSO_4^-, \qquad\qquad K_1 = 1.7 \times 10^{-3};$$
$$H^+ + Zr(SO_4)_2 = ZrSO_4^{++} + HSO_4^-, \qquad\qquad K_2 = 1.9 \times 10^{-2};$$
$$H^+ + Zr(SO_4)_3^{--} = Zr(SO_4)_2 + HSO_4^-, \qquad\qquad K_3 = 1;$$
$$H^+ + ZrF^{+++} = Zr^{+4} + HF, \qquad\qquad K_1 = 1.6 \times 10^{-6};$$
$$H^+ + ZrF_2^{++} = ZrF^{+++} + HF, \qquad\qquad K_2 = 4.8 \times 10^{-5};$$
$$H^+ + ZrF_3^+ = ZrF_2^{++} + HF, \qquad\qquad K_3 = 1.5 \times 10^{-3}.$$

HAFNIUM

Oxidation states.   Only compounds of the $+4$ oxidation state are known. No reduction of the oxide or halides, even at high temperatures, has been reported. The similarity between $+4$ compounds of hafnium and zirconium is remarkable, and the difficulties of separation are comparable to the separation of neighboring elements of the rare earth group. A few slight differences in the properties of compounds of the two elements may be noted. Hafnyl chloride is somewhat less soluble in concentrated hydrochloric acid than is zirconyl chloride. The ammonium hexofluohafniate is slightly more soluble at

---

[1] G. von Hevesy and K. Kimura, *J. Am. Chem. Soc.*, **47**, 2540 (1925).
[2] R. E. Connick and W. H. McVey, *J. Am. Chem. Soc.*, **71**, 3188 (1949).

0° C. than is the fluozirconate. Hafnium salicylate is less soluble than zirconium salicylate. In general the reactions of hafnium indicate that the oxide is slightly more basic than is zirconium oxide; hence, hafnyl compounds hydrolyze to a greater extent, and the compounds with acid oxides, for example, $HfOSO_4$ and $HfO(NO_3)_2$, decompose into their respective oxides at slightly higher temperatures.

TABLE 63

THERMODYNAMIC DATA ON HAFNIUM[1]

(Heat and free energy of formation in kcal. Entropy of substance in cal./deg.)

Formula	Description	State	$\Delta H°$	$\Delta F°$	$S°$
Hf		c			*44.65*
Hf	metal	c	0.0	0.0	*13.1*
HfO_2		c	*−271.5*	−258.	(15.8)
$Hf(OH)_2$		c		(−325.5)	

[1] Bureau of Standards values in *italics;* estimated values in parentheses.

Hafnium free energies. From the heat of formation of the dioxide and an estimated entropy, we calculate

$$Hf + 2H_2O = HfO_2 + 4H^+ + 4e^-, \qquad E° = 1.57.$$

There are no data on the free energy of hydration of the dioxide. Larsen and Gammil[1] give

$$HfO(OH)_2 = HfO^{++} + 2OH^-, \qquad K = 4 \times 10^{-26}.$$

The radii of Hf^{+4} and Zr^{+4} are almost the same, and it is to be expected that their basic character would be very similar. By comparison with zirconium we write

$$Hf = Hf^{+4} + 4e^-, \qquad E° = 1.70.$$

The free energy of solution of the hydrated oxide in alkali is doubtless nearly the same as the value for the zirconium oxide. Since the solubility is small, we shall write for the potential in alkaline solution

$$4OH^- + Hf = HfO(OH)_2 + H_2O + 4e^-, \qquad E_B° = 2.50.$$

The status of the data pertaining to the sulfides, phosphates, and oxalates is similar to that for zirconium.

[1] *Loc. cit.*

Summary of group potentials. The titanium potentials were summarized at the end of the discussion of that element. For comparison, the over-all potentials from the metals to the $+4$ state in acid solution are given below.

$$\text{Ti} \underset{(0.89)}{\overline{\hspace{3cm}}} \text{TiO}^{++}$$

$$\text{Zr} \underset{1.56}{\overline{\hspace{3cm}}} \text{Zr}^{+4}$$

$$\text{Hf} \underset{1.70}{\overline{\hspace{3cm}}} \text{Hf}^{+4}$$

CHAPTER 19

Boron, Aluminum, Scandium, and Yttrium

In the monatomic gaseous atoms of boron and aluminum, the ground state of the three valence electrons is $s^2p^1(^2P_{\frac{1}{2}})$ and in scandium and yttrium it is $s^2d^1(^2P_{\frac{3}{2}})$. However, the $+3$ ions all have similar "eight-electron" outer shells in their kernels and, since the chemistry of the ions is more important than that of the gaseous atoms, it is logical to group these elements together. Lanthanum and actinium also belong in the group, but the former will be discussed in connection with the rare earth, or lanthanide elements, and the latter with the actinide elements. The elements of the group are highly electropositive, and practically no free energies have been obtained by direct equilibrium measurements involving the elements. Thermal data are also meager and permit few accurate third-law calculations.

BORON

Oxidation states. The preparation of pure solid boron has been difficult; most of the older heat determinations refer to an amorphous form containing some oxide or metallic borides. Pure crystalline boron has now been prepared and this is taken as the standard state of the element. The oxide, BO, is known as a gas molecule from spectroscopic data, and the suboxides B_7O and B_3O have been reported. However, there is no definite proof that these substances are not small amounts of B_2O_3 in amorphous boron. A number of boron hydrogen compounds, for example, B_2H_6, B_4H_{10}, B_5H_9, are well known. No oxidation numbers will be assigned the boron in these compounds. The bonds are definitely nonpolar, but there are not enough electrons to give electron-pair bonds. Their structure has been discussed by Pauling,[1] who formulated the structures in terms of one-electron

---

[1] L. Pauling, *J. Am. Chem. Soc.*, **53**, 3225 (1931).

TABLE 64

THERMODYNAMIC DATA ON BORON[1]

(Heat and free energy of formation in kcal. Entropy of substance in cal./deg.)

Formula	Description	State	$\Delta H°$	$\Delta F°$	$S°$
B		g	*97.2*	*86.7*	*36.649*
B	crystalline	c	0.0	0.0	*1.56*
B	amorph.	c	*0.4*		
B^+		g	*290.0*		
B^{++}		g	*871.46*		
B_2		g	*124.5*		
BO		g	*−5.3*	*−11.6*	*47.22*
BO_2^-		aq	*−183.5* (?)	*−169.6* (?)	(20.)
B_2O_3		c	*−302.0*	*−283.0*	*12.91*
B_2O_3		glass	*−297.6*	*−280.4*	*18.8*
$B_4O_7^{--}$		aq		*−616.* (?)	
BH		g	*73.8*	*67.1*	*39.62*
B_2H_6	diborane	g	*7.5*	*19.8*	*55.66*
B_5H_9	pentaborane	g	*15.0*	*39.6*	*65.88*
B_5H_9		liq	*7.8*	*38.8*	*44.16*
$B_{10}H_{14}$	decaborane	c	*8.*		
HBO_2		c	*−186.9*	*−170.5*	*11.*
HBO_2		aq	*−186.9*		
$H_2BO_3^-$		aq	*−251.8*	*−217.6*	*7.3*
H_3BO_3		c	*−260.2*	*−230.2*	*21.41*
H_3BO_3		aq	*−255.2*	*−230.24*	*38.2*
$H_2B_4O_7$		c	*−676.5*		
BF		g	*−17.4*		
BF_3		g	*−265.4*	*−261.3*	*60.70*
BF_4^-		aq	*−365.*	*−343.*	*40.*
BCl		g	*25.6*		
BCl_3		g	*−94.5*	*−90.9*	*69.29*
BCl_3		liq	*−100.0*	*−90.6*	*50.0*
BBr		g	*25.0*		
BBr_3		g	*−44.6*	*−51.0*	*77.49*
BBr_3		liq	*−52.8*	*−52.4*	*54.7*
B_2S_3		c	*−57.0*	*−53.3*	(13.7)
BN		g	*90.6*		
$B_3N_3H_6$	borazole	g			*73.7*
$B(CH_3)_3$		liq	*−31.4*		
$LiBH_4$		c	*−44.15*		
$NaBH_4$		c	*−43.83*		

[1] Bureau of Standards values in *italics;* estimated values in parentheses.

bonds, and by Pitzer[1] who has suggested protonated double bonds, as for example, the following formula for diborane:

$$
\begin{array}{ccc}
\text{H} & \text{H} & \text{H} \\
\cdot\ \ \cdot & \cdot\cdot & \cdot\ \ \cdot \\
& \text{B} \quad\quad \text{B} & \\
\cdot\ \ \cdot & \cdot\cdot & \cdot\ \ \cdot \\
\text{H} & \text{H} & \text{H}
\end{array}
$$

The action of potassium hydroxide on Mg_3B gives

$$
\begin{array}{c}
\text{HB—OH} \\
\| \\
\text{HB—OH}
\end{array}
$$

and both the cis- and trans-forms are known. Compounds, such as $H_2B_4O_2$ and $H_2B_2O_4$, have been prepared. There are also compounds in which B—N resembles C—C; for example $B_3N_3H_6$, borazole, which is similar to benzene, C_6H_6, in its physical properties. Many interesting derivatives of the group BH_4^-, such as $NaBH_4$ and $Ca(BH_4)_2$, are also known, but no thermodynamic data are available.

The important oxidation state is $+3$ and the oxide, B_2O_3, is the anhydride of the weak boric acids which are discussed below in some detail. The oxide has slight basic properties. The trihalides form at high temperatures, but all except the fluoride hydrolyze completely in water with the formation of boric acid. The fluoride forms complex ions, for example, BF_4^-. The sulfide, B_2S_3, is also completely hydrolyzed in water.

Boric acids and their salts.   The solid acid, H_3BO_3, is somewhat soluble in cold water and quite soluble in hot. The solubility at 25° C. is 0.933 moles per 1000 grams H_2O. Salts of the orthoacid, H_3BO_3, may be formed by fusing the acid with alkalies, but in water the orthoion is hydrolyzed.

$$BO_3^{---} + 2H_2O = H_2BO_3^- + 2OH^-.$$

In solution one cannot distinguish between the dihydrogen orthoion, $H_2BO_3^-$, and the metaion, BO_2^-. Salts of the latter readily crystallize from water solution, but the formula $H_2BO_3^-$ will be used. At low concentrations of boric acid the molecular species is H_3BO_3 or HBO_2.

---

[1] K. S. Pitzer, *J. Am. Chem. Soc.*, **67**, 1126 (1945).

From the free energies we calculate for the ionization constant of $H_3BO_3(aq)$

$$H_3BO_3 = H_2BO_3^- + H^+, \qquad K = 6.0 \times 10^{-10}.$$

Owens[1] gave 5.8×10^{-10} for this constant. The thermal data on BO_2^- are inconsistent with the free energy of $H_2BO_3^-$. At high concentrations the acid polymerises with the formation of tetraboric acid, $H_2B_4O_7$, and possibly more complicated polyacids. This acid is considerably stronger than the orthoacid.

Kolthoff[2] has studied the concentration of hydrogen ion in these solutions. Assuming that the ionization

$$H_2B_4O_7 = H^+ + HB_4O_7^-$$

is much greater than that of the orthoacid, he has shown that at concentrations above $0.5M$

$$\frac{(H^+)^2}{(H_3BO_3)^4} = K = 9.7 \times 10^{-8} \text{ at } 18° \text{ C.}$$

Metaborates in dilute solution hydrolyze in a normal manner with the formation of the acid H_3BO_3 and hydroxide as indicated by the value for the acid constant given above. However, the tetraborate ion decomposes according to the equation

$$B_4O_7^{--} + 5H_2O = 2H_3BO_3 + 2H_2BO_3^-, \qquad K = \text{ca } 10^{-3}.$$

The value of the constant is taken from some unpublished calculations by Bray[3] on distribution ratio experiments with borate and boric acid solutions by Mueller and Abegg.[4] Hence, at concentrations of tetraborate below $0.1M$, the ion is largely decomposed and the alkalinity is determined by the hydrolysis of the $H_2BO_3^-$ ion. The constant for the complex formation in alkaline solution could be compared with the constant found by Kolthoff in acid solution if the second dissociation constant of the tetraboric acid were known.[5] It is estimated that

$$H_2B_4O_7 = H^+ + HB_4O_7^-, \qquad K = \text{ca } 10^{-4}.$$

[1] B. B. Owens, *J. Am. Chem. Soc.*, **56**, 1695 (1934).
[2] I. M. Kolthoff, *Rec. trav. chim.*, **45**, 501 (1926).
[3] W. C. Bray, unpublished material, University of California, 1928.
[4] P. Mueller and R. Abegg, *Z. physik. Chem.*, **57**, 513 (1906).
[5] The author is indebted to Professor W. C. Bray for this observation.

It may also be pointed out that, since the dissociation of the tetra-borate ion gives approximately equal concentrations of H_3BO_3 and $H_2BO_3^-$, the hydrogen ion concentration in tetraborate solutions is equal to K for H_3BO_3 at low concentration.

$$(H^+) = \frac{K(H_3BO_3)}{H_2BO_3^-} = K \qquad (\text{when } H_3BO_3 = H_2BO_3^-).$$

At high concentrations the pH is complicated by the hydrolysis of $B_4O_7^{--}$ to give $HB_4O_7^-$, which probably has a constant of around 10^{-5}.

Boron potentials. From the free energy of formation of boric acid (aqueous), -230.24 kcal., we calculate

$$3H_2O + B = H_3BO_3 + 3H^+ + 3e^-, \qquad E^\circ = 0.87.$$

In view of this comparatively small potential for the reduction of boron, it is odd that the element cannot be obtained by reduction in water solutions. Its behavior in this respect is similar to carbon. Amorphous boron has been prepared by the cathodic reduction of the fused oxide and halides or of mixtures of the two, but the process is not a satisfactory one.

From the dissociation constant of the acid, we calculate for the free energy of ionization, 12,600 cal., and for the free energy of formation of the ion, $H_2BO_3^-$, -217.6 cal. The potential in alkaline solution then is

$$4OH^- + B = H_2BO_3^- + 2H_2O + 3e^-, \qquad E_B^\circ = 1.79.$$

The potential of the B—BF_4^- couple is

$$4F^- + B = BF_4^- + 3e^-, \qquad E^\circ = 1.04.$$

Ryss[1] reported

$$BF_4^- + H_2O = BF_3OH^- + HF, \qquad K = 2.8 \times 10^{-3}.$$

In alkaline solution BF_4^- is completely hydrolyzed:

$$BF_4^- + 4OH^- = H_2BO_3^- + 4F^- + H_2O, \qquad \Delta F^\circ = -45. \text{ kcal.}$$

Heteroboric acids. The polyalcohols, especially those with hydroxyl groups on adjacent carbon atoms, combine with boric acid

---

[1] I. G. Ryss, *Compt. rend. (U.S.S.R.)*, **52**, 47 (1946).

to form heteroacids of the types

$$
\begin{array}{c}
>C\!-\!O \\
 \diagdown \\
\Big|B\!-\!OH \\
 \diagup \\
>C\!-\!O
\end{array}
\quad\text{and}\quad
\left[\;
\begin{array}{c}
>C\!-\!O \diagdown O\!-\!C< \\
\Big|B\Big| \\
>C\!-\!O \diagup O\!-\!C<
\end{array}
\;\right]
H^+.
$$

With the more complicated alcohols, such as mannitol, two or three molecules of boric acid may react with one molecule of the alcohol.

Kolthoff[1] studied the complex with glycerine, and gave the following equilibrium constants:

$$
H_3BO_3 + \text{glycerine} = H_3BO_3\cdot\text{glycerine}, \qquad K = 0.9;
$$
$$
H_3BO_3\cdot\text{glycerine} = H^+ + A^-, \qquad K = 3 \times 10^{-7}.
$$

Advantage has been taken of the increased strengths of the hetero-boric acids in the standard volumetric titration of boric acid with alkali.

Yabroff, Branch, and Bettman[2] have determined the ionization constants of a number of hydrocarbon boric acids and have discussed their results in terms of the resonance and negativity of the various groups. They gave the following constants:

PHENYLBORIC ACID, $K = 137 \times 10^{-10};$
o-TOLYLBORIC ACID, $K = 18.1 \times 10^{-10};$
BENZYLBORIC ACID, $K = 75.5 \times 10^{-10};$
β-PHENYLETHYLBORIC ACID, $K = 10.0 \times 10^{-10};$
n-BUTYLBORIC ACID, $K = 1.82 \times 10^{-10}.$

ALUMINUM

Oxidation states. The only stable oxidation state is that of $+3$ aluminum. The hydroxide is amphoteric; with acids it forms compounds of the ion, Al^{+++}, and with bases, salts of the metaluminate ion, AlO_2^-, and a few salts of orthoaluminate and polyaluminate ions. The fluoride is acidic, and many fluoaluminates are known. Aluminum sulfide and carbonate are completely hydrolyzed. The phosphate is

---

[1] I. M. Kolthoff, *Rec. trav. chim.*, **44**, 975 (1925).

[2] D. L. Yabroff, G. E. K. Branch, and B. Bettman, *J. Am. Chem. Soc.*, **56**, 1852 (1934).

but slightly soluble. Some evidence has been obtained for an unstable +1 state as an intermediate in the oxidation of aluminum in liquid ammonia.

Aluminum potentials.   Numerous attempts have been made to measure the potential of the aluminum electrode. The best results have been obtained with aluminum amalgam but the potentials, at least in acid solution, have not been reproducible. Latimer and Greensfelder[1] determined the entropy of cesium alum and aluminum ion, and calculated a potential for the couple. The data in Table 65 are a recalculation of that value.

$$Al = Al^{+++} + 3e^-, \qquad E^\circ = 1.66.$$

For the couple in alkaline solution, our calculated value for the free energy of the hydroxide gives

$$Al \quad + 3OH^- = Al(OH)_3 + 3e^-, \qquad E_B^\circ = 2.31$$

and

$$Al(OH)_3 = Al^{+++} + 3OH^-, \qquad K = 5 \times 10^{-33}.$$

For the hydrolysis of aluminum ion, Bjerrum[2] reported

$$Al^{+++} + H_2O = Al(OH)^{++} + H^+, \qquad K = 1.4 \times 10^{-5}.$$

The hydrolysis appears to be complicated by the formation of more complex ions. Thus Guiter[3] wrote, for sulfate solutions,

$$Al^{+++} + H_2O + SO_4^- = AlOHSO_4 + H^+, \qquad K = 1.25 \times 10^{-2};$$
$$2AlSO_4^+ + 2H_2O = (AlOHSO_4)_2 + 2H^+, \qquad K = 1.25 \times 10^{-8}.$$

Various investigators[4] have given values for the acid dissociation constant of aluminic acid varying from 6×10^{-12} to 1.3×10^{-14}. We shall write

$$Al(OH)_3 = H^+ + H_2AlO_3^- \text{ (or } AlO_2^- + H_2O), \qquad K = 4 \times 10^{-13}.$$

The free energy of the aluminate ion, $H_2AlO_3^-$, then is $-256,000$ cal. and the potential of the Al—$H_2AlO_3^-$ couple,

$$4OH^- + Al = H_2AlO_3^- + H_2O + 3e^-, \qquad E_B^\circ = 2.35.$$

[1] W. M. Latimer and B. S. Greensfelder, *J. Am. Chem. Soc.*, **50**, 2202 (1928).
[2] N. Bjerrum, *Z. physik. Chem.*, **59**, 350 (1907).
[3] H. Guiter, *Compt. rend.*, **226**, 1092 (1948).
[4] A. Maffei, *Gazz. chim. ital.*, **64**, 149 (1934); R. Fricke, *Koll. Z.*, **49**, 241 (1929); I. M. Kolthoff, *Z. anorg. allgem. Chem.*, **112**, 185 (1920).

TABLE 65

THERMODYNAMIC DATA ON ALUMINUM[1]

(Heat and free energy of formation in kcal. Entropy of substance in cal./deg.)

Formula	Description	State	$\Delta H°$	$\Delta F°$	$S°$
Al		g	75.0	65.3	39.303
Al	metal	c	0.0	0.0	6.769
Al+		g	214.487		
Al++		g	650.062		
Al+++		g	1307.44		
Al+++		aq	−125.4	−115.0	−74.9
AlO		g	45.3		
AlO₂⁻		aq	−218.6(?)	−204.7	(25.)
H₂AlO₃⁻		aq		−255.2	
Al₂O₃	corundum α	c	−399.09	−376.77	12.186
Al₂O₃	corundum γ	c	−384.84		
Al₂O₃·H₂O		c	−471.	−435.	23.15
Al₂O₃·3H₂O	hydragillete	c	−613.7	−547.9	33.51
Al(OH)₃	amorph		−304.9	−271.9	(17.)
AlF		g	51.4		
AlF₃		c	−311.	−294.	23.
H₃AlF₆		aq	−597.2		
AlF₆⁻⁻⁻		aq		−539.6	(−40.)
AlBr		g	1.8		
AlBr₃		c	−125.8	−120.7	44.
AlI		g	30.6		
AlI₃		c	−75.2	−75.0	48.
AlCl₃		c	−166.2	−152.2	40.
(NH₄)Al(SO₄)₂·12H₂O		−c	−1419.40	−1179.02	166.6
Al₂S₃		c	−121.6	−117.7	23.
Al₂(SO₄)₃		c	−820.98	−738.99	57.2
Al₂(SO₄)₃·6H₂O		c	−1268.14	−1105.14	112.1
AlN		c	−57.7	−50.1	5.0
Al(NO₃)₃·6H₂O		c	−680.65	−525.82	111.8
Al(NO₃)·9H₂O		c	−897.34	−700.2	136.
(NH₄)Al(SO₄)₂		c	−561.24	−485.95	51.7
Al₄C₃		c	−30.9	−29.0	25.
Al(CH₃)₃		liq	−26.9		
Al₂SiO₅	andalusite	c	−642.2	−607.8	25.0
Al₂SiO₅	disthene	c	−642.7	−607.0	20.7
Al₂SiO₅	sillimanite	c	−648.9	−615.0	27.0
LiAlH₄		c	−24.08		

[1] Bureau of Standards values in *italics;* estimated values in parentheses.

Brosset and Orring[1] have determined the successive constants for Al^{+++} and F^-

$$AlF^{++} = Al^{+++} + F^-, \qquad K_1 = 7.4 \times 10^{-7};$$
$$AlF_2^+ = Al^{+++} + 2F^-, \qquad K_2 = 7.1 \times 10^{-12};$$
$$AlF_3 = Al^{+++} + 3F^-, \qquad K_3 = 1.0 \times 10^{-15};$$
$$AlF_4^- = Al^{+++} + 4F^-, \qquad K_4 = 1.8 \times 10^{-18};$$
$$AlF_5^{--} = Al^{+++} + 5F^-, \qquad K_5 = 4.3 \times 10^{-20};$$
$$AlF_6^{---} = Al^{+++} + 6F^-, \qquad K_6 = 1.44 \times 10^{-20}.$$

From K_6 we calculate the free energy of AlF_6^{---} to be -539.6 kcal. and

$$Al + 6F^- = AlF_6^{---} + 3e^-, \qquad E^\circ = 2.07.$$

In the first edition, 2.13 was given as a rough value of the potential from the heat of formation and an estimated entropy.

SCANDIUM

Oxidation states. The chemistry of scandium is concerned only with the $+3$ oxidation state. The hydroxide is more basic than is aluminum hydroxide. Unstable scandiumates such as $K_2Sc(OH)_5 \cdot 4H_2O$ have been prepared but they decompose to give the hydroxide when washed with water. The fluoride is only slightly soluble but dissolves in ammonium fluoride with the formation of the complex fluoride, ScF_6^{---}. The oxalate, phosphate, and carbonate are also but slightly soluble.

Scandium free energies and potentials. The potential of the Sc—Sc^{+++} couple as calculated from the free energy of the formation of the ion is

$$Sc = Sc^{+++} + 3e^-, \qquad E^\circ = 2.08.$$

There are no data on the hydroxide, but by comparison with aluminum and yttrium, we shall write

$$Sc(OH)_3 = Sc^{+++} + 3OH^-, \qquad K = ca\ 10^{-27};$$
$$Sc + 3OH^- = Sc(OH)_3 + 3e^-, \qquad E_B^\circ = ca\ 2.6.$$

Brewer[2] has calculated from the figures quoted by Noyes and Bray the

[1] C. Brosset and J. Orring, *Svensk. Kemisk. Tidskrif*, **55**, 101 (1943).

[2] L. Brewer, private communication.

TABLE 66

THERMODYNAMIC DATA ON SCANDIUM[1]

(Heat and free energy of formation in kcal. Entropy of substance in cal./deg.)

Formula	Description	State	$\Delta H°$	$\Delta F°$	$S°$
Sc		g	*93.*		*41.76*
Sc	metal	c	0.0	0.0	(8.)
Sc^+		g	*245.75*		
Sc^{++}		g	*544.51*		
Sc^{+++}		g	*1116.81*		
Sc^{+++}		aq	*−148.8*	−143.7	(−56.)
$Sc(OH)_3$		c		(−293.5)	
$ScCl_3$		c	*−220.8*	−205.7	(30.4)
$ScBr_3$		c	*−179.4*	−171.5	(36.7)
ScF_3		c	*−368.*		
ScF_6^{---}		aq		−565.	

[1] Bureau of Standards values in *italics;* estimated values in parentheses.

following constants for the fluoride and fluoscandiumate:

$$ScF_3 = Sc^{+++} + 3F^-, \qquad K = 3 \times 10^{-20};$$
$$ScF_6^{---} = Sc^{+++} + 6F^-, \qquad K = 5 \times 10^{-18}.$$

These values at least give the order of magnitude of the constants.

YTTRIUM

Oxidation states. The only oxidation state is the $+3$. The hydroxide has no acid properties and the same is true of the fluoride. The phosphate, carbonate, and oxalate are but slightly soluble in water, but the latter two dissolve in excess of the negative ion.

Yttrium potentials. From the Bureau of Standards value for the heat of formation of Y^{+++}, -168.0 kcal., and an estimation of the entropy of the aqueous ion as $-48.$ cal./deg., we calculate

$$Y = Y^{+++} + 3e^-, \qquad E° = 2.37.$$

For the solubility product of the hydroxide, we have used the value of Moeller and Kremers[1]

$$Y(OH)_3 = Y^{+++} + 3OH^-, \qquad K = 8.1 \times 10^{-23}.$$

The radius of yttrium ion is 0.82 Å and this value is similar to that of Ho^{+++}. It is, therefore, to be expected that the basic character of

[1] T. Moeller and H. E. Kremers, *J. Phys. Chem.*, **48**, 395 (1944).

TABLE 67

THERMODYNAMIC DATA ON YTTRIUM[1]

(Heat and free energy of formation in kcal. Entropy of substance in cal./deg.)

Formula	Description	State	$\Delta H°$	$\Delta F°$	$S°$
Y		g	*103.*		*42.87*
Y	metal	c	0.0	0.0	(11.3)
Y+		g	*255.04*		
Y++		g	*542.37*		
Y+++		g	*1016.33*		
Y+++		aq	*−168.0*	−164.1	(−48.)
Y(OH)₃		c	−339.5	−307.1	(23.)
YCl₃		c	*−234.8*		(32.7)
YI₃		c	*−143.2*		(47.5)
Y₂(SO₄)₃·8H₂O		c	*−1512.6*	*−1327.3*	(140.6)

[1] Bureau of Standards values in *italics;* estimated values in parentheses.

yttrium hydroxide would be similar to that of the holmium hydroxide and this agrees with the results obtained by Moeller and Kremer in the reference quoted. For the potential of the couple in alkaline solution we then find,

$$Y + 3OH^- = Y(OH)_3 + 3e^-, \qquad E_B° = 2.8.$$

Summary of group potentials. The increasing positive character of the group with increasing atomic weight is shown in the following summary.

$$
\begin{array}{c}
0.87 \\
B\text{————}H_3BO_3 \\
1.66 \\
Al\text{————}Al^{+++} \\
2.08 \\
Sc\text{————}Sc^{+++} \\
2.37 \\
Y\text{————}Y^{+++}
\end{array}
$$

CHAPTER 20

Lanthanum and Rare Earth Elements: The Lanthanide Elements

The state of the three valence electrons in lanthanum is $s^2d^1(^2D_{3/2})$, the same as that of scandium and yttrium, and the element is a member of that group. Following lanthanum, the entering electrons go into the $4f$ orbitals which have become more stable than the $5d$. Fourteen electrons may enter these $4f$ orbitals; hence, we have a series of 14 elements which resemble lanthanum rather closely as they all have s^2d^1 electrons in the outer shell and the $4f$ electrons are comparatively deep and do not appreciably affect the chemical properties. The 14 members of the series are known as the rare-earth elements and, with lanthanum, are now generally called the lanthanide elements.

Oxidation states. Lanthanum readily loses its one d and two s electrons to form the $+3$ ion which has the electron structure of the noble gas, xenon. The rare-earth elements similarly form the $+3$ ions, which also have the external structure of xenon but which differ, of course, in the 1 to 14 electrons in the $4f$ level. Of these various $+3$ ions, lanthanum with no f electrons, gadolinium with $7f$ electrons (that is, one in each f eigenfunction), and lutecium with $14f$ electrons are in S states and apparently are the most stable. These facts serve to account for the anomalous oxidation states and the so-called periodicity within the rare-earth group. Thus, cerium, following lanthanum tends to revert to the latter structure by losing 4 electrons to give a $+4$ oxidation state. Similar behavior is shown by terbium, following gadolinium. On the other hand, europium and ytterbium, preceding gadolinium and lutecium, respectively, also tend to form the S-state structure of the two latter ions and thus have $+2$ oxidation states. Continuing this line of reasoning, one would expect praseodymium and dysprosium to have $+5$ as their maximum oxidation states.

286

TABLE 68

THERMODYNAMIC DATA ON RARE EARTH ELEMENTS[1]

(Heat and free energy of formation in kcal. Entropy of substance in cal./deg.)

Formula	Description	State	$\Delta H°$	$\Delta F°$	$S°$
Lanthanum					
La		g	*88.*	*79.*	*43.57*
La	metal	c, III	0.000	0.000	*13.7*
La$^+$		g	*218.95*		
La^{++}		g	*484.10*		
La^{+++}		g	*927.59*		
La^{+++}		aq	*−176.2*	−174.5	(−39.)
La$_2$O$_3$		c	*−458.*	−426.9	(29.1)
La$_3$H$_8$		c	*−382.*		
La(OH)$_3$		c	−345.0	−313.2	(25.)
LaCl$_3$	α	c	*−263.6*	−245.9	(34.5)
LaI$_3$	α	c	*−167.4*	−166.1	(51.3)
LaS$_2$		c	*−156.7*	−154.7	(18.8)
La$_2$S$_3$		c	*−306.8*	−301.2	(31.5)
LaN		c	*−72.1*		
La$_2$(CN$_2$)$_3$	cyanimide	c	*−229.*		
Cerium					
Ce		g	*85.*		
Ce$^+$		g	*245.9*		
Ce	metal	c, III	0.000	0.000	*13.8*
Ce^{++}		g	*531.1*		
Ce^{+++}		g	*994.*		
Ce^{+++}		aq		−171.75	
Ce^{++++}		g	*1842.*		
Ce^{++++}	in HClO$_4$(aq)	aq	*−134.4*		
CeO$_2$		c	*−233.*	−219.	(15.8)
CeO$_3$·2H$_2$O		c	*−389.*		
Ce$_3$H$_8$		c	*−170.*		
Ce(OH)$^{+++}$		aq		*−188.9*	
Ce(OH)$_2{}^{++}$		aq		*−245.2*	
Ce(OH)$_3$		c		−311.63	
CeCl$_3$	α	c	*−260.3*	−242.4	(34.5)
CeI$_3$	α	c	*−164.4*	−163.1	(51.3)
CeS$_2$		c	*−153.9*	−151.5	(18.8)
Ce$_2$S$_3$		c	*−298.7*	−293.1	(31.5)
Ce(SO$_4$)$_2$		c	*−560.*	−507.4	(48.2)
Ce$_2$(SO$_4$)$_3$·5H$_2$O		c	*−1308.*	−1157.	(115.7)
Ce$_2$(SO$_4$)$_3$·8H$_2$O		c		*−1340.2*	
Ce$_2$(SO$_4$)$_3$·9H$_2$O		c		*−1396.8*	
CeN		c	*−78.3*		

[1] Bureau of Standards values in *italics;* estimated values in parentheses.

TABLE 68 (Continued)

THERMODYNAMIC DATA ON RARE EARTH ELEMENTS[1]

Formula	Description	State	$\Delta H°$	$\Delta F°$	$S°$
Praseodymium					
Pr		g	87.		
Pr	metal	c	0.000	0.000	(13.7)
Pr$^+$		g	2221.4		
Pr^{+++}		aq	−172.7	−170.3	(−41.1)
PrO$_2$		c	−234.0	−220.0	(15.8)
Pr$_2$O$_3$		c	−444.5	423.1	(21.4)
Pr$_6$O$_{11}$		c	−1391.		
Pr(OH)$_3$		c		−309.7	(22.8)
PrCl$_3$	α	c	−257.8	−239.9	(34.5)
PrCl$_3$		aq	−292.8		
PrI$_3$		c	−162.0	−160.7	(51.3)
PrI$_3$		aq	−212.8		
Pr$_2$(SO$_4$)$_3$·8H$_2$O		c	−1536.	−1337.0	(153.)
Neodymium					
Nd		g	87.		
Nd	metal	c, III	0.000	0.000	(13.8)
Nd		g	234.1		
Nd^{+++}		aq	−171.2	−168.2	(−41.6)
Nd$_2$O$_3$		c	−442.0	−420.6	(29.3)
Nd(OH)$_3$		c		−309.3	
NdCl$_3$	α	c	−254.3	−236.4	(34.6)
NdCl$_3$		aq	−291.3		
NdCl$_3$·6H$_2$O		c	−692.3	−591.8	(93.0)
NdI$_3$	α	c	−158.9	−157.7	(51.4)
NdI$_3$		aq	−211.3		
Nd$_2$S$_3$		c	−281.8	−276.2	(31.6)
Nd$_2$(SO$_4$)$_3$		c	−948.1	−866.1	(68.9)
Nd$_2$(SO$_4$)$_3$		aq	−993.1		
Nd$_2$(SO$_4$)$_3$·5H$_2$O		c	−1318.4		
Nd$_2$(SO$_4$)$_3$·8H$_2$O		c	−1524.7	−1334.5	
Promethium					
Pm	metal	c	0.000	0.000	(13.9)
Pm^{+++}		aq	−170.4	−167.6	(−41.2)
PmCl$_3$		c	−251.9	−234.	(34.6)
PmCl$_3$		aq	−290.5		
Pm(OH)$_3$		c		−309.0	
Samarium					
Sm		g	87.		43.74
Sm	metal	c	0.000	0.000	(13.95)
Sm$^+$		g	217.7		

[1] Bureau of Standards values in *italics;* estimated values in parentheses.

TABLE 68 (*Continued*)

THERMODYNAMIC DATA ON RARE EARTH ELEMENTS[1]

Formula	Description	State	$\Delta H°$	$\Delta F°$	$S°$
Samarium					
Sm^{++}		g	*482.*		
Sm^{+++}		aq	*−169.8*	−167.0	(−42.3)
Sm(OH)$_3$		c		−308.7	
SmCl$_3$	α	c	*−249.8*	−231.9	(34.8)
SmCl$_3$		aq	*−289.9*	*−259.9*	
SmI$_3$	β	c	*−153.4*	−152.1	(51.6)
SmI$_3$		aq	*−209.9*		
Sm$_2$(SO$_4$)$_3$·8H$_2$O		c	*−1522.*	*−1332.6*	(154.1)
Europium					
Eu		g	*87.*		*45.10*
Eu	metal	c	0.000	0.000	(14.0)
Eu$^+$		g	*219.23*		
Eu^{++}		g	*480.0*		
Eu^{++}		aq		−156.6	
Eu^{+++}		aq	*−169.3*	−166.5	(−42.3)
EuCl$_3$	α	c	−247.1	−229.2	(34.8)
EuCl$_3$		aq	*−289.4*		
Eu$_2$(SO$_4$)$_3$·8H$_2$O		c	−1523.4	*−1331.0*	(156)
Eu(OH)$_3$				−308.6	
Gadolinium					
Gd		g	*87.*	*77.*	*46.41*
Gd	metal	c	0.000	0.000	*14.*
Gd$^+$		g	*230.55*		
Gd^{+++}		aq	−168.8	−165.8	−43.
Gd(OH)$_3$		c		−308.0	
GdCl$_3$	α	c	*−245.5*	−227.6	(34.9)
GdCl$_3$		aq	*−288.9*		
GdI$_3$		c	*−147.6*	−146.3	(51.8)
GdI$_3$	β	aq	*−208.9*		
Gd$_2$(SO$_4$)$_3$·8H$_2$O		c	*−1518.9*	*−1329.8*	*155.8*
Terbium					
Tb		g	*87.*		
Tb		c	0.000	0.000	(14.15)
Tb$^+$		g	*244.0*		
Tb^{+++}		aq	*−168.4*	−165.4	(−42.8)
TbCl$_3$	β	c	*−241.6*	−123.7	(34.9)
TbCl$_3$		aq	*−288.5*		
Tb$_2$(SO$_4$)$_3$·8H$_2$O		c	−1517.3	*−1328.2*	(155.8)
Tb(OH)$_3$		c		−305.7	

[1] Bureau of Standards values in *italics*; estimated values in parentheses.

TABLE 68 (*Continued*)

THERMODYNAMIC DATA ON RARE EARTH ELEMENTS[1]

Formula	Description	State	$\Delta H°$	$\Delta F°$	$S°$
Dysprosium					
Dy		g	*87.*		
Dy	metal	c	0.000	0.000	(14.2)
Dy$^+$		g	*245.8*		
Dy^{+++}		aq	*−166.0*	−162.8	(−43.3)
Dy(OH)$_3$		c		−305.4	
DyCl$_3$	β	c	*−237.8*	−219.9	(35.0)
DyCl$_3$	γ	c	*−234.8*		
DyCl$_3$		aq	*−286.1*		
DyI$_3$	β	c	*−144.5*	−143.2	(51.9)
Dy$_2$(SO$_4$)$_3$·8H$_2$O		c		*−1322.0*	(155.9)
Holmium					
Ho	metal	c	0.000	0.000	(14.24)
Ho^{+++}		aq	*−163.7*	−160.4	(−43.7)
HoCl$_3$	γ	c	*−232.8*	(−215.0)	(35.1)
HoCl$_3$		aq	*−283.8*		
HoI$_3$	β	c	*−141.7*	−140.5	(52.)
Ho$_2$(SO$_4$)$_3$·8H$_2$O		c		*−1318.0*	(−156.1)
Ho(OH)$_3$		c		−304.1	
Erbium					
Er	metal	c	0.000	0.000	(14.3)
Er^{+++}		aq	*−162.3*	−158.86	(−44.)
Er(OH)$_3$		c		−302.8	
ErCl$_3$	γ	c	*−231.8*	−214.	(35.1)
ErCl$_3$		aq	*−282.4*		
ErI$_3$	β	c	*−140.0*	−138.8	(52.)
Er$_2$(SO$_4$)$_3$·8H$_2$O		c		*−1313.9*	
Thulium					
Tm		g			*45.2*
Tm		c	0.000	0.000	(14.4)
Tm^{+++}		aq	*−161.3*	−157.6	−44.8
TmCl$_3$	γ	c	*−229.5*	−111.7	(35.2)
TmI$_3$	β	c	*−137.8*	−136.6	(52.1)
Tm(OH)$_3$		c		−302.4	
Ytterbium					
Yb		g	*87.*		*41.30*
Yb		c	0.000	0.000	(14.45)
Yb$^+$		g	*231.5*		
Yb^{++}		g	*511.*		

[1] Bureau of Standards values in *italics;* estimated values in parentheses.

TABLE 68 (Continued)

THERMODYNAMIC DATA ON RARE EARTH ELEMENTS[1]

Formula	Description	State	$\Delta H°$	$\Delta F°$	$S°$
Ytterbium					
Yb^{++}		aq		−129.0	
Yb^{+++}		aq	−160.6	−156.8	(−45.4)
YbCl$_3$	γ	c	−228.7	−110.9	(35.3)
Yb$_2$(SO$_4$)$_3$·8H$_2$O		c		−1308.8	(156.6)
Yb(OH)$_3$		c		−301.7	
Lutecium					
Lu		g	87.		44.14
Lu	metal	c	0.000	0.000	(14.5)
Lu$^+$		g	203.8		
Lu^{+++}		aq	−160.1	−156.0	(−45.7)
Lu(OH)$_3$		aq		−301.0	
LuCl$_3$		c	−227.9	(−110.1)	(35.4)
LuCl$_3$		aq	−280.2		
LuI$_3$		c	−133.2	−131.	(51.3)
Lu$_2$(SO$_4$)$_3$·8H$_2$O		c		−1308.1	(156.8)

[1] Bureau of Standards values in *italics;* estimated values in parentheses.

TABLE 69

SUMMARY OF RARE EARTH POTENTIALS AND
SOLUBILITY PRODUCTS

	Free Energy M^{+++}	$E°$ for M = M^{+++} + 3e$^-$	Free Energy M(OH)$_3$	M(OH)$_3$ = M^{+++} + 3OH$^-$ K
La	−174.5	2.52	−313.2	1.0×10^{-19}
Ce	−171.75	2.48	−311.6	1.5×10^{-20}
Pr	−170.3	2.47	−309.7	2.7×10^{-20}
Nd	−168.2	2.44	−309.3	1.9×10^{-21}
Pm	−167.6	2.42	−309.0	$1. \times 10^{-21}$
Sm	−167.0	2.41	−308.7	6.8×10^{-22}
Eu	−166.5	2.41	−308.6	3.4×10^{-22}
Gd	−165.8	2.40	−308.0	2.1×10^{-22}
Tb	−165.4	2.39	−307.8	2.0×10^{-22}
Dy	−162.8	2.35	−305 4	1.4×10^{-22}
Ho	−160.4	2.32	−304.1	$5. \times 10^{-23}$
Er	−158.8	2.30	−302.8	1.3×10^{-23}
Tm	−157.6	2.28	−302.4	3.3×10^{-24}
Yb	−156.8	2.27	−301.7	2.9×10^{-24}
Lu	−156.0	2.25	−301.0	2.5×10^{-24}

Prandtl and Huttner[1] have shown that the oxidation product of praseodymium is Pr_6O_{11}, which they considered to be the praseodymium praseodymate, $2Pr_2O_3 \cdot Pr_2O_5$, but the oxide may be a mixture of Pr_2O_3 and PrO_2, as the latter oxide has been prepared in practically pure form. There is no evidence of higher oxidation states in dysprosium. Neodymium forms the dioxide.

Samarium and thulium might be expected to form $+1$ compounds, but so far none have been prepared. However, samarium, definitely, and thulium, probably, form compounds of the $+2$ oxidation state.

Properties of the $+3$ state. The values for the heats of solution of the elements in acid to give the $+3$ ions are fairly accurate. There is only one value for the entropy of a $+3$ ion, that of Gd^{+++}. We have recalculated the value given by Coulter and Latimer,[2] giving considerable weight to the new heat of dilution of $Gd_2(SO_4)_3$, determined by Nathan, Wallace, and Robinson.[3] For the entropies of the other $+3$ ions we have used a smoothed out series of estimated values consistent with the crystal radii. These have been employed to calculate the free energies given in Table 69. The elements are all highly electropositive and for comparison the potentials of the M—M^{+++} couples are given in Table 69. It will be observed that $E°$ decreases from 2.52 for lanthanum to 2.25 for lutecium. Klemm and Bommer[4] have found that the molecular volumes of europium and ytterbium, as metals, are much larger than those of the other rare-earth elements and correspond more closely to the value for barium. These authors suggest that these elements may have $7f$ and $14f$ electrons, respectively, in the metallic state; i.e., they have only two valence electrons in the metal. It would seem likely that this would lead to a difficult lattice energy of the metal, which should show up in the heat of solution, but such deviations have not been observed experimentally.

The ionic radii decrease from 1.0 Å for La^{+++} to 0.93 Å for Ce^{+++} and then decrease quite regularly to 0.78 Å for Lu^{+++}. This decrease in ionic size is reflected in the decreasing basicity of the hydroxide. Various experimental values have been reported for the solubility products, but we have given the results of Moeller and Kremers[5] for

[1] W. Prandtl and K. Huttner, Z. anorg. allgem. Chem., **136**, 289 (1924).

[2] L. V. Coulter and W. M. Latimer, J. Am. Chem. Soc., **62**, 2557 (1940).

[3] C. Nathan, W. E. Wallace and A. L. Robinson, J. Am. Chem. Soc., **65**, 790 (1943).

[4] W. Klemm and H. Bommer, Z. anorg. allgem. Chem., **231**, 154 (1937).

[5] T. Moeller and H. E. Kremers, J. Phys. Chem., **48**, 395 (1944).

the freshly precipitated hydroxides in Table 69. Upon aging the precipitates, the values of K become smaller by almost one power of ten. The solubility products have been employed to calculate the free energies of formation listed in Table 69.

The potential of the lanthanum and lutecium couples in alkaline solution are

$$La + 3OH^- = La(OH)_3 + 3e^-, \qquad E_B^\circ = 2.90;$$
$$Lu + 3OH^- = Lu(OH)_3 + 3e^-, \qquad E_B^\circ = 2.72.$$

Rimbach and Schubert[1] gave the following solubility products for cerium oxalate and tartrate:

$$Ce_2(C_2O_4)_3 \cdot 10H_2O = 2Ce^{+++} + 3C_2O_4^{--} + 10H_2O,$$
$$K = 2.5 \times 10^{-29};$$
$$Ce_2(C_4H_4O_6)_3 \cdot 9H_2O = 2Ce^{+++} + 3C_4H_4O_6^{--}, \qquad K = 9.7 \times 10^{-20}.$$

The constants are based upon concentrations and not activites. The same authors reported similar values for the oxalates of praseodymium, neodymium, and samarium. These authors reported the solubility of cerium iodate, $Ce(IO_3)_3 \cdot 2H_2O$ as $0.0074M$ and lanthanum iodate, $2La(IO_3)_3 \cdot 3H_2O$, as $0.0085M$.

The oxalates are not appreciably soluble in hydrogen ion but tend to form complex oxalate ions with excess oxalate, especially in the case of the heavier rare earths. Crouthamel and Martin[2] gave the following constants for $Yb_2(C_2O_4)_3$:

$$Yb_2(C_2O_4)_3 = YbC_2O_4^+ + Yb(C_2O_4)_2^-, \qquad K = 1.9 \times 10^{-10};$$
$$YbC_2O_4^+ = Yb^{+++} + C_2O_4^{--}, \qquad K = 5 \times 10^{-8};$$
$$Yb(C_2O_4)_2^- = YbC_2O_4^+ + C_2O_4^{--}, \qquad K = 2.6 \times 10^{-5}.$$

The fluorides are but slightly soluble and do not dissolve in ammonium fluoride. The phosphates and carbonates are also insoluble but the heavier carbonates dissolve in ammonium carbonate with complex ion formation.

The dioxides. Cerium dioxide is a well-defined compound. Praseodymium, neodymium, and terbium form oxides in which their oxidation number is greater than $+3$. However, the preparation of the pure dioxide is difficult. Cerium dioxide, when hydrated, dissolves

[1] E. Rimbach and A. Schubert, *Z. physik. Chem.*, **67**, 198 (1909).
[2] C. E. Crouthamel and D. S. Martin, Jr., *J. Am. Chem. Soc.*, **72**, 1382 (1950).

readily in sulfuric acid, but the other dioxides evolve oxygen in acid solution.

Ceric sulfate has become a valuable volumetric reagent.[1] Its use in analysis closely parallels that of permanganate. Kunz[2] studied the potential of the Ce^{+3}—Ce^{+4} couple against the hydrogen couple in sulfuric acid. In $1M$ acid and equal concentration of the two ions, he reported

$$(\text{In } 1M \text{ H}_2\text{SO}_4)\text{Ce}^{+++} = \text{Ce}^{+4} + e^-, \qquad E = -1.44.$$

Noyes and Garner[3] studied the potential in nitric acid. They found that the potential varied but little on changing the concentration of nitric acid between 0.5 and $2M$, indicating little tendency toward complex nitrate formation. They wrote, without correcting for the difference in the activities of the $+3$ and $+4$ ions,

$$\text{Ce}^{+3} = \text{Ce}^{+4} + e^-, \qquad E^\circ = -1.61.$$

Hugus[4] has discussed the Ce^{+3}—Ce^{+4} potential in perchloric acid and gave for the formal potential in $1M$ $HClO_4$ -1.70 volts. On the basis of this value it would seem that the sulfate solution investigated by Kunz must be subject to considerable complex formation.

Cunningham and Eyring[5] report

$$\text{Pr}^{+3} = \text{Pr}^{+4} + e^-, \qquad E^\circ = -2.86.$$

The $+4$ praseodymium evolves oxygen from water in acid solution.

Properties of the $+2$ ions. Europous ion is stable in water solutions at low hydrogen-ion concentrations, and the slightly soluble ytterbous and samarous sulfates are not rapidly oxidized by water. These elements also form $+2$ halides by reduction of the $+3$ compounds by hydrogen at high temperatures.

McCoy[6] prepared europous solutions by reduction with zinc. He gave for the Eu^{++}—Eu^{+++} couple

$$\text{Eu}^{++} = \text{Eu}^{+++} + e^-, \qquad E^\circ = 0.43.$$

---

[1] H. H. Willard and P. Young, *J. Am. Chem. Soc.*, **50**, 1322 (1928); N. H. Furman, *J. Am. Chem. Soc.*, **50**, 755 (1928).

[2] A. H. Kunz, *J. Am. Chem. Soc.*, **50**, 98 (1931).

[3] A. A. Noyes and C. S. Garner, *J. Am. Chem. Soc.*, **58**, 1265 (1936).

[4] Z. Z. Hugus, Univ. Calif. Radiation Lab. Report UCRL-1379.

[5] B Cunningham and L. Eyring, *Paper Am. Chem. Soc. Chicago*, 1950.

[6] H. N. McCoy, *J. Am. Chem. Soc.*, **58**, 1579 (1936).

Walters and Pearce[1] determined by direct measurement

$$Yb^{++} = Yb^{+++} + e^-, \qquad E^\circ = 0.578$$

but there is some question with regard to the reversibility of the electrode. From chemical behavior we estimate

$$Sm^{++} = Sm^{+++} + e^-, \qquad E^\circ = >0.9.$$

In their solubilities, the compounds of the $+2$ rare-earth ions appear to be similar to the corresponding barium compounds.

---

[1] G. C. Walters and D. W. Pearce, *J. Am. Chem. Soc.*, **62**, 3331 (1940).

CHAPTER 21

The Actinide Elements

The point at which the energy of the $5f$ electrons drops below that of the $6d$ electrons is somewhat uncertain, but it seems to be in the region of thorium or protactinium, although it probably depends somewhat upon the oxidation state and also the physical state of the several elements with atomic numbers in this region. An interpretation of the spectroscopic data appears to give the following electron assignments for the valence electrons in the gaseous atoms

89 actinium $6d$, $7s^2$

90 thorium $6d^2$, $7s^2$

  or $5f$, $6d$, $7s^2$

91 protactinium $5f^2$, $6d$, $7s^2$

  or $5f$, $6d^2$, $7s^2$

92 uranium $5f^3$, $6d$, $7s^2$

93 neptunium $5f^5$, $7s^2$

  or $5f^4$, $6d$, $7s^2$

94 plutonium $5f^6$, $7s^2$

  or $5f^5$, $6d$, $7s^2$

95 americium $5f^7$, $7s^2$

96 curium $5f^7$, $6d$, $7s^2$

97 berkelium $5f^8$, $6d$, $7s^2$

98 californium $5f^9$, $6d$, $7s^2$

We thus have a series of elements which resemble the rare earths, or lanthanide, elements in many respects, but in the first part of the series the $5f$ and $6d$ levels are so close together that these elements also resemble, to a certain extent, the heavier elements of subgroups IV, V, and VI. In analogy to the lanthanide elements, this group is called the actinide elements. They are all radioactive and several of them are so unstable that they are known only in microgram (or smaller) amounts. For such elements there are no quantitative thermodynamic data and we can only discuss their chemistry in qualitative terms.

The solubilities of the actinide elements in the +3 and +4 states are similar to those of the lanthanides, since the ionic radii are about the same. The following table of radii has been given by Fried, Hagemann, and Zachariasen.[1]

---

[1] S. Fried, F. Hagemann and W. H. Zachariasen, *J. Am. Chem. Soc.*, **72**, 771 (1950).

TABLE 70

CRYSTAL RADII OF LANTHANIDE AND ACTINIDE ELEMENTS

(Values in Å)

Th^{+4}	0.95	Ac^{+3}	1.11	La^{+3}	1.04
Pa^{+4}	(0.91)	Th^{+3}	(1.08)	Ce^{+3}	1.02
U^{+4}	0.89	Pa^{+3}	(1.06)	Pr^{+3}	1.00
Np^{+4}	0.88	U^{+3}	1.04	Nd^{+3}	0.99
Pu^{+4}	0.86	Np^{+3}	1.02	Pm^{+3}	(0.98)
Am^{+4}	0.85	Pu^{+3}	1.01	Sm^{+3}	0.97
		Am^{+3}	1.00	Eu^{+3}	0.97

ACTINIUM

The instability of the actinium nuclei precludes the accumulation of any appreciable quantity of the element, the half-life of Ac^{227}, the most stable isotope, being only 21.7 years, and the abundance of its parent element, protactinium, being also very low. The chemical properties of actinium compounds resemble those of lanthanum. The only oxidation state is the +3. The potassium complex sulfate, the fluoride, and the oxalate are slightly soluble, although the latter dissolves readily in dilute acids. Unlike thorium, it is not precipitated by hydrogen peroxide. The sulfide is also soluble like lanthanum sulfide. The hydroxide is somewhat soluble in ammonium ion,[1] which satisfies the expectation that the hydroxide is more basic than lanthanum hydroxide. The metal must be highly electropositive.

$$Ac = Ac^{+++} + 3e^-, \qquad E^\circ = ca\ 2.6.$$

For an additional discussion of the tracer chemistry of actinium, reference may be made to the work of McLane and Peterson.[2]

THORIUM

Oxidation states. The only oxidation state in water solution is the +4. The +3 iodide, ThI_3, and the +2 sulfide, ThS, have been prepared. The dioxide ThO_2 is much more basic than the dioxides of the lighter elements of group IV and shows no tendency to form thorates even when fused with alkalies. The hydrated oxide dissolves

---

[1] D. E. Hull, W. F. Libby, and W. M. Latimer, *J. Am. Chem. Soc.*, **57**, 1649 (1935).

[2] C. K. McLane and S. Peterson, *Nat. Nuclear Energy Series*, **IV**, 14B, paper 19.3.

readily in strong acids, and the hydrated normal salts may be crystallized from the solutions, for example, $Th(SO_4)_2 \cdot 8H_2O$ and $Th(NO_3)_4 \cdot 12H_2O$. The addition of alkalies to these solutions precipitates basic salts, for example, $ThOSO_4 \cdot H_2O$ and $Th(OH)_2Cl_2 \cdot 4H_2O$. Double salts of almost every negative ion may also be prepared, for example, $K_4Th(SO_4)_2 \cdot 2H_2O$ and $KTh(NO_3)_5 \cdot 9H_2O$. The tetrafluoride, $ThF_4 \cdot 4H_2O$, may be precipitated. Sodium carbonate precipitates $ThOCO_3 \cdot$

TABLE 71

THERMODYNAMIC DATA ON THORIUM[1]

(Heat and free energy of formation in kcal. Entropy of substance in cal./deg.)

Formula	Description	State	$\Delta H°$	$\Delta F°$	$S°$
Th		g			*45.43*
Th	metal	c	0.0	0.0	*13.6*
Th++++		aq	*−183.0*	−175.2	(−75.)
ThO₂		c	*−292.*	−278.4	(16.9)
ThH₄		c	*−43.*		
Th(OH)₄	"soluble"	c	*−421.5*	−379.	(32.)
ThF₄		c	*−477.*	−454.7	(35.9)
ThCl₄		c	*−285.*	−263.9	(48.3)
ThOCl₂		c	*−274.8*		
ThBr₄		c	*−227.1*	−218.0	(55.9)
ThOBr₂		c	*−252.8*		
ThI₄		c	*−131.*	−131.	(67.9)
Th₂S₃		c	*−262.0*	−257.7	(35.7)
ThOSO₄		c	*−487.*		
Th(SO₄)₂		c	*−602.*		
Th₃N₄		c	*−308.*		
ThC₂		c	−45.		

[1] Bureau of Standards values in *italics;* estimated values in parentheses.

$8H_2O$, soluble in excess of the reagent. Oxalic acid precipitates the oxalate, which is soluble in ammonium oxalate. Other slightly soluble compounds are the iodate, $Th(IO_3)_4$, and the phosphate, $Th_3(PO_4)_4 \cdot 4H_2O$. The heats of precipitation of many of these compounds have been measured but the data cannot be used to calculate solubility products inasmuch as little is known regarding the activities or entropies of the ions in solution. Sulfides are formed only at high temperatures. A slightly soluble peroxyacid is precipitated from dilute acid solutions by hydrogen peroxide. The formula has been given as H_2ThO_4, with an indefinite amount of water, but it appears to be more complicated, and the precipitate generally contains negative ions.

Free energies and potentials. From the Bureau of Standards values for the heats of formation a number of free energies may be calculated using estimated entropy values. Using these free energies we find

$$Th = Th^{++++} + 4e^-, \qquad E^\circ = 1.90;$$
$$Th + 4OH^- = Th(OH)_4 + 4e^-, \qquad E_B^\circ = 2.48;$$
$$Th(OH)_4 = Th^{++++} + 4OH^-, \qquad K = 1.0 \times 10^{-39}.$$

The metal is thus somewhat more electropositive than aluminum.

The fluoride is one of the few slightly soluble compounds for which we have data.

$$ThF_4 = Th^{++++} + 4F^-, \qquad K = 7. \times 10^{-12}.$$

Dodgen and Rollefson[1] reported the following:

$$ThF_4 \cdot 4H_2O + 2H^+ = ThF_2^{++} + 2HF + 4H_2O, \qquad K = 5.9 \times 10^{-8};$$
$$Th^{+4} + HF = ThF^{+3} + H^+, \qquad K = 4.5 \times 10^4;$$
$$ThF^{+3} + HF = ThF_2^{++} + H^+, \qquad K = 6.5 \times 10^2;$$
$$ThF_2^{++} + HF = ThF_3^+ + H^+, \qquad K = 3.2.$$

Fry, Barney, and Stoughton[2] have studied the solubility of thorium iodate Th $(IO_3)_4$ and the basic iodate $ThOH(IO_3)_3$. They give

$$Th(IO_3)_4 = Th^{+4} + 4IO_3^-, \qquad K = 2.4 \times 10^{-15};$$
$$Th(IO_3)_4 = ThIO_3^{+3} + 3IO_3^-, \qquad K = 1.8 \times 10^{-12};$$
$$Th(IO_3)_4 = Th(IO_3)_2^{++} + 2IO_3^-, \qquad K = 1.6 \times 10^{-10};$$
$$Th(IO_3)_4 + 2IO_3^- = Th(IO_3)_6^{--}, \qquad K = 2.5 \times 10^{-4};$$
$$ThOH(IO_3)_3 = ThOH(IO_3)_2^+ + IO_3^-, \qquad K = 3.6 \times 10^{-8};$$
$$ThOH(IO_3)_3 = ThOH(IO_3)^{++} + 2IO_3^-, \qquad K = 4.4 \times 10^{-10};$$
$$Th(OH)(IO_3)_3 + H^+ = Th^{+4} + H_2O + 3IO_3^-, \qquad K = 1.8 \times 10^{-10}.$$

PROTACTINIUM

The isotope Pa^{231}, with a half-life of 3.4×10^4 years is one of the longest lived radioactive products of the disintegration of uranium.

---

[1] H. W. Dodgen and G. K. Rollefson, *J. Am. Chem. Soc.*, **71**, 2600 (1949).

[2] A. J. Fry, J. E. Barney and R. W. Stoughton, Oak Ridge Nat. Lab. Paper RONL 63.

Grosse[1] has isolated a few tenths of a gram of the element. Although no quantitative values are yet available, the following facts are of interest. The metal is not readily oxidized in air. The pentoxide, Pa_2O_5, is more basic than the corresponding tantalum oxide, and the hydrated oxide dissolves appreciably in sulfuric acid, probably with the formation of PaO_2^+. No protoactinates are formed by fusion of the oxide with soldium carbonate. The element is precipitated from acid solution by the formation of the peroxyacid and by the addition of phosphoric acid. The pentachloride is formed at 500° C. by the reaction

$$Pa_2O_5 + 5COCl_2 = 2PaCl_5 + 5CO_2.$$

The metal was prepared by the decomposition of the chloride by heating on a tungsten filament in a high vacuum.

The oxide dissolves in HF and salts such as K_2PaF_7 have been prepared. In general, the fluoride PaF_5 appears to resemble the $+5$ tantalum fluoride. There is some evidence for a $+4$ state in solution. Maddock and Miles[2] have summarized the results of tracer experiments and confirmed the assumption that the solution of the pentoxide in HCl is a positive ion.

$$Pa + 2H_2O = PaO_2^+ + 4H^+ + 5e^-, \qquad E° = ca\ 1.0.$$

URANIUM

Oxidation states. The oxides UO_2 and UO_3 as well as the intermediate oxide, U_3O_8, and probably $UO_2 \cdot 2UO_3$ or $U(UO_4)_2$ are stable. The $+3$ oxide, U_2O_3, does not appear to be stable above 100° C., but the hydroxide $U(OH)_3$ may be precipitated. Complex ions of the $+3$ and $+4$ states exist in solution. The penta- and hexachlorides and fluorides have been prepared, but the hexachloride is not very stable. Hydrates of the trioxide, $UO_3 \cdot H_2O$ and $UO_3 \cdot 2H_2O$, are quite soluble in acids, forming compounds of the uranyl ion, UO_2^{++}. This ion is remarkably stable, and has the properties of a large, simple, doubly charged metallic ion.[3] Most of its salts are soluble. The addition of alkalies to uranyl solutions precipitates alkali diuranates, for example, $K_2U_2O_7$. The monosalts may also be prepared—for example, Na_2UO_4.

[1] A. von Grosse, *J. Am. Chem. Soc.*, **52**, 1745 (1930); **56**, 2501 (1934).

[2] A. G. Maddock and G. L. Miles, *J. Chem. Soc.*, S249 (1949).

[3] H. W. Crandall, *J. Chem. Phys.*, **17**, 602 (1949), for proof of formula.

The tendency to form complicated polyacids, which is characteristic of the trioxides of this group, is somewhat repressed in the case of uranium by the formation of uranyl ion in acid solutions, and by the very slight solubility of the diuranates in general. The diuranates are somewhat soluble in excess of carbonate with the formation of carbonate complex ions.

Free energies and potentials. Because of the role of the chemistry of uranium in the nuclear energy programs, most of the important free energies have been determined and we shall use the values tabulated by the Bureau of Standards. Much of the basic experimental work is published in the National Nuclear Energy Series.

The following calculations are based upon the free energies:

$$U = U^{+++} + 3e^-, \qquad E° = 1.80;$$
$$U^{+++} = U^{++++} + e^-, \qquad E° = 0.61.$$

The $+3$ ion is thus highly unstable with respect to the evolution of hydrogen.

$$U + 4OH^- = UO_2 + 2H_2O + 4e^-, \qquad E_B° = 2.39;$$
$$U^{++++} + 2H_2O = UO_2^+ + 4H^+ + e^-, \qquad E° = -0.62;$$
$$UO_2^+ = UO_2^{++} + e^-, \qquad E° = -0.05.$$

The UO_2^+ is unstable with respect to its disproportionation, and the significant couple in acid solution is U^{+4}—UO_2^{++}.

$$U^{++++} + 2H_2O = UO_2^{++} + 4H^+ + 2e^-, \qquad E° = -0.334.$$

R. Luther and A. C. Michie[1] reported

$$U(SO_4)_2(aq) + 2H_2O = UO_2^{++} + 2SO_4^{--} + 4H^+ + 2e^-, \quad E = -0.42.$$

From this value, there appears to be considerable complexing of U^{+4} ion with sulfate.

From the similarity of the radii of U^{+3} and La^{+++} we estimate

$$U(OH)_3 = U^{+++} + 3OH^-, \qquad K = 1 \times 10^{-19}.$$

Hence,

$$U + 3OH^- = U(OH)_3 + 3e^-, \qquad E_B° = 2.17.$$

Comparing the ionic radii and the solubility products of $Th(OH)_4$ and $Pu(OH)_4$, we estimate

$$U(OH)_4 = U^{+4} + 4OH^-, \qquad K = 10^{-45}.$$

[1] R. Luther and A. C. Michie, *Z. Elektrochem.*, **14**, 826 (1908).

TABLE 72

THERMODYNAMIC DATA ON URANIUM[1]

(Heat and free energy of formation in kcal. Entropy of substance in cal./deg.)

Formula	Description	State	$\Delta H°$	$\Delta F°$	$S°$
U		g	*125.*		
U	metal	c, III	0.000	0.000	*12.03*
U$^+$		g	*218.*		
U^{+++}		aq	*−123.0*	*−124.4*	*−30.* (?)
U^{++++}		aq	*−146.7*	*−138.4*	*−78.*
UO$_2$		c	*−270.*	*−257.*	*18.6*
UO$_2{}^+$		aq	*−247.4*	*−237.6*	*12.*
UO$_2{}^{++}$		aq	*−250.4*	*−236.4*	*−17.*
UO$_3$		c	*−302.*	*−283.*	*23.57*
UO$_3$·H$_2$O		c	*−375.4*	*−343.*	(*33.*)
UO$_3$·2H$_2$O		c	*−446.2*		
UO$_4$·2H$_2$O		c	*−436.*		
U$_3$O$_8$		c	*−898.*		
UH$_3$		c	*−30.4*		
U(OH)$^{+++}$		aq	*−204.1*	*−193.5*	*−30.*
UF$_3$		c	*−357.*	*−339.*	*26.*
UF$_4$		c	*−443.*	*−421.*	*36.1*
UF$_5$		c	*−488.*	*−461.*	*43.*
UF$_6$		g	*−505.*	*−485.*	*90.76*
UF$_6$		c	*−517.*	*−486.*	*54.45*
U(OH)$_3$		c		(−263.2)	
U(OH)$_4$		c		(−351.6)	
UCl$_3$		c	*−213.0*	*−196.9*	*37.99*
UCl$_4$		c	*−251.2*	*−230.0*	*47.4*
UCl$_5$		c	*−262.1*	*−237.4*	*62.*
Na$_2$UO$_4$		c	*−501.*	*−475.*	(*47.*)
UCl$_6$		c	*−272.4*	*−241.5*	*68.3*
UO$_2$Cl$_2$		aq	*−331.*		
UBr$_3$		c	*−170.1*	*−164.7*	*49.*
UBr$_4$		c	*−196.6*	*−188.5*	*58.*
UO$_2$Br$_2$		aq	*−308.2*		
UI$_3$		c	*−114.7*	*−115.3*	*56.*
UI$_4$		c	*−127.0*	*−126.1*	*65.*
UCl$_3$I		c	*−219.9*	*−204.4*	*54.*
UBr$_3$I		c	*−177.1*		
UO$_2$SO$_4$		aq	*−467.3*	*−413.7*	*−13.*
UO$_2$SO$_4$·3H$_2$O		c	*−666.8*	*−586.0*	*63.*
U(SO$_4$)$_2$		c	*−563.*	*−515.6*	(*64.*)
UN		c	*−80.*	*−75.*	*18.*
U$_2$N$_3$		c	*−213.*	*−194.*	*29.*
UO$_2$(NO$_3$)$_2$		c	*−329.2*	*−273.1*	*66.*
UO$_2$(NO$_3$)$_2$		aq	*−349.1*	*−289.2*	*53.*
UO$_2$(NO$_3$)$_2$·H$_2$O		c	*−404.8*	*−335.3*	*76.*

[1] Bureau of Standards values in *italics;* estimated values in parentheses.

TABLE 72 (*Continued*)

THERMODYNAMIC DATA ON URANIUM[1]

Formula	Description	State	$\Delta H°$	$\Delta F°$	$S°$
$UO_2(NO_3)_2 \cdot 2H_2O$		c	*−480.0*	*−396.6*	*85.*
$UO_2(NO_3)_2 \cdot 3H_2O$		c	*−552.2*	*−454.7*	*94.*
$UO_2(NO_3)_2 \cdot 6H_2O$		c	*−764.3*	*−625.0*	*120.85*
UC_2		c	*−42.*	*−42.*	*14.*
$UO_2(C_2H_3O_2)_2$	uranyl acetate	aq	*−484.0*		
$UO_2(C_2H_3O_2) \cdot 2H_2O$		c	*−624.9*		
$UO_2(C_2H_3O_2)_2 \cdot 6H_2O$		c	*−1045.8*		

[1] Bureau of Standards values in *italics;* estimated values in parentheses.

Hence,

$$U(OH)_3 + OH^- = U(OH)_4 + e^-, \qquad E_B° = 2.14.$$
$$U(OH)_4 + 2Na^+ + 4OH^- = Na_2UO_4 + 4H_2O + 2e^-, \quad E_B° = 1.61.$$

Sutton[1] has written for the hydrolysis of UO_2^{++} the following constants:

$$2UO_2^{++} + H_2O = U_2O_5^{++} + 2H^+, \qquad K = 1.1 \times 10^{-6};$$
$$U_2O_5^{++} + UO_2^{++} + H_2O = U_3O_8^{++} + 2H^+, \qquad K = 5 \times 10^{-9};$$
$$U_3O_8^{++} + H_2O = U_3O_8OH^+ + H^+, \qquad K = 2.8 \times 10^{-4}.$$

There are no thermal data for the diuranates. The following equilibrium constants may be given:

$$H_2UO_4 = UO_2^{++} + 2OH^-, \qquad K = 2 \times 10^{-23};$$
$$UF_4 = U^{+4} + 4F^-, \qquad K = 3.7 \times 10^{-14};$$
$$UF_3 = U^{+++} + 3F^-, \qquad K = 1 \times 10^{-12}.$$

Foley and Anderson[2] gave for the complex of uranyl ion with sulfosalicylic acid, $C_6H_3OHCOOHSO_3H,$

$$UO_2R^{++} = UO_2^{++} + R, \qquad K = 1.93 \times 10^{-4}.$$

For the hydrolysis of the hexafluoride we find

$$UF_6 + 2H_2O = UO_2^{++} + 6F^- + 4H^+, \qquad \Delta F = -34.5 \text{ kcal.}$$

However, the reaction is extremely slow.

[1] J. Sutton, *J. Chem. Soc.*, S275 (1949).
[2] R. T. Foley and R. C. Anderson, *J. Am. Chem. Soc.*, 71, 910 (1949).

Potential diagram.   The potentials relating the various oxida-
'ion states are summarized in the following diagram.

Acid Solution

$$
\begin{array}{ccccccc}
1.80 & & 0.61 & & -0.62 & & -0.05 \\
U\text{------}U^{+++}\text{------}U^{+4}\text{------}UO_2^+\text{------}UO_2^{++}
\end{array}
$$

$$
\phantom{U\text{------}U^{+++}\text{------}}\big|\text{------}-0.334\text{------}\big|
$$

Basic Solution

$$
\begin{array}{ccccc}
2.17 & & 2.14 & & 0.62 \\
U\text{------}U(OH)_3\text{------}U(OH)_4\text{------}UO_2(OH)_2
\end{array}
$$

NEPTUNIUM

Oxidation states.   The important oxidation states of neptunium,
like those of uranium, are the $+3$, $+4$, $+5$, and $+6$, and the formulas
of the ions are also similar to the uranium ions. Unlike uranium the
$+5$ state is stable in acid solution.

Free energies and potentials.   We have estimated the entropies of the neptunium ions and salts as similar to those of uranium
and calculated free energies from the heat values listed by the Bureau
of Standards. Their values for ΔH of the ions are all in $1M$ HCl and
true ΔH° values are not known. Hence, our calculated ΔF values are
subject to this correction. However, we shall use these free energies to
calculate potentials for the various couples.

$$
\begin{array}{ll}
Np = Np^{+++} + 3e^-, & E^\circ = 1.86; \\
Np^{+++} = Np^{+4} + e^-, & E^\circ = -0.147; \\
Np^{+4} + 2H_2O = NpO_2^+ + 4H^+ + e^-, & E^\circ = -0.75; \\
NpO_2^+ = NpO_2^{++} + e^-, & E^\circ = -1.15.
\end{array}
$$

Hindman, Magnusson, and La Chapelle[1] and also Hindman and
Kritchevsky[2] have reported for the formal potentials in $1M$ HCl;
Np^{+++}—Np^{+4}, 0.137 and 0.142; Np^{+4}—NpO_2^+, -0.74; and NpO_2^+—
NpO_2^{++}, -1.14. These potentials were obtained by spectrophotometric

---

[1] J. C. Hindman, L. B. Magnusson and T. J. La Chapelle, *J. Am. Chem. Soc.*, **71**,
687 (1949).

[2] J. C. Hindman and E. S. Kritchevsky, *J. Am. Chem. Soc.*, **72**, 953 (1950).

TABLE 73

THERMODYNAMIC DATA FOR NEPTUNIUM[1]

(Heat and free energy of formation in kcal. Entropy of substance in cal./deg.)

Formula	Description	State	$\Delta H°$	$\Delta F°$	$S°$
Np	metal	c	0.000	0.000	(12.1)
Np^{+++}	in $HCl\cdot55H_2O$	aq	-127.3	ca -128.4	$(-31.)$
Np^{++++}	in $HCl\cdot55H_2O$	aq	-133.2	ca -124.9	$(-78.)$
NpO_2^+	in $HCl\cdot55H_2O$	aq	-230.8	ca -221.0	$(12.)$
NpO_2^{++}	in $HCl\cdot55H_2O$	aq	-208.5	ca -194.5	$(-17.)$
NpF_3		c	$-360.$	$-342.$	$(26.)$
NpF_4		c	$-428.$	$-406.$	$(36.)$
$NpCl_3$		c	$-216.$	$-200.$	$(38.)$
$NpCl_3$	in $HCl\cdot55H_2O$	aq	-291.2		
$NpCl_4$		c	$-237.$	$-216.$	(47.5)
$NpCl_5$		c	$-246.$	$-221.$	$(62.)$
$NpBr_3$		c	$-174.$	$-169.$	$(49.)$
$NpBr_4$		c	$-183.$	$-175.$	$(58.)$
NpI_2		c	$-120.$	$-121.$	$(56.)$

[1] Bureau of Standards values in *italics;* estimated values in parentheses.

titrations with oxidizing and reducing agents and by polarographic reductions. These authors report that the $+4$—$+5$ couple is irreversible and the other two couples are reversible.

The solubility products for the fluorides may be calculated as follows:

$$NpF_3 = Np^{+++} + 3F^-, \qquad K = 1 \times 10^{-11};$$
$$NpF_4 = Np^{+4} + 4F^-, \qquad K = 5 \times 10^{-13}.$$

Potential diagram. The following diagram summarizes the potentials:

Acid Solution

```
     1.86        -0.147       -0.75        -1.15
 Np———Np^{+++}————Np^{+4}————NpO_2^+————NpO_2^{++}
```

We have no values for the potentials in alkaline solution, but assuming the same solubility products which we gave for plutonium, we estimate

Basic Solution

```
   2.25          1.76         -0.39         -0.48
 Np——Np(OH)_3——Np(OH)_4———NpO_2OH———NpO_2(OH)_2
```

PLUTONIUM

Oxidation states. Plutonium resembles neptunium and uranium in having the important oxidation states $+3$, $+4$, $+5$, and $+6$, and also in the formulas and general chemical properties of the compounds of these oxidation states. Its chemistry is unlike that of tungsten in most respects. Thus, the metal is much more electropositive and the

TABLE 74

THERMODYNAMIC DATA ON PLUTONIUM[1]

(Heat and free energy of formation in kcal. Entropy of substance in cal./deg.)

Formula	Description	State	$\Delta H°$	$\Delta F°$	$S°$
Pu		c	0.000	0.000	(12.1)
Pu^{+++}		aq	-141.8	-140.5	$-39.$
Pu^{++++}	in $HClO_4 \cdot 110H_2O$	aq	-129.1	-118.2	$-87.$
PuO_2		c	$-251.$		
PuO_2^+	in $HClO_4 \cdot 55H_2O$	aq	$-213.$	-204.9	19.
PuO_2^{++}	in $HClO_4 \cdot 110H_2O$	aq	-196.3	-183.5	$-13.$
PuH_2		c	-31.7		(12.)
PuF_3		aq	-374.6		
$PuCl_3$		c	-230.0	$-214.$	(38.)
$PuCl_3$		aq	-261.9		
$PuOCl$		c	-222.8		
$PuBr_3$		c	-187.8	-182.4	(49.)
$PuBr_3$		aq	-228.5		
PuI_3		c	$-133.$	-133.6	(56.)
$Pu(OH)_3$		c		-280.2	
$Pu(OH)_4$		c		$-340.$	
PuO_2OH		c		-246.7	
$PuO_2(OH)_2$		c		-278.9	

[1] Bureau of Standards values in *italics;* estimated values in parentheses.

higher oxidation states are much more powerful oxidizing agents. The dioxide is more soluble, and both the $+5$ and $+6$ states form important oxygenated ions, PuO_2^+ and PuO_2^{+4}.

Free energies and potentials. The principal sources of thermodynamic data are the summary of heats of formation by the Bureau of Standards, the heats of reaction and entropy relationships by Evans[1] and the summary of potential values by Kraus.[2] We have used the former for all of the $\Delta H°$ values except that of Pu^{+4}. In this case we have given more weight to the difference in heat content of Pu^{+++}

[1] M. W. Evans, *National Nuclear Energy Series*, **IV**, 14B, Paper 3.30.
[2] K. A. Kraus, *National Nuclear Energy Series*, **IV**, 14B, Paper 3.16.

and Pu^{+4} as determined by Evans. We have adjusted the entropies to agree with our new value for Gd^{+++} through the comparison of its radius with that of Pu^{+++}. The resulting free energies are in excellent agreement with the potentials summarized by Kraus. From these free energies we calculate the following:

$$Pu = Pu^{+++} + 3e^-, \qquad E^\circ = 2.03;$$
$$Pu^{+3} = Pu^{+4} + e^-, \qquad E^\circ = -0.97.$$

This potential agrees with the value given by Kraus.

$$Pu^{+4} + 2H_2O = PuO_2^{++} + 4H^+ + 2e^-, \qquad E^\circ = -1.04.$$

Kraus favored -1.02 for this potential, but Hindman[1] gave -1.067.

$$PuO_2^+ = PuO_2^{++} + e^-, \qquad E^\circ = -0.93.$$

This is in agreement with the value given by Connick[2]

$$Pu^{+4} + 2H_2O = PuO_2^+ + 4H^+ + e^-, \qquad E^\circ = -1.15.$$

This potential is determined by the values for the PuO_2^+—PuO_2^{++} and Pu^{+4}—PuO_2^{++} couples.

$$Pu + 3OH^- = Pu(OH)_3 + 3e^-, \qquad E_B^\circ = 2.42.$$

The value is calculated by assuming that the solubility product is similar to that of the rare-earth element with the same ionic radius.

$$Pu(OH)_3 = Pu^{+++} + 3OH^-, \qquad K = 2 \times 10^{-20}.$$

The following potentials are given by Kraus by extrapolation from low acid solutions:

$$Pu(OH)_3 + OH^- = Pu(OH)_4 + e^-, \qquad E_B^\circ = 0.95;$$
$$Pu(OH)_4 + OH^- = PuO_2OH + e^-, \qquad E_B^\circ = -0.76;$$
$$PuO_2OH + OH^- = PuO_2(OH)_2 + e^-, \qquad E_B^\circ = -0.26.$$

These potentials, together with our free energies, give the following solubility products:

$$Pu(OH)_4 = Pu^{+4} + 4OH^-, \qquad K = 10^{-52};$$
$$PuO_2OH = PuO_2^+ + OH^-, \qquad K = 1 \times 10^{-3};$$
$$PuO_2(OH)_2 = PuO_2^{++} + 2OH^-, \qquad K = 1.6 \times 10^{-15}.$$

---

[1] J. C. Hindman, Metallurgical Project Report CN-2289 (Nov. 1944).
[2] R. E. Connick, *National Nuclear Energy Series*, **IV**, 14B, 256.

These constants are most reasonable and give added confirmation of our free energy values. Connick and Kasha[1] reported 7×10^{-56} for the $Pu(OH)_4$ constant by noting the pH at which the colloidal precipitate forms.

Potential diagrams. The following diagrams summarize the potentials of the various couples.

Acid Solution

$$\text{Pu} \xrightarrow{2.03} \text{Pu}^{+++} \xrightarrow{-0.97} \text{Pu}^{+4} \xrightarrow{-1.15} \text{PuO}_2^+ \xrightarrow{-0.93} \text{PuO}_2^{++}$$
$$\underset{-1.04}{\underline{}}$$

Basic Solution

$$\text{Pu} \xrightarrow{2.42} \text{Pu}(\text{OH})_3 \xrightarrow{0.95} \text{Pu}(\text{OH})_4 \xrightarrow{-0.76} \text{PuO}_2\text{OH} \xrightarrow{-0.26} \text{PuO}_2(\text{OH})_2$$
$$\underset{-0.51}{\underline{}}$$

From these potentials it is obvious that the $+5$ state is unstable in both acid and base, but the free energy of the reaction in acid is not large and a measurable concentration of PuO_2^+ exists in the solution. Also in acid solution we have the equilibrium

$$3Pu^{+4} + 2H_2O = 2Pu^{+++} + PuO_2^{++} + 4H^+, \qquad K = 1 \times 10^{-3}.$$

Kasha[2] gave 0.0018 for this constant in $0.05M$ $HClO_4$ and 0.014 in $0.5M$ $HClO_4$.

Connick[3] has discussed the disproportionation of PuO_2^+ and suggested the mechanism

$$Pu(V) + Pu(III) = 2Pu(IV),$$
$$Pu(V) + Pu(IV) = Pu(VI) + Pu(III),$$

where the first reaction is the rate-determining step and the second is a rapid reversible equilibrium.

---

[1] R. E. Connick and M. Kasha, *National Nuclear Energy Series*, IV, 14B, Paper 3.10.

[2] M. Kasha, *National Nuclear Energy Series*, **IV**, 14B, Paper 3.10.

[3] R. C. Connick, *National Nuclear Energy Series*, **IV**, 14B, Paper 3.8.

Hindman[1] has given the following constants:

$$PuCl^{+3} = Pu^{+4} + Cl^-, \qquad K = 2.6;$$
$$PuNO_3^{+3} = Pu^{+4} + NO_3^-, \qquad K = 0.34.$$

For the corresponding fluoride complex, McLane[2] found
$$PuF^{+3} = Pu^{+4} + F^-, \qquad K = 1.6 \times 10^{-7}.$$

Reas[3] studied the solubility of the $+4$ oxalate in acid.

$$Pu(C_2O_4)_2 6H_2O = Pu(C_2O_4)_2(aq) + 6H_2O, \quad K = 3 \times 10^{-5};$$
$$Pu(C_2O_4)_2(aq) + 2H^+ = Pu(C_2O_4)^{++} + H_2C_2O_4, \quad K = 1.03 \times 10^{-3};$$
$$Pu(C_2O_4)_3^{--} + 2H^+ = Pu(C_2O_4) + H_2C_2O_4, \quad K = 4 \times 10^{-2}.$$

With excess of hydrogen peroxide, Pu^{+4} forms slightly soluble peroxides of complex structure. With low concentration of peroxide, two soluble complex ions are formed. Both contain two $+4$ plutonium atoms; and one, the brown, has one peroxide, and the other, the red, has two peroxides. Connick and McVey[4] have reported for $0.5M$ HCl solutions

$$2Pu^{+4} + H_2O_2 = \text{brown complex}, \qquad K = 7 \times 10^7;$$
$$\text{brown complex} + H_2O_2 = \text{red complex}, \qquad K = 1.5 \times 10^5.$$

AMERICIUM

Oxidation states. Americium should resemble europium in its electronic structure. The oxidation states are $+3$, $+4$, $+5$, and $+6$. There is no verified evidence for the existence of the $+2$ state. In general, the chemistry is similar to that of plutonium with the exception that the potential of the Am(III)—Am(IV) is highly negative and Am^{+4} is unstable in acid solutions.

Free energies and potentials. The heat of solution of the metal has been measured by Lohr and Cunningham,[5] who also gave the heat of formation of $AmCl_3$. The heats of formation of AmO_2 and Am^{+4}

[1] J. C. Hindman, *National Nuclear Energy Series*, **IV**, 145, Papers 4.5 and 4.7.
[2] C. K. McLane, *National Nuclear Energy Series*, **IV**, 14, Paper 4.8.
[3] W. H. Reas, *National Nuclear Energy Series*, **IV**, 14, Paper 4.9.
[4] R. E. Connick and W. H. McVey, *National Nuclear Energy Series*, **IV**, 14B, Paper 4.12.
[5] H. R. Lohr and B. B. Cunningham, *J. Am. Chem. Soc. Chicago* 73, 2025 (1951).

are by Eyring, Lohr and Cunningham.[1] From the free energies based upon these heats,

$$Am = Am^{+++} + 3e^-, \qquad E° = 2.32;$$
$$Am^{+++} = Am^{+4} + e^-, \qquad E° = -2.18.$$

Since the radius of Am^{+++} is similar to that of Pr^{+++}, we estimate

$$Am(OH)_3 = Am^{+++} + 3OH^-, \qquad K = 2.7 \times 10^{-20};$$
$$Am + 3OH^- = Am(OH)_3 + 3e^-, \qquad E_B° = 2.71.$$

For the solubility product of $Am(OH)_4$, we estimate

$$Am(OH)_4 = Am^{+4} + 4OH^-, \qquad K = ca\ 10^{-56}.$$

TABLE 75

THERMODYNAMIC DATA ON AMERICIUM[1]

(Heat and free energy of formation in kcal. Entropy of substance in cal./deg.)

Formula	Description	State	$\Delta H°$	$\Delta F°$	$S°$
Am	metal	c	0.000	0.000	15.0
Am^{+++}		aq	-163.2	-160.5	(-38.0)
Am^{+4}		aq	-122.3	-110.2	(-89.)
AmO_2^+		aq		(-194.5)	
AmO_2^{++}		aq		(-156.7)	
AmO_2		c	-240.3	-231.	(20)
$Am(OH)_3$		c		(-300.0)	
$Am(OH)_4$		c		(-347.0)	
$AmCl_3$		c	-251.3		

[1] Estimated values in parentheses.

Hence,

$$Am(OH)_3 + OH^- = Am(OH)_4 + e^-, \qquad E_B° = 0.4.$$

Penneman and Asprey[2] have measured the formal potential of the 5—6 couple,

$$AmO_2^+ = AmO_2^{++}, \qquad E_f = -1.64.$$

---

[1] L. Eyring, H. R. Lohr, and B. B. Cunningham, *Paper Am. Chem. Soc. Chicago* (1950).

[2] R. A. Penneman and L. B. Asprey, *Paper Am. Chem. Soc. Chicago*, 1950.

AmO_2^+ is unstable in acid with respect to the disproportionation reaction,

$$3AmO_2^+ + 4H^+ = 2AmO_2^{++} + Am^{+++} + 2H_2O.$$

Hence, as a rough value, we estimate

$$Am^{+++} + 2H_2O = AmO_2^+ + 4H^+ + 2e^- \qquad E^\circ = -1.72.$$

The following potentials are derived from the various couples given above

$$Am^{+4} + 2H_2O = AmO_2^+ + 4H^+ + e^-, \qquad E^\circ = -1.26;$$
$$Am^{+3} + 2H_2O = AmO_2^{++} + 4H^+ + 3e^-, \qquad E^\circ = -1.69.$$

Summary of americium potentials. The following diagrams summarize the various couples

Acid Solution

$$-1.72$$

```
          ┌─────────────────────────────┐
   2.32   │  -2.18       -1.26          │   -1.64
Am────────Am⁺³─────────Am⁺⁴──────────AmO₂⁺────────AmO₂⁺⁺
          └─────────────────────────────┘
                    -1.69
```

Basic Solution

```
  2.71          0.4           (-0.7)         (-1.1)
Am ──────Am(OH)₃── Am(OH)₄────AmO₂OH────────AmO₂(OH)₂
```

It appears that all of the states are stable in alkaline solution.

CURIUM

Oxidation states. Curium should resemble gadolinium from its electron configuration, and like this element it seems to have only the $+3$ state. There are no data on the free energy of Cm^{+++}. The solubility product of $Cm(OH)_3$ is probably about 1.9×10^{-21} in comparison to that of $Nd(OH)_3$, since the radii of the two ions are similar.

BERKELIUM

Oxidation states. The $+3$ and $+4$ states are known. The free energies of these ions have not been determined, but in tracer experiments Bk^{+++} is oxidized to the Bk^{++++} by ceric perchlorate in perchloric acid.

$$Bk^{+++} = Bk^{++++} + e^-, \qquad E^\circ = ca\ -1.6.$$

CALIFORNIUM

Oxidation states. The $+3$ state is known but experiments with tracer amounts have not given evidence for any higher state.

CHAPTER 22

Beryllium, Magnesium, Calcium, Strontium, Barium, and Radium

The elements of this group have two valence electrons and, in the monatomic gas atoms, the ground state is $s^2(^1S_0)$. The elements are highly electropositive and the only oxidation state, stable in water solutions, is the $+2$. The electronic structure of the ions is that of the preceding noble gas. Because of the small ionic radius, the oxide of beryllium is amphoteric, but with increasing size of the heavier members of the group, the oxides become strong bases.

BERYLLIUM

Oxidation states. Spectroscopic evidence has been obtained on the unstable $+1$ fluoride, BeF; however, only the $+2$ state has chemical significance. As stated above, the oxide or hydroxide is amphoteric. The hydroxide and phosphate are only slightly soluble, but the normal salts of most of the acid ions are soluble. However, insoluble basic salts form at low acid concentration. The basic carbonate is soluble in excess carbonate ion, and the ion, $BeFe^+$, forms at high fluoride concentration.

Beryllium free energies and potentials. From the free energy of Be^{++} we calculate

$$Be = Be^{++} + 2e^-, \qquad E^\circ = 1.85.$$

Bodforss[1] and others have sought to determine the beryllium potential by direct cell measurements. The value obtained was around 0.6. The electrode is obviously not reversible.

[1] S. Bodforss, *Z. physik. Chem.*, **124**, 66 (1926); **130**, 85 (1927). Cf. also B. Neumann and H. Richter, *Z. Elektrochem.*, **31**, 296 (1925).

TABLE 76

THERMODYNAMIC DATA ON BERYLLIUM[1]

(Heat and free energy of formation in kcal. Entropy of substance in cal./deg.)

Formula	Description	State	$\Delta H°$	$\Delta F°$	S
Be		g	76.63	67.60	32.545
Be	metal	c	0.0	0.0	2.28
Be$^+$		g	293.049		
Be^{++}		g	714.393		
Be^{++}		aq	−93.	−85.2	(−55.)
BeO		g	11.8	5.7	47.18
BeO		c	−146.0	−139.0	3.37
BeO$_2^{--}$		aq	−187.8	−155.3	−27.
Be$_2$O$_3^{--}$		aq		−298.	
Be$_2$O^{++}		aq		−218.	
BeH		g	78.1	71.3	40.84
Be(OH)$_2$	α	c	−216.8	−196.2	(13.3)
Be(OH)$_2$	β	c	−216.1	−195.5	(13.3)
BeO·Be(OH)$_2$	ppt.	c	−366.2	−338.	(16.7)
BeCl$_2$		c	−122.3	−111.8	(20.5)
BeCl$_2$·4H$_2$O		c	−436.8	−376.	(58.1)
BeBr$_2$		c	−88.4	−84.6	(26.1)
BeI$_2$		c	−50.6	−51.	(31.5)
BeS		c	−55.9	−55.9	(9.3)
BeSO$_4$		c	−286.9	−260.2	21.5
Be$_3$N$_2$		c	−135.7		
BeMoO$_4$		c	−330.	−306.	(26.)

[1] Bureau of Standards values in *italics;* estimated values in parentheses.

From the free energies of Be$_2$O(OH)$_2$ and Be(OH)$_2\alpha$ we calculate

$$\tfrac{1}{2}\text{Be}_2\text{O(OH)}_2 + \tfrac{1}{2}\text{H}_2\text{O} = \text{Be}^{++} + 2\text{OH}^-, \qquad K = 9 \times 10^{-28};$$

$$\text{Be}_2\text{O(OH)}_2 + \text{H}_2\text{O} = 2\text{Be(OH)}_2\alpha \qquad \Delta F° = 2. \text{ kcal.};$$

$$\text{Be(OH)}_2\alpha = \text{Be}^{++} + 2\text{OH}^-, \qquad K = 1.6 \times 10^{-26}.$$

Thus Be$_2$O(OH)$_2$, which appears to be in the formula of the freshly precipitated hydroxide, is not metastable with respect to the α form as is generally stated. However, the calculated ΔF is only $+2$ kcal., and a small negative value would be within the limits of accuracy of the heats and our estimated entropies and we will use the calculated free energies of the hydroxide in spite of this probable error.

For the equilibrium constant of the solid and its acid ions, Bleyer and Kaufmann[1] reported,

$$\text{H}_2\text{Be}_2\text{O}_3 = 2\text{H}^+ + \text{Be}_2\text{O}_3^{--}, \qquad K = 7.3 \times 10^{-30}.$$

[1] B. Bleyer and S. W. Kaufmann, *Z. anorg. Chem.*, **82**, 83 (1913).

The free energy of $Be_2O_3^{--}$ is then $-298.$ kcal., and for the couple in alkaline solution

$$6OH^- + 2Be = Be_2O_3^{--} + 3H_2O + 4e^-, \qquad E_B^o = 2.62.$$

These authors also gave

$$H_2BeO_2\alpha = 2H^+ + BeO_2^{--}, \qquad K = 1.4 \times 10^{-30};$$
$$H_2BeO_2\beta = 2H^+ + BeO_2^{--}, \qquad K = 2.8 \times 10^{-30}.$$

The corresponding free energies of BeO_2^{--} are -155.5 and -155.2 kcal. We shall use -155.3 to calculate the entropy of BeO_2^{--} from the heat of formation. The calculated value -27 appears very reasonable in comparison with -13.0 for CO_3^{--}.

Prytz[1] gave slightly different data for the hydrolysis of various halide solutions, but the following is representative:

$$2Be^{++} + H_2O = Be_2O^{++} + 2H^+, \qquad K = 4 \times 10^{-7}.$$

From this, the free energy of Be_2O^{++} is -218 kcal. and we calculate

$$Be_2O(OH)_2 = Be_2O^{++} + 2OH^-, \qquad K = 10^{-33}.$$

Prytz gave 4×10^{-19} for this constant. He also gave 10^{-20} for the dissociation into Be^{++} and OH^- as compared with the value 5.5×10^{-28} calculated above. We are unable to resolve this discrepancy.

Beryllium does not form the complex ion BeF_4^{--}, but there is evidence for BeF^+ with a dissociation constant around 10^{-5}.

MAGNESIUM

Oxidation states. Although the $+2$ oxidation state is the only one of importance, claims are made for the formation of compounds of the $+1$ state by high temperature reduction. The probable free energies will be discussed. The $+2$ hydroxide is distinctly basic. The hydroxide, carbonate fluoride, and ammonium phosphate are the more important slightly soluble compounds.

Magnesium free energies and potentials. The $\Delta H°$, $\Delta F°$, and $S°$ values of the Bureau of Standards have been accepted, although the author believes that the values given by Stevensen[2] may be better.

[1] M. Prytz, *Z. anorg. allgem. Chem.*, **197**, 111 (1931).
[2] C. C. Stevensen, *J. Am. Chem. Soc.*, **68**, 721 (1946).

TABLE 77

THERMODYNAMIC DATA ON MAGNESIUM[1]

(Heat and free energy of formation in kcal. Entropy of substance in cal./deg.)

Formula	Description	State	$\Delta H°$	$\Delta F°$	$S°$
Mg		g	*35.9*	*27.6*	*35.504*
Mg	metal	c	0.0	0.0	7.77
Mg⁺		g	*213.663*		
Mg⁺⁺		g	*561.788*		
Mg⁺⁺		aq	*−110.41*	*−108.99*	*−28.2*
MgO		c	*−143.84*	*−136.13*	*6.4*
MgO	finely divided	c	*−142.95*	*−135.31*	*6.66*
MgO₂		c	*−148.9*		
MgH		g	*41.*	34.	47.61
Mg(OH)₂		c	*−221.00*	*−199.27*	*15.09*
MgF		g	*−20.*	*−27.*	*54.85*
MgF₂		c	*−263.5*	*−250.8*	*13.68*
MgCl		g	*2.*		
MgCl		c	(−53.)	(−46.5)	(17.3)
MgCl₂		c	*−153.40*	*−141.57*	*21.4*
Mg(ClO₄)₂		c	*−140.6*	−79.4	(51.6)
MgOHCl		c	*−191.3*	*−175.0*	*19.8*
MgBr₂		c	*−123.7*	−119.3	(29.4)
MgI₂		c	*−86.0*	−86.0	(34.8)
MgS		c	*−83.*	−83.6	(12.6)
MgSO₃		c	*−241.0*	−221.2	(22.5)
MgSO₄		c	*−305.5*	*−280.5*	*21.9*
MgTe		c	*−50.*	−50.	(19.)
Mg(NO₃)₂		c	*−188.72*	*−140.63*	*39.2*
Mg₃(PO₄)₂		c	*−961.5*	−904.	(56.8)
Mg₃(AsO₄)₂		c	*−731.3*	−679.3	(53.8)
MgCO₃		c	*−266.*	*−246.*	*15.7*
MgCN₂	cyanamide	c	*−60.3*		
Mg₂Si		c	*−18.6*		
MgNH₄PO₄				−390.	
MgC₂O₄				−273.9	

[1] Bureau of Standards values in *italics;* estimated values in parentheses.

From the values in Table 77, the potential of the Mg—Mg⁺⁺ couple is

$$Mg = Mg^{++} + 2e^-, \qquad E° = 2.37.$$

From the free energy of magnesium hydroxide we may write

$$2OH^- + Mg = Mg(OH)_2 + 2e^-, \qquad E_B° = 2.69;$$
$$Mg(OH)_2 = Mg^{++} + 2OH^-, \qquad K = 8.9 \times 10^{-12}.$$

The solubility product may be compared with the value given by Kline[1] of 5.5×10^{-12}, and the more recent value of 3.07×10^{-11} given by Nasanen.[2]

Kelley and Anderson[3] have given ΔF° for MgO as -136.37 kcal. and ΔF° of $MgCO_3$ as -246.63 kcal. The Bureau of Standards free energy for the carbonate corresponds to a solubility product of 8×10^{-9}. Kline[4] reported for the trihydrate

$$MgCO_3 \cdot 3H_2O = Mg^{++} + CO_3^{--} + 3H_2O, \qquad K = ca\ 1 \times 10^{-5}.$$

The solubility of magnesium ammonium phosphate was studied by Bube.[5] He found

$$Mg(NH_4)PO_4 = Mg^{++} + NH_4^+ + PO_4^{---}, \qquad K = 2.5 \times 10^{-13}.$$

The corresponding free energy of the compound is $-390.$ kcal. We also calculate from the free energies

$$Mg_3(AsO_4)_2 = 3Mg^{++} + 2AsO_4^{---}, \qquad K = 10^{-35};$$
$$MgF_2 = Mg^{++} + 2F^-, \qquad K = 8 \times 10^{-8}.$$

For the latter constant Kohlrausch[6] recorded from conductivity measurement, a value of K of 6.4×10^{-9}. The same author gave

$$MgC_2O_4 = Mg^{++} + C_2O_4^{--}, \qquad K = 8.6 \times 10^{-5}.$$

The free energy of Mg^+. The monohalides exist as gas molecules at high temperatures and various authors[7] have postulated the existence of the $+1$ state as an intermediate in the reduction of magnesium compounds. If we assume that the heat of sublimation of MgCl would be approximately the same as that for NaCl, we may calculate, from the heat of formation of MgCl(g), the data given for solid MgCl in Table 77. Thus,

$$2MgCl(c) = Mg + MgCl_2(c), \qquad \Delta F^\circ = -50.\ kcal.$$

and it may be concluded that the solid $+1$ compounds (and also the aqueous $+1$ ion) are highly unstable at room temperature.

[1] W. D. Kline, *J. Am. Chem. Soc.*, **51**, 2096 (1929).
[2] R. Nasanen, *Z. physik. Chem.*, **A188**, 272 (1941).
[3] K. K. Kelley and C. T. Anderson, *U. S. Bur. Mines Bull.*, No. 384 (1935).
[4] W. D. Kline, *J. Am. Chem. Soc.*, **51**, 2093 (1929).
[5] K. Bube, *Z. anal. Chem.*, **49**, 557 (1910).
[6] F. Kohlrausch, *Z. physik. Chem.*, **64**, 164 (1908).
[7] H. G. Grimm and K. F. Herzfeld, *Z. Physik*, **16**, 77, (1923).

TABLE 78

THERMODYNAMIC DATA ON CALCIUM[1]

(Heat and free energy of formation in kcal. Entropy of substance in cal./deg.)

Formula	Description	State	$\Delta H°$	$\Delta F°$	$S°$
Ca		g	46.04	37.98	36.99
Ca	metal	c	0.0	0.0	9.95
Ca$^+$		g	188.459		
Ca^{++}		g	463.64		
Ca^{++}		aq	−129.77	−132.18	−13.2
CaO		c	−151.9	−144.4	9.5
CaO$_2$		c	−157.5	143.	(10.3)
CaH		g	58.7		
CaH$_2$		c	−45.1	−35.8	10.
Ca(OH)$_2$		c	−235.8	−214.33	18.2
CaF		g	−9.3		
CaF$_2$		c	−290.3	−277.7	16.46
CaCl		g	6.7		
CaCl$_2$		c	−190.0	−179.3	27.2
CaOCl$_2$		c	−178.6		
CaBr$_2$		c	−161.3	−156.8	31.
CaI$_2$		c	−127.8	−126.6	34.
CaS		c	−115.3	−114.1	13.5
CaSO$_4$		c			24.2
CaC$_2$		c	−15.0	−16.2	16.8
CaCO$_3$	calcite	c	−288.45	−269.78	22.2
CaCO$_3$	aragonite	c	−288.49	−269.53	21.2
CaC$_2$O$_4$·H$_2$O	precipitated	c	−399.1	−360.6	37.28
CaC$_2$O$_4$·2H$_2$O		c	−469.1	−416.9	47.
Ca(HCO$_2$)$_2$	formate	c	−323.5	−300.8	(37.3)
Ca(CH$_2$CO$_2$)$_2$		c	−355.0	−309.7	(47.3)
CaCN$_2$		c	−84.0		
Ca(CN)$_2$		c	−44.2	−33.1	(21.3)
CaSiO$_3$	pseudowollastonite	c	−377.4	−357.4	20.9
CaSiO$_3$	wollastonite	c	−378.6	−358.2	19.6
Ca$_2$SiO$_4$	β	c	−538.0	−512.7	(37.6)
Ca$_2$SiO$_4$	γ	c	−539.0	−513.7	(37.6)
Ca$_3$SiO$_5$		c	−688.4		
CaCrO$_4$		c	−337.1	−312.8	(32.)
CaSO$_4$	anhydrite	c	−342.42	−315.56	25.5
CaSO$_4$	soluble α	c	−340.27	−313.52	25.9
CaSO$_4$	soluble β	c	−339.21	−312.46	25.9
CaSO$_4$·½H$_2$O	α	c	−376.47	−343.02	31.2
CaSO$_4$·½H$_2$O	β	c	−375.97	−342.78	32.1
CaSO$_4$·2H$_2$O		c	−483.06	−429.19	46.36
Ca(N$_3$)$_2$	azide	c	75.8		
Ca$_3$N$_2$		c	−103.2	−88.1	25.
CaN$_2$O$_2$·4H$_2$O		c	−405.7		

[1] Bureau of Standards values in *italics;* estimated values in parentheses.

Table 78 (*Continued*)

THERMODYNAMIC DATA ON CALCIUM[1]

Formula	Description	State	$\Delta H°$	$\Delta F°$	$S°$
$Ca(NO_2)_2$		c	*−178.3*	−144.2	(39.3)
$Ca(NO_3)_2$		c	*−224.00*	−177.34	*46.2*
$Ca_3(PO_4)_2$	α	c	*−986.2*	*−929.7*	*57.6*
$Ca_3(PO_4)_2$	β	c	*−988.9*	*−932.0*	*56.4*
$CaHPO_4$		c	*−435.2*	*−401.5*	*21.*
$CaHPO_4·2H_2O$		c	*−576.0*	*−514.6*	*40.*
$Ca(H_2PO_4)_2$	precipitated	c	*−744.4*	*−672.*	(45.3)
$CaHAsO_4·H_2O$		c	*−410.*	*−363.*	*35.*(?)
$CaWO_4$		c	*−392.5*	−368.7	(36.1)
$CaO·B_2O_3$		c	*−483.3*	*−457.7*	*25.1*
$CaO·2B_2O_3$		c	*−798.3*	*−752.4*	*32.2*
$CaO·2B_2O_3$		glass	*−786.2*		
$2CaO·B_2O_3$		c	*651.6*	*−618.6*	*34.7*
$3CaO·B_2O_3$		c	*817.7*	*−777.1*	*43.9*

[1] Bureau of Standards values in *italics;* estimated values in parentheses.

CALCIUM

Oxidation states. Like magnesium, highly unstable +1 halides may exist, but the only oxidation state which is stable in water solutions is the +2. The hydroxide is more basic than magnesium hydroxide and the solubilities of the sulfate and oxalate are much lower.

Calcium free energies and potentials. For the potential of the Ca—Ca^{++} couple, we compute from the free energy of the ion

$$Ca = Ca^{++} + 2e^-, \qquad E° = 2.87.$$

The best experimental value for this potential appears to be that of Tamele,[1] who obtained 2.76, using an amalgam electrode. For the couple in alkaline solution we find

$$2OH^- + Ca = Ca(OH)_2 + 2e^-, \qquad E_B° = 3.03.$$

The corresponding value for the solubility product of the hydroxide is

$$Ca(OH)_2 = Ca^{++} + 2OH^-, \qquad K = 1.3 \times 10^{-6}.$$

For calcium carbonate we calculate from the free energies

$$CaCO_3 \text{ (calcite)} = Ca^{++} + CO_3^{--}, \qquad K = 4.7 \times 10^{-9};$$
$$CaCO_3 \text{ (aragonite)} = Ca^{++} + CO_3^{--}, \qquad K = 6.9 \times 10^{-9}.$$

[1] M. Tamele, *J. Phys. Chem.*, **28**, 502 (1924).

Frear and Johnston[1] reported 4.82×10^{-9} for the calcite. The free energy of the aragonite-calcite transition is

$$CaCO_3 \text{ (aragonite)} = CaCO_3 \text{ (calcite)}, \qquad \Delta F^\circ = 0.25 \text{ kcal.}$$

From the values in Table 78 the following additional solubility products may be calculated.

$$CaSO_4 \cdot 2H_2O = Ca^{++} + SO_4^{--} + 2H_2O, \qquad K = 2.4 \times 10^{-5};$$
$$CaC_2O_4 \cdot H_2O = Ca^{++} + C_2O_4^{--} + H_2O, \qquad K = 1.3 \times 10^{-9};$$
$$CaHPO_4 = Ca^{++} + HPO_4^{--}, \qquad K = 2 \times 10^{-6};$$
$$Ca_3(PO_4)_2 = 3Ca^{++} + 2PO_4^{---}, \qquad K = 1.3 \times 10^{-32};$$
$$CaF_2 = Ca^{++} + 2F^-, \qquad K = 1.7 \times 10^{-10};$$

$$CaWO_4 = Ca^{++} + WO_4^{--}, \qquad K = 8 \times 10^{-13}.$$

The first two constants agree with the values summarized by Latimer, Hicks, and Schutz.[2] The third constant agrees with the work of Britton,[3] but the same author gave $K = 1 \times 10^{-25}$ for $Ca_3(PO_4)_2$. From conductive measurements Kohlrausch[4] reported

$$K = 3.9 \times 10^{-11} \text{ for } CaF_2.$$

The solubility of calcium iodate was studied by Kilde.[5] He recorded

$$Ca(IO_3)_2 \cdot 6H_2O = Ca^{++} + 2IO_3^- + 6H_2O, \qquad K = 1.73 \times 10^{-6}.$$

Paul[6] gave for the solubility product of the tartrate

$$CaC_4H_4O_6 \cdot 2H_2O = Ca^{++} + C_4H_4O_6^{--} + 2H_2O, \qquad K = 7.7 \times 10^{-7}.$$

Calcium in the +1 state. Guntz and Benoit[7] claim the formation of the subhalides by reduction with the metal at 1000°. It has been pointed out by Bichowsky and Rossini that their heat of solution

---

[1] G. L. Frear and J. Johnston, *J. Am. Chem. Soc.*, **51**, 2082 (1929).

[2] W. M. Latimer, J. F. G. Hicks, Jr., and P. W. Schutz, *J. Chem. Phys.*, **1**, 620 (1933); W. M. Latimer, P. W. Schutz, and J. F. G. Hicks, *J. Am. Chem. Soc.*, **55**, 974 (1933).

[3] H. T. S. Britton, *J. Chem. Soc.*, 614 (1927).

[4] F. Kohlrausch, *Z. physik. Chem.*, **64**, 145 (1908).

[5] G. Kilde, *Z. anorg. allgem. Chem.*, **218**, 115 (1934).

[6] T. Paul, *Z. Elektrochem.*, **21**, 549 (1915).

[7] A. Guntz and F. Benoit, *Bull. soc. chim.*, **35**, 709 (1924).

of CaCl in acid is exactly the value which would be given by a mixture of the metal and the dichloride. The heat of formation of the subchloride from their work is -96.9 kcal., the value calculated from a Born-Haber cycle is -40.3 kcal., and the corresponding free energies would be about -92 and -35 kcal. From band spectra data the heat of formation of the gaseous subfluoride, CaF, is -9.3 kcal. Estimating the heat of sublimation to be the same as that for potassium fluoride, 53 kcal., we find the heat of formation of the solid CaF to be -62 kcal. This value would make the fluoride highly unstable.

$$2CaF(c) = Ca + CaF_2, \qquad \Delta H^\circ = \Delta F^\circ = -166 \text{ kcal.}$$

See also the discussion of $+1$ magnesium.

STRONTIUM

Oxidation states. The $+1$ halides are known as unstable gas molecules, and claims are made for the solids (cf. magnesium and calcium). The $+2$ hydroxide is more basic than calcium, and the solubilities of the $+2$ sulfates and chromates are less than those of the calcium salts.

Strontium free energies and potentials. From the free energy of the ion, the potential of the Sr—Sr^{++} couple is

$$Sr = Sr^{++} + 2e^-, \qquad E^\circ = 2.89.$$

Cell measurements using amalgam electrode do not appear to be completely reversible.[1]

The solubility of the octahydrated hydroxide, $Sr(OH)_2 \cdot 8H_2O$, is $0.086M$. Using 0.5 as a rough value for the activity coefficient and neglecting the change in the activity of the water, we find the free energy of solution to be 4780 cal. and

$$Sr(OH)_2 \cdot 8H_2O = Sr^{++} + 2OH^- + 8H_2O, \qquad K = 3.2 \times 10^{-4}.$$

For the potential of the strontium couple in alkaline solution we then compute

$$8H_2O + 2OH^- + Sr = Sr(OH)_2 \cdot 8H_2O + 2e^-, \qquad E_B^\circ = 2.99.$$

---

[1] P. S. Danner, *J. Am. Chem. Soc.*, **46**, 2390 (1924).

TABLE 79

THERMODYNAMIC DATA ON STRONTIUM[1]

(Heat and free energy of formation in kcal. Entropy of substance in cal./deg.)

Formula	Description	State	$\Delta H°$	$\Delta F°$	$S°$
Sr		g	39.2	26.3	39.325
Sr	metal	c	0.0	0.0	13.0
Sr	amalgam	liq	−50.4		
Sr⁺		g	171.96		
Sr⁺⁺		aq	−130.38	−133.2	−9.4
SrO		c	−141.1	−133.8	13.0
SrO₂		c	−153.6	−139.	(13.)
SrH		g	52.4	45.8	49.43
SrH₂		c	−42.3		
Sr(OH)₂		c	−229.3	−207.8	(21.)
SrF		g	−5.		
SrF₂		c	−290.3	−277.8	(21.4)
SrCl		g	9.		
SrCl₂		c	−198.0	−186.7	28.
SrBr₂		c	−171.1	166.3	(33.8)
SrI₂		g	−135.5	−135.	(39.2)
SrS		c	19.		
SrS		c	−108.1	−97.4	(17.)
SrSO₄		c	−345.3	−318.9	29.1
Sr(N₃)₂		c	48.9	80.0	(46.)
Sr₃N₂		c	−93.4		
Sr(NO₂)₂		c	−179.3	−145.1	(42.)
Sr(NO₃)₂		c	−233.25	−186.	(47.4)
SrCrO₄		c		−315.3	
SrC₂O₄·H₂O		c		−359.6	
Sr₃(PO₄)₂		c	−987.3	−932.1	(70.)
SrHPO₄		c	−431.3	−399.7	(31.2)
Sr₃(AsO₄)₂		c	−800.7	−770.1	(74.6)
SrCO₃	strontianite	c	−291.9	−271.9	23.3
Sr(HCO₂)₂	formate	c	−325.5	−295.	(40.)
SrSiO₃		c	−371.2	−350.8	(22.5)
SrSiO₃		glass	−367.4		
Sr₂SiO₄		c	−520.6	−495.7	(43.)
Sr(WO₄)		c	−398.3	−366.5	(37.8)

[1] Bureau of Standards values in *italics;* estimated values in parentheses.

The following solubility products may be calculated.

$$SrCO_3 = Sr^{++} + CO_3^{--}, \qquad K = 7 \times 10^{-10};$$

$$SrSO_4 = Sr^{++} + SO_4^{--}, \qquad K = 7.6 \times 10^{-7};$$

$$SrF_2 = Sr^{++} + 2F^{-}, \qquad K = 7.9 \times 10^{-10};$$

$$SrCrO_4 = Sr^{++} + CrO_4^{--}, \qquad K = 3.6 \times 10^{-5};$$

$$SrHPO_4 = Sr^{++} + HPO_4^{--}, \qquad K = 2 \times 10^{-4};$$
$$Sr_3(PO_4)_2 = 3Sr^{++} + 2PO_4^{---}, \qquad K = 1 \times 10^{-31}.$$
$$Sr_3(AsO_4)_2 = 3Sr^{++} + 2AsO_4^{---}, \qquad K = 2 \times 10^{-49};$$
$$SrWO_4 = Sr^{++} + WO_4^{--}, \qquad K = 1.7 \times 10^{-10}.$$

For strontium carbonate, McCoy and Smith[1] report 9.42×10^{-10}. Kohlrausch[2] reported 2.8×10^{-7} for the sulfate and 3×10^{-9} for the fluoride. Kohlrausch also reported

$$SrC_2O_4 \cdot H_2O = Sr^{++} + C_2O_4^{--} + H_2O, \qquad K = 5.61 \times 10^{-8}.$$

The iodate $Sr(IO_3)_2 \cdot 6H_2O$ is also slightly soluble, but no data can be given.

Randall[3] gave for strontium bicarbonate

$$Sr(HCO_3)_2 = Sr^{++} + 2HCO_3^-, \qquad K = 1.83 \times 10^{-6}.$$

BARIUM

Oxidation states.   The $+1$ halides exist as gas molecules at high temperatures, but like the other $+1$ halides of this group are unstable as solids at room temperature. From the Bureau of Standards value for the heat of formation of $BaCl_e$, we calculate

$$2BaCl = Ba + BaCl_2, \qquad \Delta F^\circ = -17. \text{ kcal.}$$

The $+2$ state is only slightly more electropositive than strontium, but the hydroxide is more basic. The solubilities of the sulfate and chromate are less than those of the lighter elements of the family.

Barium free energies and potentials.   The potential of the Ba—Ba^{++} couple is

$$Ba = Ba^{++} + 2e^-, \qquad E^\circ = 2.90.$$

Devoto[4] computed 2.86 from measurements of the decomposition potential of the molten chloride. The free energy of solution of barium

[1] H. N. McCoy and H. J. Smith, *J. Am. Chem. Soc.*, **33**, 468 (1911); K. K. Kelley and C. T. Anderson, *U. S. Bur. Mines Bull.*, No. 384 (1935).

[2] F. Kohlrausch, *Z. physik. Chem.*, **64**, 152 and 168 (1908).

[3] M. Randall, *International Critical Tables*, **VII**, 299.

[4] G. Devoto, *Z. Elektrochem.*, **34**, 21 (1928).

TABLE 80

THERMODYNAMIC DATA ON BARIUM[1]

(Heat and free energy of formation in kcal. Entropy of substance in cal./deg.)

Formula	Description	State	$\Delta H°$	$\Delta F°$	$S°$
Ba		g	41.96	34.60	40.699
Ba	metal	c	0.0	0.0	16.
Ba$^+$		g	163.582		
Ba^{++}		aq	−128.67	−134.0	3.
Ba^{++}		g	395.705		
BaO		c	−133.4	−126.3	16.8
BaO$_2$		c	−150.5	−135.3	(15.7)
BaO$_2$·H$_2$O		c	−223.5	−195.	(25.1)
BaH		g	52.	46.	52.97
BaH$_2$		c	−40.9		
Ba(OH)$_2$		c	−226.2	−204.7	(22.7)
Ba(OH)$_2$·8H$_2$O			−799.5	−666.8	
BaF		g	−9.		
BaF$_2$		c	−286.9	−272.5	(23.1)
BaCl		g	24.		
BaCl		c	−111.	−105.3	(23.4)
BaCl$_2$		c	−205.56	−193.8	30.
BaCl$_2$·H$_2$O		c	−278.4	−253.1	40.
BaCl$_2$·2H$_2$O		c	−349.35	−309.8	48.5
Ba(ClO$_2$)$_2$		c	−158.2	−136.8	(47.7)
Ba(ClO$_3$)$_2$		c	−181.7	−133.1	(53.7)
Ba(ClO$_4$)$_2$		c	−192.8	−127.9	(57.7)
BaBr$_2$		c	−180.4	−174.4	(35.5)
BaI$_2$		c	−144.0	−143.1	(40.9)
BaS		g	41.		
BaS		c	−106.0	−104.5	(18.7)
BaSO$_3$		c	−282.6	−262.4	(28.6)
BaSO$_4$		c	−350.2	−323.4	31.6
BaS$_2$O$_8$·4H$_2$O		c	−738.7		
BaS$_4$O$_6$·2H$_2$O		c	−554.5		
BaSeO$_4$		c	−280.0	−253.8	(36.1)
Ba(N$_3$)$_2$		c	−8.	23.5	(47.7)
Ba$_3$N$_2$		c	−86.9		
Ba(NO$_2$)$_2$		c	−174.0	−126.0	(43.7)
Ba(NO$_3$)$_2$		c	−237.06	−190.0	51.1
BaNH		c	−53.8		
Ba(NH$_2$)$_2$		c	−78.9		
Ba$_3$(PO$_4$)$_2$		c	−998.0	−944.4	(85.1)
Ba$_3$(PO$_4$)$_2$	colloidal	aq	−981.4		
BaCO$_3$	witherite	c	−291.3	−272.2	26.8
BaC$_2$O$_4$·2H$_2$O		c	−470.1	−416.3	
BaCN$_2$		c	−63.8		
Ba(CN)$_2$		c	−47.9	−46.7	(25.7)

[1] Bureau of Standards values in *italics;* estimated values in parentheses.

TABLE 80 (Continued)

THERMODYNAMIC DATA ON BARIUM[1]

Formula	Description	State	$\Delta H°$	$\Delta F°$	$S°$
$Ba(IO_3)_2 \cdot H_2O$				−211.1	
$Ba(BrO_3)_2 \cdot H_2O$				−192.9	
$Ba(CNO)_2$		c	−209.6		
$BaSiO_3$		c	−359.5	−338.7	(24.2)
Ba_2SiO_3		c	−496.8	−470.6	(46.4)
$BaSiF_6$		c	−691.6		
$BaMnO_4$		c	−282.	−257.	(36.8)
$BaCrO_4$		c	−348.8	−324.0	(36.7)
$BaMoO_4$		c	−373.8	349.3	(38.7)
$BaWO_4$		c	−407.7	373.6	(41.)

[1] Bureau of Standards values in *italics;* estimated values in parentheses.

hydroxide and the potential in alkaline solution have been given by Lewis and Randall[1]

$$Ba(OH)_2 \cdot 8H_2O = Ba^{++} + 2OH^- + 8H_2O, \quad \Delta F° = 3140 \text{ cal.},$$
$$K = 5.0 \times 10^{-3};$$
$$Ba + 8H_2O + 2OH^- = Ba(OH)_2 \cdot 8H_2O + 2e^-, \quad E_B° = 2.97.$$

The following solubility products are calculated from the free energies.

$$BaCO_3 = Ba^{++} + CO_3^{--}, \qquad\qquad K = 1.6 \times 10^{-9};$$
$$BaSO_4 = Ba^{++} + SO_4^{--}, \qquad\qquad K = 1.5 \times 10^{-9};$$
$$BaCrO_4 = Ba^{++} + CrO_4^{--}, \qquad\qquad K = 8.5 \times 10^{-11};$$
$$BaF_2 = Ba^{++} + 2F^-, \qquad\qquad K = 2.4 \times 10^{-5};$$
$$BaSO_3 = Ba^{++} + SO_3^{--}, \qquad\qquad K = 9.5 \times 10^{-10};$$
$$BaSeO_4 = Ba^{++} + SeO_4^{--}, \qquad\qquad K = 2.8 \times 10^{-11};$$
$$Ba_3(PO_4)_2 = 2Ba^{++} + 3PO_4^{---}, \qquad\qquad K = 6 \times 10^{-39};$$
$$BaC_2O_4 \cdot 2H_2O = Ba^{++} + C_2O_4^{--} + 2H_2O, \qquad\qquad K = 1.5 \times 10^{-8}.$$

From the investigations of McCoy and Smith,[2] we calculate

[1] G. N. Lewis and M. Randall, *Thermodynamics,* New York: McGraw-Hill Book Company, Inc., 1923, p. 490.

[2] H. N. McCoy and H. J. Smith, *J. Am. Chem. Soc.,* **33,** 468 (1911); K. K. Kelley and C. T. Anderson, *U. S. Bur. Mines Bull.,* No. 384 (1935).

4.93×10^{-9} as the constant for the carbonate. Latimer, Hicks, and Schutz[1] gave 9.9×10^{-11} for the sulfate. Kohlrausch[2] reported 2×10^{-10} for the chromate, 1.7×10^{-6} for the fluoride and 1.1×10^{-7} for $BaCrO_4 \cdot 2H_2O$.

The solubility of barium sulfate in sulfuric acid has been studied by Hammett and Deyrup,[3] who report

$$Ba(HSO_4)_2 = Ba^{++} + 2HSO_4^-, \qquad K = ca\ 2.7.$$

The free energies agree with this value.

Kohlrausch in the reference cited above also gave

$$BaC_2O_4 \cdot 3\tfrac{1}{2}H_2O = Ba^{++} + C_2O_4^{--} + 3\tfrac{1}{2}H_2O, \qquad K = 1.62 \times 10^{-7}.$$

A recalculation of the work of Schlesinger and Siem[4] gives

$$BaMnO_4 = Ba^{++} + MnO_4^{--}, \qquad K = 1.5 \times 10^{-10}.$$

The thermal data do not agree with this value and are certainly wrong.

Using the activity coefficient, 0.85, and the solubility of barium iodide, $7.9 \times 10^{-4}M$, given by Harkins and Winninghoff,[5]

$$Ba(IO_3)_2 \cdot H_2O = Ba^{++} + 2BrO_3^- + H_2O, \qquad K = 1.25 \times 10^{-9}.$$

The free energy of solution of barium bromate was given by Greensfelder and Latimer[6] as 7171 cal. The solubility product is

$$Ba(BrO_3)_2 \cdot H_2O = Ba^{++} + 2BrO_3^- + H_2O, \qquad K = 5.5 \times 10^{-6}.$$

The solubilities of both the chloride and nitrate at 25° C. are not large. From the free energies of solution, -280 cal. and 3200 cal., respectively,[7] we calculate

$$BaCl_2 \cdot 2H_2O = Ba^{++} + 2Cl^- + 2H_2O, \qquad K = 1.6;$$

$$Ba(NO_3)_2 = Ba^{++} + 2NO_3^-, \qquad K = 4.5 \times 10^{-3}.$$

[1] W. M. Latimer, J. F. G. Hicks, Jr., and P. W. Schutz, *J. Chem. Phys.*, **1**, 620 (1933).

[2] F. Kohlrausch, *Z. physik. Chem.*, **64**, 145 and 158 (1908).

[3] L. P. Hammett and A. J. Deyrup, *J. Am. Chem. Soc.*, **55**, 1908 (1933).

[4] H. I. Schlesinger and H. B. Siem, *J. Am. Chem. Soc.*, **46**, 1971 (1924); Landolt-Bornstein, *Tabellen* **III**, p. 2134.

[5] W. D. Harkins and W. J. Winninghoff, *J. Am. Chem. Soc.*, **33**, 1827 (1911).

[6] B. S. Greensfelder and W. M. Latimer, *J. Am. Chem. Soc.*, **50**, 3289 (1928).

[7] O. L. Brown, W. V. Smith, and W. M. Latimer, *J. Am. Chem. Soc.*, **58**, 1758 (1936); W. M. Latimer and J. E. Ahlberg, *Z. physik. Chem.*, **A148**, 464 (1930).

RADIUM

Oxidation states.   As with the other members of this group, only the $+2$ state is stable. The chemistry of the $+2$ ion resembles closely that of Ba^{++}. The sulfate is slightly less soluble than $BaSO_4$ and the same is doubtless true of the chromate. The hydroxide is the most basic of the group.

Radium free energies.   From the data in Table 81 the following potential and solubility products may be calculated.

TABLE 81

THERMODYNAMIC DATA ON RADIUM[1]

(Heat and free energy of formation in kcal. Entropy of substance in cal./deg.)

Formula	Description	State	$\Delta H°$	$\Delta F°$	$S°$
Ra		g	*31.*	*23.*	*42.15*
Ra	metal	c	0.0	0.0	*17.*
Ra^+		g	*153.1*		
Ra^{++}		g	*388.5*		
Ra^{++}		aq	*−126.*	*−134.5*	*13.*
RaO		c	*−125.*	−117.5	(16.3)
$RaCl_2 \cdot 2H_2O$		c	*−351.*	*−311.7*	*50.*
$RaSO_4$		c	*−352.*	*−326.0*	*34.*
$Ra(NO_3)_2$		c	*−237.*	*−190.3*	*52.*

[1] Bureau of Standards values in *italics;* estimated values in parentheses.

$$Ra = Ra^{++} + 2e^-, \qquad\qquad E° = 2.92;$$
$$RaCl_2 \cdot 2H_2O = Ra^{++} + 2Cl^- + 2H_2O, \qquad K = 4 \times 10^{-1};$$
$$RaSO_4 = Ra^{++} + SO_4^{--}, \qquad\qquad K = 4 \times 10^{-11};$$
$$Ra(NO_3)_2 = Ra^{++} + 2NO_3^-, \qquad\qquad K = 6.3 \times 10^{-3}.$$

The solubility product of $RaSO_4$ has been given by Nikitin and Tolmatscheff[1] as 4.25×10^{-11}.

Summary of group potentials.   For comparison, the following summary of the group potentials is given,

$$\begin{array}{ll} Be—Be^{++} & E° = 1.85 \\ Mg—Mg^{++} & E° = 2.37 \\ Cu—Cu^{++} & E° = 2.87 \\ Sr—Sr^{++} & E° = 2.89 \\ Ba—Ba^{++} & E° = 2.90 \\ Ra—Ra^{++} & E° = 2.92 \end{array}$$

[1] B. Nikitin and P. Tolmatscheff, *Z. physik. Chem.*, **A167**, 269 (1933).

CHAPTER 23

Lithium, Sodium, Potassium, Rubidium, Cesium, and Francium

The elements of this group have but one valence electron and the state of the monatomic gas atoms is $s^1(^2S_{1/2})$. Because of the similarity and simplicity of the chemistry the various thermodynamic properties will be discussed for the group as a whole, with the exception of francium.

Oxidation states. The only oxidation state is the $+1$. The so-called "subhalides" are obviously solid solutions or "colloidal solution" of the metals in the halides. Because of the low charge and large size of the $+1$ ions, the hydroxides are all soluble, strong bases. The salts of the alkali metals with the common negative ions, with few exceptions, are readily soluble. In fact, salts with a solubility of less than $0.01M$ are very rare. The standard thermodynamic states of the elements are, of course, the solid metals. At low concentrations of the metal vapors, the gases are monatomic, but at higher concentration appreciable formation of the diatomic molecules occurs.

Alkali element free energies and potentials. The following potentials for the metal-metal ion couples are calculated from the free energies in Table 82.

$$Li = Li^+ + e^-, \qquad E° = 3.045;$$
$$Na = Na^+ + e^-, \qquad E° = 2.714;$$
$$K = K^+ + e^-, \qquad E° = 2.925;$$
$$Rb = Rb^+ + e^-, \qquad E° = 2.925;$$
$$Cs = Cs^+ + e^-, \qquad E° = 2.923.$$

Since the hydroxides are soluble strong bases, the potentials in $1M$ OH^- are the same. Lewis and his co-workers[1] have measured the po-

---

[1] G. N. Lewis and M. Randall, *Thermodynamics*, New York: McGraw-Hill Book Company, Inc., 1923, p. 414.

TABLE 82

THERMODYNAMIC DATA ON THE ALKALI METALS AND
THEIR COMPOUNDS[1]

(Heat and free energy of formation in kcal. Entropy of substance in cal./deg.)

Formula	Description	State	$\Delta H°$	$\Delta F°$	$S°$
Lithium					
Li		g	*37.07*	*29.19*	*33.143*
Li	metal	c	*0.000*	*0.000*	*6.70*
Li$^+$		g	*160.860*		
Li$^+$		aq	*−66.554*	*−70.22*	*3.4*
Li^{++}		g	*1908.2*		
Li^{+++}		g	*4732.9*		
Li$_2$		g	*47.6*	*37.6*	*47.06*
Li$_2$O		c	*−142.4*	−133.9	9.06
Li$_2$O$_2$		c	*−151.7*	−135.	(8.)
LiH		g	*30.7*	*25.2*	*40.77*
LiH		c	*−21.61*	*−16.72*	*5.9*
LiOH		c	*−116.45*	−105.9	10.2
LiOH		aq	*−121.511*	*−107.82*	*0.9*
LiOH·H$_2$O		c	*−188.77*	−163.3	17.07
LiF		c	*−146.3*	−139.6	8.57
LiF		aq	*−145.210*	*−136.30*	*1.1*
LiCl		g	*−53.*	*−58.*	*51.01*
LiCl		c	*−97.70*	−91.7	(13.2)
LiCl		aq	*−106.577*	*−101.57*	*16.6*
LiCl·H$_2$O		c	*−170.31*	−151.2	24.8
LiBr		g	*−41.*	*−50.*	*53.78*
LiBr		c	*−83.72*	−81.2	(16.5)
LiBr		aq	*−95.45*	*−94.79*	*22.7*
LiI		g	*−16.*	*−26.*	*55.68*
LiI		c	*−64.79*	−64.	(18.1)
LiI		aq	*−79.92*	*−82.57*	*29.5*
Li$_2$SO$_4$		c, II	*−342.83*	−316.6	(27.)
Li$_2$SO$_4$		aq	*−350.01*	*−317.78*	*10.9*
Li$_3$N		c	*−47.2*		
LiNO$_2$		c	*−96.6*	−79.5	(21.3)
LiNO$_3$		c	*−115.279*	−93.1	(25.2)
LiNO$_3$		aq	*−115.926*	*−96.63*	*38.4*
LiNH$_2$		c	*−43.50*		
Li$_2$C$_2$		c	*−14.2*		
Li$_2$CO$_3$		c	*−290.54*	−270.66	21.60
Li$_2$CO$_3$		aq	*−294.74*	*−266.66*	*−5.9*
Li$_2$SiO$_3$		glass	*−376.7*	−356.1	(23.8)
Li$_2$SiF$_6$		c	*−688.9*		
LiReO$_4$		c	*−253.4*		
LiBH$_4$		c	*−44.6*		
LiAlH$_4$		c	*−24.2*		

[1] Bureau of Standards values in *italics;* estimated values in parentheses.

TABLE 82 *(Continued)*

THERMODYNAMIC DATA ON THE ALKALI METALS AND THEIR COMPOUNDS[1]

(Heat and free energy of formation in kcal. Entropy of substance in cal./deg.)

Formula	Description	State	$\Delta H°$	$\Delta F°$	$S°$
Sodium					
Na		g	*25.98*	*18.67*	*36.715*
Na	metal	c	*0.000*	*0.000*	*12.2*
Na^+		g	*146.015*		
Na^+		aq	*−57.279*	*−62.589*	*14.4*
Na^{++}		g	*1238.10*		
Na^{+++}		g	*2891.89*		
Na_2		g	*33.97*	*24.85*	*55.02*
NaO_2		c	*−61.9*	*−46.5*	(9.5)
Na_2O		c	*−99.4*	*−90.0*	*17.4*
Na_2O_2		c	*−120.6*	*−102.8*	(16.)
NaH		g	*29.88*	*24.78*	*44.93*
NaH		c	*−13.7*		
NaOH		c, II	*−101.99*	*−90.1*	(12.5)
NaOH		aq	*−112.236*	*−100.184*	*11.9*
$NaOH·H_2O$		c	*−175.17*	*−149.00*	*20.2*
NaF		g	*−72.*		
NaF		c	*−136.0*	*−129.3*	*14.0*
NaF		aq	*−135.94*	*−128.67*	*12.1*
$NaHF_2$		c	*−216.6*		
NaCl		g	*−43.50*		
NaCl		c	*−98.232*	*−91.785*	*17.30*
NaCl		aq	*−97.302*	*−93.939*	*27.6*
$NaClO_2$		c	*−72.65*	*−54.45*	(26.7)
$NaClO_3$		c	*−85.73*		
$NaClO_4$		c, II	*−92.18*	*−61.4*	(33.5)
$NaClO_4$		aq	*−88.69*	*−65.16*	*57.9*
NaBr		g	*−36.33*		
NaBr		c	*−86.030*	*−83.1*	(20.5)
NaBr		aq	*−86.18*	*−87.163*	*33.7*
NaI		g	*−20.94*		
NaF		c	*−68.84*	*−56.7*	(22.1)
NaI		aq	*−70.65*	*−70.94*	*40.5*
Na_2S		c	*−89.2*	*−86.6*	(23.2)
Na_2S_2		aq	*−104.6*		
Na_2SO_3		c	*−260.6*	*−239.5*	*34.9*
Na_2SO_4		c, II	*−330.90*	*−302.78*	*35.73*
Na_2SO_4		aq	*−331.46*	*−302.52*	*32.9*
$Na_2S_2O_3$		c	*−267.0*		
$Na_2S_2O_5$		c	*−349.1*		
$Na_2S_2O_6$		c	*−399.9*		
NaHS		c, II	*−56.5*		

[1] Bureau of Standards values in *italics;* estimated values in parentheses.

TABLE 82 (*Continued*)

THERMODYNAMIC DATA ON THE ALKALI METALS AND THEIR COMPOUNDS[1]

(Heat and free energy of formation in kcal. Entropy of substance in cal./deg.)

Formula	Description	State	$\Delta H°$	$\Delta F°$	$S°$
Sodium					
$NaHSO_4$		c	*−269.2*		
Na_2SeO_3		aq	*−236.6*		
Na_2SeO_4		c	*−258.*		
$NaHSe$		c, II	*−27.8*		
Na_2Te		c, II	*−84.0*	−82.6	(31.5)
Na_2TeO_4		c	*−313.*		
$NaNO_2$		c, II	*−85.9*	−67.8	(25.3)
$NaNO_3$		c, II	*−101.54*	*−87.45*	*27.8*
$NaNO_3$		aq	*−106.651*	*−89.00*	*49.4*
$NaNH_2$		c	*−28.4*		
$NaPO_3$		c	*−288.6*		
Na_3PO_4		c	*−460.*	−430.6	(46.5)
$Na_4P_2O_7$		c	*−760.8*		
NaH_2PO_3		c	*−289.4*		
Na_2HPO_3		c	*−338.0*		
Na_2HPO_4		c	*−417.4*		
Na_3ASO_4		c	*−365.*		
Na_2C_2	sodium carbide	c	*4.1*		
Na_2CO_3		c	*−270.3*	−250.4	(32.5)
Na_2CO_3		aq		−251.4	
$Na_2C_2O_4$	sodium oxalate	c	*−314.3*	−308.	(37.)
$NaCHO_2$	sodium formate	c	*−155.03*		
$NaHCO_3$		c	*−226.5*	−203.6	*24.4*
$NaHCO_3$		aq	*−222.5*	−202.89	(37.1)
$NaHC_2O_4·H_2O$		c	*−330.2*		
$NaC_2H_3O_2$	sodium acetate	c	*−169.8*		
$NaCN$		c, III	*−21.46*	−14.7	(21.8)
$NaCNO$	sodium cyanate	c	*−95.6*		
$NaCO_2NH_2$	sodium carbamate	c	*−179.4*		
$NaCNS$		c	*−41.73*		
Na_2SiO_3		c	*−363.*	*−341.*	*27.2*
Na_2SiO_3		glass	*−360.*		
$Na_2Si_2O_5$		c			*39.4*
Na_4SiO_4		c			*46.8*
Na_2SiF_6		c	*−677.*	−610.4	(51.3)
Na_2SnO_3		c	*−276.*		
Na_2PbO_3		c	*−205.*		
Na_2ZnO_2		c	*−188.*		

[1] Bureau of Standards values in *italics;* estimated values in parentheses.

TABLE 82 (*Continued*)

THERMODYNAMIC DATA ON THE ALKALI METALS AND THEIR COMPOUNDS[1]

(Heat and free energy of formation in kcal. Entropy of substance in cal./deg.)

Formula	Description	State	$\Delta H°$	$\Delta F°$	$S°$
Sodium					
Na_2PtCl_6		c	−273.6		
$Na_2PtBr_6·6H_2O$		c	−650.1		
Na_2PtI_6		aq	−170.1		
Na_2IrCl_6		c	−233.4		
Na_3IrCl_6		c	−318.7 (?)		
Na_2OsCl_6		c	−295.8		
$NaReO_4$		c	−249.4		
Na_3RhCl_6		c	−371.7		
Na_2FeO_4		c	−251.		
Na_2MnO_4		c	−274.		
Na_2CrO_4		c	−325.1		
Na_2MoO_4		c, II	−368.		
Na_2WO_4		c	−395.		
Na_3VO_4		c	−420.		
$NaBO_2$		c	−253.		
$Na_2B_4O_7·10H_2O$		c	−1497.2		
$NaBH_4$	sodium boro-hydride	c, I	−43.82	−28.57	25.02
$NaAlO_2$		c	−273.		
Na_3AlF_6		c, II	−759.6		
Na_2UO_4		c	−501.		
Potassium					
K		g	21.51	14.62	38.296
K	metal	c	0.000	0.000	15.2
K^+		g	123.07		
K^+		aq	−60.04	−67.46	24.5
K^{++}		g	858.15		
K^{+++}		g	1913.		
K_2		g	30.8	22.1	59.69
K_2O		c	−86.4	−76.2	(20.8)
K_2O_2		c	−118.	−100.1	(19.4)
K_2O_3		c	−125.	−100.	(19.9)
K_2O_4		c	−134.	−99.6	(22.4)
KH		g	30.0	25.1	47.3
KH		c	−13.6		
KOH		c	−101.78	−89.5	(14.2)
KOH		aq	−115.00	−105.061	22.0
KF		c	−134.46	−127.42	15.91
$KF·2H_2O$		c	−277.00	−242.7	36.
KHF_2		c	−219.98	203.73	24.92

[1] Bureau of Standards values in *italics;* estimated values in parentheses.

TABLE 82 (*Continued*)

THERMODYNAMIC DATA ON THE ALKALI METALS AND THEIR COMPOUNDS[1]

(Heat and free energy of formation in kcal. Entropy of substance in cal./deg.)

Formula	Description	State	$\Delta H°$	$\Delta F°$	$S°$
Potassium					
KCl		g	−51.6	−56.2	57.24
KCl		c	−104.175	−97.592	19.76
KCl		aq	−100.06	−98.816	37.7
KClO₃		c	−93.50	−69.29	34.17
KClO₃		aq	−83.54	−68.09	63.5
KClO₄		c	−103.6	−72.7	36.1
KClO₄		aq	−91.45	−70.04	68.0
KBr		g			59.87
KBr		c	−93.73	−90.63	23.05
KBr		aq	−88.94	−92.040	43.8
KBrO₃		c	−79.4	−58.2	35.65
KBrO₃		aq	−69.6	−56.6	63.4
KI		g			61.64
KI		c	−78.31	−77.03	24.94
KI		aq	−73.41	−79.816	50.6
KI₃		c	−76.6	−73.5	(46.7)
KIO₃		c	−121.5	−101.7	36.20
KIO₃		aq	−115.0	−99.9	52.2
K₂S		c	−100.	−96.6	(26.6)
K₂S₄		c	−113.0	−110.8	(38.4)
K₂SO₃		c	−266.9	−244.8	(37.4)
K₂SO₄		c, II	−342.66	−314.62	42.0
K₂S₂O₅		c	−362.6		
K₂S₂O₆		c	−413.6		
K₂S₂O₈		c	−458.3		
K₂S₄O₆		c	−422.		
KHS		c	−63.2		
KHSO₄		c	−276.8		
KHSe		c	−35.9		
KNO₂		c	−88.5	−67.3	(28.)
KNO₃		c	−117.76	−93.96	31.77
KNO₃		aq	−109.412	−93.88	69.5
KH₂PO₄		c	−374.9	−339.2	(34.3)
KH₂AsO₄		c	−271.5	−237.0	37.08
K₂CO₃		c	−273.93	−255.5	(33.6)
K₂CO		aq		−261.2	
K₂C₂O₄	potassium oxalate	c	−320.8	−296.7	(40.4)
KCHO₂	potassium formate	c	−158.0	−141.3	(25.2)
KHCO₃		c	−229.3	−205.7	(26.6)

[1] Bureau of Standards values in *italics;* estimated values in parentheses.

TABLE 82 (*Continued*)

THERMODYNAMIC DATA ON THE ALKALI METALS AND
THEIR COMPOUNDS[1]

(Heat and free energy of formation in kcal. Entropy of substance in cal./deg.)

Formula	Description	State	$\Delta H°$	$\Delta F°$	$S°$
Potassium					
KCN		c	*−26.90*	−20.	(16.4)
KCNO		c	*−98.5*		
KCNS		c	*−48.62*		
K_2SiF_6		c	*−671.*	−651.	(54.7)
K_2SnCl_6		c	*−362.9*	−327.2	(75.1)
$KAg(CN)_2$		c	*−3.9*	8.6	(34.0)
K_2PtCl_4		c	*−254.2*	−229.0	(67.6)
K_2PtCl_6		c	*−301.0*	−265.1	79.8
K_2PtBr_4		c	*−220.7*	−209.7	(81.6)
K_2PtBr_6		c	*−248.6*	−22.4	(77.2)
K_2IrCl_6		c	*−286.*	−244.	(82.6)
K_3IrCl_6		c	*−374.*	−330.4	(91.4)
K_2OsCl_6		c	*−280.*	−242.5	(82.5)
$KReO_4$		c	*−264.02*		
K_2PdCl_4		c	*−261.6*	−238.1	(67.1)
K_2PdCl_6		c	*−283.8*	−247.9	(77.7)
K_2PdBr_4		c	*−217.2*	−211.6	(79.1)
K_3RhCl_6		c	*−343.*	−307.5	(94.1)
$K_3Fe(CN)_6$		c	*−41.4*	−3.3	(77.)
$K_4Fe(CN)_6$		c	*−125.1*	−84.0	(86.2)
$K_3FeCO(CN)_5$		c	*−137.4*		
$KMnO_4$		c	*−194.4*	*−170.6*	*41.04*
K_2CrO_4		c	*−338.0*	−310.5	(44.6)
$K_2Cr_2O_7$		c	*−500.9*		
$KCr(SO_4)_2$		c	*−562.*	−510.	(57.4)
$KCr(SO_4)_2·12H_2O$		c	*−1383.1*	−1164.	(169.2)
KVO_4		c	*−273.9*		
$KCl·AlCl_3$		c	*−284.7*	−260.7	(48.8)
$3KCl·2AlCl_3$		c	*−677.6*	−622.	(114.3)
$KAl(SO_4)_2$		c	*−589.24*	*−534.29*	*48.9*
$KAl(SO_4)_2·12H_2O$		c	*−1447.74*	*−1227.8*	*164.3*
Rubidium					
Rb		g	*20.51*	*13.35*	*40.628*
Rb	metal	c, I	*0.000*	*0.000*	*16.6*
Rb^+		g	*118.297*		
Rb^+		aq	*58.9*	*−67.45*	*29.7*
Rb^{++}		g	*753.95*		
Rb_2		g	*29.6*		
Rb_2O		c	*−78.9*	−69.5	(26.2)
Rb_2O_2		c	*−101.7*	−83.6	(24.8)

[1] Bureau of Standards values in *italics;* estimated values in parentheses.

Table 82 (*Continued*)

THERMODYNAMIC DATA ON THE ALKALI METALS AND THEIR COMPOUNDS[1]

(Heat and free energy of formation in kcal. Entropy of substance in cal./deg.)

Formula	Description	State	$\Delta H°$	$\Delta F°$	$S°$
Rubidium					
Rb_2O_3		c	−116.7	−92.4	(25.3)
Rb_2O_4		c	−126.2	−94.6	(27.8)
RbH		g	33.		
$RbOH$		c, II	−98.9	−87.1	(16.9)
$RbOH$		aq	−113.9	−105.05	27.2
RbF		c	−131.28	−124.3	(17.4)
RbF		aq	−137.6	−133.53	27.4
$RbHF_2$		c	−217.3		
$RbCl$		c	−102.91	−96.8	(22.6)
$RbCl$		aq	−98.9	−98.80	42.9
$RbClO_3$		c	−93.8	−69.8	36.3
$RbClO_3$		aq	−82.4	−68.07	68.7
$RbClO_4$		c, II	−103.87	−73.19	38.4
$RbClO_4$		aq	−90.3	−70 02	73.2
$RbBr$		c	−93.03	−90.38	25.88
$RbBr$		aq	−87.8	−92.02	49.0
RbI		c	−78.5	−77.8	28.21
RbI		aq	−72.3	−79.80	55.8
Rb_2S		c	−83.2	−80.8	(32.)
Rb_2SO_4		c	−340.50	−312.8	(45.8)
Rb_2SO_4		aq	−334.7	−312.24	33.8
$RbHS$		c	−62.4		
$RbNO_3$		c, II	−117.04	−93.3	(33.6)
$RbNO_3$		aq	−108.3	−93.86	64.7
$RbNH_2$		c	−25.7		
Rb_2CO_3		c	−269.6	−249.3	(23.3)
$RbHCO_3$		c	−228.5	−204.4	(29.3)
Rb_2CO_3		aq		−261.2	
$RbReO_4$		c	−256.9		
Cesium					
Cs		g	18.83	12.24	41.944
Cs	metal	c	0.000	0.000	19.8
Cs^+		g	110.081		
Cs^+		aq	−59.2	−67.41	31.8
Cs^{++}		g	652.5		
Cs_2		g	27.0		
Cs_2O		c	−75.9	−65.6	(29.6)
Cs_2O_2		c	−96.2	−78.2	(28.2)
Cs_2O_3		c	−111.2	−86.1	(28.7)
Cs_2O_4		c	−124.2	−92.5	(31.2)

[1] Bureau of Standards values in *italics:* estimated values in parentheses.

TABLE 82 (*Continued*)

THERMODYNAMIC DATA ON THE ALKALI METALS AND THEIR COMPOUNDS[1]

(Heat and free energy of formation in kcal. Entropy of substance in cal./deg.)

Formula	Description	State	$\Delta H°$	$\Delta F°$	$S°$
Cesium					
CsH		g	*29.0*	*24.3*	*51.25*
CsOH		c, II	*−97.2*	−84.9	(18.6)
CsOH		aq	*−114.2*	−105.00	29.3
CsF		c	*−126.9*	−119.5	(19.1)
CsF		aq	*−135.9*	*−133.49*	29.5
$CsHF_2$		c	*−216.1*		
CsCl		c, II	*−103.5*	−96.6	(23.3)
CsCl		aq	*−99.2*	−88.76	45.0
$CsClO_4$		c	*−103.86*	−73.28	41.89
$CsClO_4$		aq	*−90.6*	−69.98	75.3
CsBr		c	*−94.3*	−91.6	29.
CsBr		aq	*−88.1*	−91.98	51.1
CsI		c	*−80.5*	−79.7	31.
CsI		aq	*−72.6*	−79.76	57.9
Cs_2S		c	*−81.1*	−77.6	(35.4)
Cs_2SO_4		c, II	*−339.38*	−310.7	(49.2)
Cs_2SO_4		aq	*−335.3*	*−312.16*	67.7
CsHS		c	*−62.9*		
$CsNO_3$		c, II	*−118.11*	−94.	(35.3)
$CsNO_3$		aq	*−108.6*	−93.82	86.8
$CsCO_3$		c	*−267.4*	−243.6	(42.4)
Cs_2CO_3		aq		−261.0	
$CsHCO_3$		c	*−228.4*	−198.8	(31.)
Cs_2SiF_6		c	*−669.5*	−629.6	(63.5)
$CsAl(SO_4)·12H_2O$		c	*−1449.5*	−1218.5	164.

[1] Bureau of Standards values in *italics;* estimated values in parentheses.

tentials of all the alkali ions, except cesium, against the alkali metal-amalgam electrodes at such low concentrations of the metal that the decomposition of the water did not occur. They then measured the e.m.f. of the amalgam against the pure metal in nonaqueous solvents. These investigations were carried out with remarkable skill and ingenuity and their $E°$ values for sodium and potassium are probably accurate to one thousandth of a volt. However, the experimental difficulties in the case of lithium and rubidium were somewhat greater and the results were not so accurate. The Lewis values are Li—Li+, 2.957; Na—Na+, 2.712; K—K+, 2.922; Rb—Rb+, 2.924. We are unable to account for the large discrepancy in the case of lithium.

One frequently wishes to know a free energy or heat of solution of a group I salt. For that reason the data for the aqueous solution of many salts have been included in Table 83. This is done for convenience, since the values can always be calculated as the sum of the properties of the individual ions. In order to illustrate trends within the group, a summary of the free energies of solution of the more important compounds is given in Table 83.

TABLE 83

SUMMARY OF FREE ENERGIES OF SOLUTION OF CERTAIN ALKALI COMPOUNDS

(Values in calories at 25° C.)

	OH^-	Cl^-	SO_4^{--}	CO_3^{--}
Li^+	−1,720	−9,870	−1,180	−4,000
Na^+	−10,087	−2,154	260	−1,000
K^+	−15,560	−1,224	2,360	−5,700
Rb^+	−17,150	−2,000	−400	−11,900
Cs^+	−20,100	−2,150	−1,460	−17,400

There are not many slightly soluble compounds in this group. The solubility products for a number of the less soluble have been calculated from the free energy data.

$$Li_2CO_3 = 2Li^+ + CO_3^{--}, \qquad K = 3.1 \times 10^{-1};$$
$$NaHCO_3 = Na^+ + HCO_3^-, \qquad K = 1.2 \times 10^{-3};$$
$$K_2PtCl_6 = 2K^+ + PtCl_6^{--}, \qquad K = 1.4 \times 10^{-6};$$
$$KClO_4 = K^+ + ClO_4^-, \qquad K = 8.9 \times 10^{-3};$$
$$RbClO_4 = Rb^+ + ClO_4^-, \qquad K = 3.8 \times 10^{-3};$$
$$CsClO_4 = Cs^+ + ClO_4^-, \qquad K = 3.2 \times 10^{-3}.$$

Francium. The most stable francium isotope is Fr^{223} which is formed from Ac^{227} by alpha-decay. Its half-life is only 21 minutes and consequently its chemistry is known only from experiments using less than microgram amounts. The results of such experiments indicate that its chemistry is very similar to that of cesium. No thermodynamic data can be given, but all values are probably very close to the corresponding values for cesium.

Summary of Oxidation-Reduction Potentials

It is often desirable to know the various couples which have potentials around a given voltage. For this reason a summary, with the couples arranged in order of decreasing $E°$ values, is given. The couples have been separated into two tables, one for acid solutions and one for basic solutions. This has been done, in part, for facility in comparisons and, in part, because the free energy of the completed reactions with the hydrogen couple requires the use of the acid value for this couple in the first case and the alkaline value in the second (see Chap. 1). This chapter should also be consulted for the definition of $E°$ and conventions regarding sign. There are, of course, a large number of couples whose potentials are independent of the acid concentration. These might have been listed in a third table, but they have been given in the table for the acid solutions, although a few of the more common are repeated in the table for basic solutions. Values for many additional couples of lesser importance are to be found in the text.

TABLE 84

OXIDATION-REDUCTION COUPLES IN ACID SOLUTIONS

Couple	$E°$
$HN_3 = \frac{3}{2}N_2 + H^+ + e^-$	3.09
$Li = Li^+ + e^-$	3.045
$K = K^+ + e^-$	2.925
$Rb = Rb^+ + e^-$	2.925
$As = As^+ + e^-$	2.923
$Ra = Ra^{++} + 2e^-$	2.92
$Ba = Ba^{++} + 2e^-$	2.90
$Sr = Sr^{++} + 2e^-$	2.89
$Ca = Ca^{++} + 2e^-$	2.87
$Na = Na^+ + e^-$	2.714
$La = La^{+++} + 3e^-$	2.52
$Ce = Ce^{+++} + 3e^-$	2.48
$Nd = Nd^{+++} + 3e^-$	2.44
$Sm = Sm^{+++} + 3e^-$	2.41
$Gd = Gd^{+++} + 3e^-$	2.40
$Mg = Mg^{++} + 2e^-$	2.37
$Y = Y^{+++} + 3e^-$	2.37
$Am = Am^{+++} + 3e^-$	2.32
$Lu = Lu^{+++} + 3e^-$	2.25
$H^- = \frac{1}{2}H_2 + e^-$	2.25
$H(g) = H^+ + e^-$	2.10
$Sc = Sc^{+++} + 3e^-$	2.08
$Pu = Pu^{+++} + 3e^-$	2.07
$Al + 6F^- = AlF_6^{---} + 3e^-$	2.07
$Th = Th^{+4} + 4e^-$	1.90
$Np = Np^{+++} + 3e^-$	1.86
$Be = Be^{++} + 2e^-$	1.85
$U = U^{+++} + 3e^-$	1.80
$Hf = Hf^{+4} + 4e^-$	1.70
$Al = Al^{+++} + 3e^-$	1.66
$Ti = Ti^{++} + 2e^-$	1.63
$Zr = Zr^{+4} + 4e^-$	1.53
$Si + 6F^- = SiF_6^{--} + 4e^-$	1.2
$Ti + 6F^- = TiF_6^{--} + 4e^-$	1.19
$Mn = Mn^{++} + 2e^-$	1.18
$V = V^{++} + 2e^-$	ca 1.18
$Nb = Nb^{+++} + 3e^-$	ca 1.1
$Ti + H_2O = TiO^{++} + 2H^+ + 4e^-$	0.89
$B + 3H_2O = H_3BO_3 + 3H^+ + 3e^-$	0.87
$Si + 2H_2O = SiO_2 + 4H^+ + 4e^-$	0.86
$2Ta + 5H_2O = Ta_2O_5 + 10H^+ + 10e^-$	0.81
$Zn = Zn^{++} + 2e^-$	0.763
$Tl + I^- = TlI + e^-$	0.753
$Cr = Cr^{+++} + 3e^-$	0.74
$H_2Te = Te + 2H^+ + 2e^-$	0.72
$Tl + Br^- = TlBr + e^-$	0.658

TABLE 84 (*Continued*)

OXIDATION-REDUCTION COUPLES IN ACID SOLUTIONS

Couple	$E°$
$2Nb + 5H_2O = Nb_2O_5 + 10H^+ + 10e^-$	0.65
$U^{+++} = U^{+4} + e^-$	0.61
$AsH_3 = As + 3H^+ + 3e^-$	0.60
$Tl + Cl^- = TlCl + e^-$	0.557
$Ga = Ga^{+++} + 3e^-$	0.53
$SbH_3(g) = Sb + 3H^+ + 3e^-$	0.51
$P + 2H_2O = H_3PO_2 + H^+ + e^-$	0.51
$H_3PO_2 + H_2O = H_3PO_3 + 2H^+ + 2e^-$	0.50
$Fe = Fe^{++} + 2e^-$	0.440
$Eu^{++} = Eu^{+++} + e^-$	0.43
$Cr^{++} = Cr^{+++} + e^-$	0.41
$Cd = Cd^{++} + 2e^-$	0.403
$H_2Se = Se + 2H^+ + 2e^-$	0.40
$Ti^{++} = Ti^{+++} + e^-$	ca 0.37
$Pb + 2I^- = PbI_2 + 2e^-$	0.365
$Pb + SO_4^{--} = PbSO_4 + 2e^-$	0.356
$In = In^{+++} + 3e^-$	0.342
$Tl = Tl^+ + e^-$	0.3363
$Pt + H_2S = PtS + 2H^+ + 2e^-$	0.30
$Pb + 2Br^- = PbBr_2 + 2e^-$	0.280
$Co = Co^{++} + 2e^-$	0.277
$H_3PO_3 = H_3PO_4 + 2H^+ + 2e^-$	0.276
$Pb + 2Cl^- = PbCl_2 + 2e^-$	0.268
$V^{++} = V^{+++} + e^-$	0.255
$V + 4H_2O = V(OH)_4^+ + 4H^+ + 5e^-$	0.253
$Sn + 6F^- = SnF_6^{--} + 4e^-$	0.25
$Ni = Ni^{++} + 2e^-$	0.250
$N_2H_5^+ = N_2 + 5H^+ + 4e^-$	0.23
$S_2O_6^{--} = 2SO_4^{--} + 4H^+ + 2e^-$	0.22
$Mo = Mo^{+++} + 3e^-$	ca 0.2
$HCOOH(aq) = CO_2 + 2H^+ + 2e^-$	0.196
$Cu + I^- = CuI + e^-$	0.185
$Ag + I^- = AgI + e^-$	0.151
$Sn = Sn^{++} + 2e^-$	0.136
$HO_2 = O_2 + H^+ + e^-$	0.13
$Pb = Pb^{++} + 2e^-$	0.126
$Ge + 2H_2O = GeO_2 + 4H^+ + 4e^-$	0.15
$W + 3H_2O = WO_3(c) + 6H^+ + 6e^-$	0.09
$HS_2O_4^- + 2H_2O = 2H_2SO_3 + H^+ + 2e^-$	0.08
$Hg + 4I^- = HgI_4^{--} + 2e^-$	0.04
$H_2 = 2H^+ + 2e^-$	0.00
$Ag + 2S_2O_3^{--} = Ag(S_2O_3)_2^{---} + e^-$	−0.01
$Cu + Br^- = CuBr + e^-$	−0.033
$UO_2^+ = UO_2^{++} + e^-$	−0.05
$HCHO(aq) + H_2O = HCOOH(aq) + 2H^+ + 2e^-$	−0.056
$PH_3(g) = P + 3H^+ + 3e^-$	−0.06

TABLE 84 *(Continued)*

OXIDATION-REDUCTION COUPLES IN ACID SOLUTIONS

Couple	$E°$
$Ag + Br^- = AgBr + e^-$	-0.095
$Ti^{+++} + H_2O = TiO^{++} + 2H^+ + e^-$	-0.1
$SiH_4 = Si + 4H^+ + 4e^-$	-0.102
$CH_4 = C + 4H^+ + 4e^-$	-0.13
$Cu + Cl^- = CuCl + e^-$	-0.137
$H_2S = S + 2H^+ + 2e^-$	-0.141
$Np^{+++} = Np^{+4} + e^-$	-0.147
$Sn^{++} = Sn^{+4} + 2e^-$	-0.15
$2Sb + 3H_2O = Sb_2O_3 + 6H^+ + 6e^-$	-0.152
$Cu^+ = Cu^{++} + e^-$	-0.153
$Bi + H_2O + Cl^- = BiOCl + 2H^+ + 3e^-$	-0.16
$H_2SO_3 + H_2O = SO_4^{--} + 4H^+ + 2e^-$	-0.17
$CH_3OH(aq) = HCHO(aq) + 2H^+ + 2e^-$	-0.19
$Hg + 4Br^- = HgBr_4^{--} + 2e^-$	-0.21
$Ag + Cl^- = AgCl + e^-$	-0.222
$(CH_3)_2SO + H_2O = CH_3SO_2 + 2H^+ + 2e^-$	-0.23
$As + 2H_2O = HAsO_2(aq) + 3H^+ + 3e^-$	-0.247
$Re + 2H_2O = ReO_2 + 4H^+ + 4e^-$	-0.252
$Bi + H_2O = BiO^+ + 2H^+ + 3e^-$	-0.32
$\frac{1}{2}C_2N_2 + H_2O = HCNO + H^+ + e^-$	-0.33
$U^{+4} + 2H_2O = UO_2^{++} + 4H^+ + 2e^-$	-0.334
$Cu = Cu^{++} + 2e^-$	-0.337
$Ag + IO_3^- = AgIO_3 + e^-$	-0.35
$Fe(CN)_6^{-4} = Fe(CN)_6^{---} + e^-$	-0.36
$V^{+++} + H_2O = VO^{++} + 2H^+ + e^-$	-0.361
$Re + 4H_2O = ReO_4^- + 8H^+ + 7e^-$	-0.363
$HCN(aq) = \frac{1}{2}C_2N_2 + H^+ + e^-$	-0.37
$S_2O_3^{--} + 3H_2O = 2H_2SO_3 + 2H^+ + 4e^-$	-0.40
$Rh + 6Cl^- = RhCl_6^{---} + 3e^-$	-0.44
$2Ag + CrO_4^{--} = Ag_2CrO_4 + 2e^-$	-0.446
$S + 3H_2O = H_2SO_3 + 4H^+ + 4e^-$	-0.45
$Sb_2O_4 + H_2O = Sb_2O_5 + 2H^+ + 2e^-$	-0.48
$2Ag + MoO_4^{--} = Ag_2MoO_4 + 2e^-$	-0.49
$2NH_3OH^+ = H_2N_2O_2 + 6H^+ + 4e^-$	-0.496
$ReO_2 + 2H_2O = ReO_4^- + 4H^+ + 3e^-$	-0.51
$S_4O_6^{--} + 6H_2O = 4H_2SO_3 + 4H^+ + 6e^-$	-0.51
$C_2H_6 = C_2H_4 + 2H^+ + 2e^-$	-0.52
$Cu = Cu^+ + e^-$	-0.521
$Te + 2H_2O = TeO_2(c) + 4H^+ + 4e^-$	-0.529
$2I^- = I_2 + 2e^-$	-0.5355
$3I^- = I_3^- + 2e^-$	-0.536
$CuCl = Cu^{++} + Cl^- + e^-$	-0.538
$Ag + BrO_3^- = AgBrO_3 + e^-$	-0.55
$Te + 2H_2O = TeOOH^+ + 3H^+ + 4e^-$	-0.559
$HAsO_2 + 2H_2O = H_3AsO_4 + 2H^+ + 2e^-$	-0.559
$Ag + NO_2^- = AgNO_2 + e^-$	-0.564

TABLE 84 (*Continued*)

OXIDATION-REDUCTION COUPLES IN ACID SOLUTIONS

Couple	$E°$
$MnO_4^{--} = MnO_4^- + e^-$	-0.564
$2H_2SO_3 = S_2O_6^{--} + 4H^+ + 2e^-$	-0.57
$Pt + 4Br^- = PtBr_4^{--} + 2e^-$	-0.58
$2SbO^+ + 3H_2O = Sb_2O_5 + 6H^+ + 4e^-$	-0.581
$CH_4 + H_2O = CH_3OH(aq) + 2H^+ + 2e^-$	-0.586
$Pd + 4Br^- = PdBr_4^{--} + 2e^-$	-0.6
$Ru + 5Cl^- = RuCl_5^{--} + 3e^-$	$-0\ 60$
$U^{+4} + 2H_2O = UO_2^{++} + 4H^+ + 2e^-$	-0.62
$Pd + 4Cl^- = PdCl_4^{--} + 2e^-$	-0.62
$CuBr = Cu^{++} + Br^- + e^-$	-0.640
$Ag + C_2H_3O_2^- = AgC_2H_3O_2 + e^-$	-0.643
$2Ag + SO_4^{--} = Ag_2SO_4 + 2e^-$	-0.653
$Au + 4CNS^- = Au(CNS)_4^- + 3e^-$	-0.66
$PtCl_4^{--} + 2Cl^- = PtCl_6^{--} + 2e^-$	-0.68
$H_2O_2 = O_2 + 2H^+ + 2e^-$	-0.682
$3NH_4^+ = HN_3 + 11H^+ + 8e^-$	-0.69
$H_2Te = Te + 2H^+ + 2e^-$	-0.70
$H_2N_2O_2 = 2NO + 2H^+ + 2e^-$	-0.71
$OH + H_2O = H_2O_2 + H^+ + e^-$	-0.72
$Pt + 4Cl^- = PtCl_4^{--} + 2e^-$	-0.73
$C_2H_4 = C_2H_2 + 2H^+ + 2e^-$	-0.73
$Se + 3H_2O = H_2SeO_3 + 4H^+ + 4e^-$	-0.74
$Np^{+4} + 2H_2O = NpO_2^+ + 4H^+ + e^-$	-0.75
$2CNS^- = (CNS)_2 + 2e^-$	-0.77
$Ir + 6Cl^- = IrCl_6^{---} + 3e^-$	-0.77
$Fe^{++} = Fe^{+++} + e^-$	-0.771
$2Hg = Hg_2^{++} + 2e^-$	-0.789
$Ag = Ag^+ + e^-$	-0.7991
$N_2O_4 + 2H_2O = 2NO_3^- + 4H^+ + 2e^-$	-0.80
$Rh = Rh^{+++} + 3e^-$	ca -0.8
$Os + 4H_2O = OsO_4(c) + 8H^+ + 8e^-$	-0.85
$H_2N_2O_2 + 2H_2O = 2HNO_2 + 4H^+ + 4e^-$	-0.86
$CuI = Cu^{++} + I^- + e^-$	-0.86
$Au + 4Br^- = AuBr_4^- + 3e^-$	-0.87
$Hg_2^{++} = 2Hg^{++} + 2e^-$	-0.920
$HNO_2 + H_2O = NO_3^- + 3H^+ + 2e^-$	-0.94
$PuO_2^+ = PuO_2^{++} + e^-$	-0.93
$NO + 2H_2O = NO_3^- + 4H^+ + 4e^-$	-0.96
$Au + 2Br^- = AuBr_2^- + e^-$	-0.96
$Pu^{+3} = Pu^{+4} + e^-$	-0.97
$Pt + 2H_2O = Pt(OH)_2 + 2H^+ + 2e^-$	-0.98
$Pd = Pd^{++} + 2e^-$	-0.987
$IrBr_6^{-4} = IrBr_6^{-3} + e^-$	-0.99
$NO + H_2O = HNO_2 + H^+ + e^-$	-1.00
$Au + 4Cl^- = AuCl_4^- + 3e^-$	-1.00
$VO^{++} + 3H_2O = V(OH)_4^+ + 2H^+ + e^-$	-1.00

TABLE 84 (*Continued*)

OXIDATION-REDUCTION COUPLES IN ACID SOLUTIONS

Couple	$E°$
$IrCl_6^{---} = IrCl_6^{--} + e^-$	-1.017
$TeO_2 + 4H_2O = H_6TeO_6(c) + 2H^+ + 2e^-$	-1.02
$NO + 2H_2O = N_2O_4 + 4H^+ + 4e^-$	-1.03
$Pu^{+4} + 2H_2O = PuO_2^{++} + 4H^+ + 2e^-$	-1.04
$2Cl^- + \frac{1}{2}I_2 = ICl_2^- + e^-$	-1.06
$2Br^- = Br_2(l) + 2e^-$	-1.0652
$2HNO_2 = N_2O_4 + 2H^+ + 2e^-$	-1.07
$Cu(CN)_2^- = Cu^{++} + 2CN^- + e^-$	-1.12
$Pu^{+4} + 2H_2O = PuO_2^+ + 4H^+ + e^-$	-1.15
$H_2SeO_3 + H_2O = SeO_4^{--} + 4H^+ + 2e^-$	-1.15
$NpO_2^+ = NpO_2^{++} + e^-$	-1.15
$4Cl^- + C + 4H^+ = CCl_4 + 4H^+ + 4e^-$	-1.18
$ClO_3^- + H_2O = ClO_4^- + 2H^+ + 2e^-$	-1.19
$\frac{1}{2}I_2 + 3H_2O = IO_3^- + 6H^+ + 5e^-$	-1.195
$HClO_2 + H_2O = ClO_3^- + 3H^+ + 2e^-$	-1.21
$2H_2O = O_2 + 4H^+ + 4e^-$	-1.229
$2S + 2Cl^- = S_2Cl_2 + 2e^-$	-1.23
$Mn^{++} + 2H_2O = MnO_2 + 4H^+ + 2e^-$	-1.23
$Tl^+ = Tl^{+++} + 2e^-$	-1.25
$Am^{+4} + 2H_2O = AmO_2^+ + 4H^+ + e^-$	-1.26
$2NH_4^+ = N_2H_5^+ + 3H^+ + 2e^-$	-1.275
$HClO_2 = ClO_2 + H^+ + e^-$	-1.275
$PdCl_4^{--} + 2Cl^- = PdCl_6^{--} + 2e^-$	-1.288
$N_2O + 3H_2O = 2HNO_2 + 4H^+ + 4e^-$	-1.29
$2Cr^{+++} + 7H_2O = Cr_2O_7^{--} + 14H^+ + 6e^-$	-1.33
$NH_4^+ + H_2O = NH_3OH^+ + 2H^+ + 2e^-$	-1.35
$2Cl^- = Cl_2 + 2e^-$	-1.3595
$N_2H_5^+ + 2H_2O = 2NH_3OH^+ + H^+ + 2e^-$	-1.42
$Au + 3H_2O = Au(OH)_3 + 3H^+ + 3e^-$	-1.45
$\frac{1}{2}I_2 + H_2O = HIO + H^+ + e^-$	-1.45
$Pb^{++} + 2H_2O = PbO_2 + 4H^+ + 2e^-$	-1.455
$Au = Au^{+++} + 3e^-$	-1.50
$H_2O_2 = HO_2 + H^+ + e^-$	-1.5
$Mn^{++} = Mn^{+++} + e^-$	-1.51
$Mn^{++} + 4H_2O = MnO_4^- + 8H^+ + 5e^-$	-1.51
$\frac{1}{2}Br_2 + 3H_2O = BrO_3^- + 6H^+ + 5e^-$	-1.52
$Br_2 + H_2O = HBrO + H^+ + e^-$	-1.59
$2BiO^+ = Bi_2O_4 + 2H_2O + 4H^+ + 2e^-$	-1.59
$IO_3^- + 3H_2O = H_5IO_6 + H^+ + 2e^-$	-1.6
$Bk^{+++} = Bk^{+4} + e^-$	-1.6
$Ce^{+++} = Ce^{+4} + e^-$	-1.61
$\frac{1}{2}Cl_2 + H_2O = HClO + H^+ + e^-$	-1.63
$AmO_2^+ = AmO_2^{++} + e^-$	-1.64
$HClO + H_2O = HClO_2 + 2H^+ + 2e^-$	-1.64
$Au = Au^+ + e^-$	ca -1.68
$Ni^{++} + 2H_2O = NiO_2 + 4H^+ + 2e^-$	-1.68

T<small>ABLE</small> 84 (Continued)

OXIDATION-REDUCTION COUPLES IN ACID SOLUTIONS

Couple	E°
$PbSO_4 + 2H_2O = PbO_2 + SO_4^{--} + 4H^+ + 2e^-$	-1.685
$Am^{+3} + 2H_2O = AmO_2^{++} + 4H^+ + 3e^-$	-1.69
$MnO_2 + 2H_2O = MnO_4^- + 4H^+ + 3e^-$	-1.695
$Am^{+++} + 2H_2O = AmO_2^+ + 4H^+ + 2e^-$	-1.725
$2H_2O = H_2O_2 + 2H^+ + 2e^-$	-1.77
$Co^{++} = Co^{+++} + e^-$	-1.82
$Fe^{+++} + 4H_2O = FeO_4^{--} + 8H^+ + 3e^-$	-1.9
$NH_4^+ + N_2 = HN_3 + 3H^+ + 2e^-$	-1.96
$Ag^+ = Ag^{++} + e^-$	-1.98
$2SO_4^{--} = S_2O_8^{--} + 2e^-$	-2.01
$O_2 + H_2O = O_3 + 2H^+ + 2e^-$	-2.07
$H_2O + 2F^- = F_2O + 2H^+ + 4e^-$	-2.1
$Am^{+++} = Am^{+4} + e^-$	-2.18
$H_2O = O(g) + 2H^+ + 2e^-$	-2.42
$2F^- = F_2 + 2e^-$	-2.87
$H_2O = OH + H^+ + e^-$	-2.8
$N_2 + 2H_2O = H_2N_2O_2 + 2H^+ + 2e^-$	-2.85
$2HF(aq) = F_2 + 2H^+ + 2e^-$	-3.06

T<small>ABLE</small> 85

OXIDATION-REDUCTION COUPLES IN BASIC SOLUTIONS

Couple	E°
$Ca + 2OH^- = Ca(OH)_2 + 2e^-$	3.03
$Sr + 2OH^- + 8H_2O = Sr(OH)_2 \cdot 8H_2O + 2e^-$	2.99
$Ba + 8H_2O + 2OH^- = Ba(OH) \cdot 8H_2O + 2e^-$	2.97
$H(g) + OH^- = H_2O + e^-$	2.93
$La + 3OH^- = La(OH)_3 + 3e^-$	2.90
$Lu + 3OH^- = Lu(OH)_3 + 3e^-$	2.72
$Mg + 2OH^- = Mg(OH)_2 + 2e^-$	2.69
$2Be + 6OH^- = Be_2O_3^{--} + 3H_2O + 4e^-$	2.62
$Sc + 3OH^- = Sc(OH)_3 + 3e^-$	ca 2.6
$Hf + 4OH^- = HfO(OH)_2 + H_2O + 4e^-$	2.50
$Th + 4OH^- = Th(OH)_4 + 4e^-$	2.48
$Pu + 3OH^- = Pu(OH)_3 + 3e^-$	2.42
$U + 4OH^- = UO_2 + 2H_2O + 4e^-$	2.39
$Al + 4OH^- = H_2AlO_3^- + H_2O + 3e^-$	2.35
$Zr + 4OH^- = H_2ZrO_3 + H_2O + 4e^-$	2.36
$U(OH)_3 + OH^- = U(OH)_4 + e^-$	2.2
$U + 3OH^- = U(OH)_3 + 3e^-$	2.17
$P + 2OH^- = H_2PO_2^- + e^-$	2.05
$B + 4OH^- = H_2BO_3^- + 3e^-$	1.79
$Si + 6OH^- = SiO_3^{--} + 3H_2O + 4e^-$	1.70

TABLE 85 (*Continued*)

OXIDATION-REDUCTION COUPLES IN BASIC SOLUTIONS

Couple	$E°$
$U(OH)_4 + 2Na^+ + 4OH^- = Na_2UO_4 + 4H_2O + 2e^-$	1.61
$H_2PO_2^- + 3OH^- = HPO_3^{--} + 2H_2O + 2e^-$	1.57
$Mn + 2OH^- = Mn(OH)_2 + 2e^-$	1.55
$Mn + CO_3^{--} = MnCO_3 + 2e^-$	1.48
$Zn + S^{--} = ZnS + 2e^-$	1.44
$Cr + 3OH^- = Cr(OH)_3 + 3e^-$	1.3
$Zn + 4CN^- = Zn(CN)_4^{--} + 2e^-$	1.26
$Zn + 2OH^- = Zn(OH)_2 + 2e^-$	1.245
$Ga + 4OH^- = H_2GaO_3^- + H_2O + 3e^-$	1.22
$Zn + 4OH^- = ZnO_2^{--} + 2H_2O + 2e^-$	1.216
$Cr + 4OH^- = CrO_2^- + H_2O + 3e^-$	1.2
$Cd + S^{--} = CdS + 2e^-$	1.21
$6V + 33OH^- = 16H_2O + HV_6O_{17}^{---} + 30e^-$	1.15
$Te^{--} = Te + 2e^-$	1.14
$HPO_3^{--} + 3OH^- = PO_4^{---} + 2H_2O + 2e^-$	1.12
$S_2O_4^{--} + 4OH^- = 2SO_3^{--} + 2H_2O + 2e^-$	1.12
$Zn + CO_3^{--} = ZnCO_3 + 2e^-$	1.06
$W + 8OH^- = WO_4^{--} + 4H_2O + 6e^-$	1.05
$Mo + 8OH^- = MoO_4^{--} + 4H_2O + 6e^-$	1.05
$Cd + 4CN^- = Cd(CN)_4^{--} + 2e^-$	1.03
$Zn + 4NH_3 = Zn(NH_3)_4^{++} + 2e^-$	1.03
$Fe + S^{--} = FeS_{(\alpha)} + 2e^-$	1.01
$In + 3OH^- = In(OH)_3 + 3e^-$	1.0
$Pb + S^{--} = PbS + 2e^-$	0.95
$CN^- + 2OH^- = CNO^- + H_2O + 2e^-$	0.97
$Tl + S^{--} = Tl_2S + 2e^-$	0.96
$Pu(OH)_3 + OH^- = Pu(OH)_4 + e^-$	0.95
$Sn + S^{--} = SnS + 2e^-$	0.94
$SO_3^{--} + 2OH^- = SO_4^{--} + H_2O + 2e^-$	0.93
$Se^{--} = Se + 2e^-$	0.92
$Sn + 3OH^- = HSnO_2^- + H_2O + 2e^-$	0.91
$Ge + 5OH^- = HGeO_3^- + 2H_2O + 4e^-$	0.9
$HSnO_2^- + H_2O + 3OH^- = Sn(OH)_6^- + 2e^-$	0.90
$PH_3 + 3OH^- = P + 3H_2O + 3e^-$	0.89
$Fe + 2OH^- = Fe(OH)_2 + 2e^-$	0.877
$Ni + S^{--} = NiS_{(\alpha)} + 2e^-$	0.83
$H_2 + 2OH^- = 2H_2O + 2e^-$	0.828
$Cd + 2OH^- = Cd(OH)_2 + 2e^-$	0.809
$Fe + CO_3^{--} = FeCO_3 + 2e^-$	0.756
$Cd + CO_3^{--} = CdCO_3 + 2e^-$	0.74
$Co + 2OH^- = Co(OH)_2 + 2e^-$	0.73
$Hg + S^{--} = HgS + 2e^-$	0.72
$Ni + 2OH^- = Ni(OH)_2 + 2e^-$	0.72
$2Ag + S^{--} = Ag_2S + 2e^-$	0.69
$As + 4OH^- = AsO_2^- + 2H_2O + 3e^-$	0.68
$AsO_2^- + 4OH^- = AsO_4^{---} + 2H_2O + 2e^-$	0.67

TABLE 85 (*Continued*)

OXIDATION-REDUCTION COUPLES IN BASIC SOLUTIONS

Couple	$E°$
$2FeS + S^{--} = Fe_2S_3 + 2e^-$	0.67
$Sb + 4OH^- = SbO_2^- + 2H_2O + 3e^-$	0.66
$Co + CO_3^{--} = CoCO_3 + 2e^-$	0.64
$Cd + 4NH_3 = Cd(NH_3)_4^{++} + 2e^-$	0.597
$ReO_2 + 4OH^- = ReO_4^- + 2H_2O + 3e^-$	0.594
$Re + 8OH^- = ReO_4^- + 4H_2O + 7e^-$	0.584
$S_2O_3^{--} + 6OH^- = 2SO_3^{--} + 3H_2O + 4e^-$	0.58
$Re + 4OH^- = ReO_2 + H_2O + 4e^-$	0.576
$Te + 6OH^- = TeO_3^{--} + 3H_2O + 4e^-$	0.57
$Fe(OH)_2 + OH^- = Fe(OH)_3 + e^-$	0.56
$O_2^- = O_2 + e^-$	0.56
$2Cu + S^{--} = Cu_2S + 2e^-$	0.54
$Pb + 3OH^- = HPbO_2^- + H_2O + 2e^-$	0.54
$Pb + CO_3^{--} = PbCO_3 + 2e^-$	0.506
$S^{--} = S + 2e^-$	0.48
$Ni + 6NH_3(aq) = Ni(NH_3)_6^{++} + 2e^-$	0.47
$Ni + CO_3^{--} = NiCO_3^{--} + 2e^-$	0.45
$2Bi + 6OH^- = Bi_2O_3 + 3H_2O + 6e^-$	0.44
$Cu + 2CN^- = Cu(CN)_2^- + e^-$	0.43
$Hg + 4CN^- = Hg(CN)_4^- + 2e^-$	0.37
$Se + 6OH^- = SeO_3^{--} + 3H_2O + 4e^-$	0.366
$2Cu + 2OH^- = Cu_2O + H_2O + 2e^-$	0.358
$Tl + OH^- = Tl(OH) + e^-$	0.3445
$Ag + 2CN^- = Ag(CN)_2^- + e^-$	0.31
$Cu + CNS^- = Cu(CNS) + e^-$	0.27
$OH + 2OH^- = HO_2^- + H_2O + e^-$	0.24
$Cr(OH)_3 + 5OH^- = CrO_4^{--} + 4H_2O + 3e^-$	0.13
$Cu + 2NH_3 = Cu(NH_3)_2^+ + e^-$	0.12
$Cu_2O + 2OH^- + H_2O = 2Cu(OH)_2 + 2e^-$	0.080
$HO_2^- + OH^- = O_2 + H_2O + 2e^-$	0.076
$TlOH + 2OH^- = Tl(OH)_3 + 2e^-$	0.05
$Ag + CN^- = AgCN + e^-$	0.017
$Mn(OH)_2 + 2OH^- = MnO_2 + H_2O + 2e^-$	0.05
$NO_2^- + 2OH^- = NO_3^- + H_2O + 2e^-$	-0.01
$Os + 9OH^- = HOsO_5^- + 4H_2O + 8e^-$	-0.02
$2Rh + 6OH^- = Rh_2O_3 + 3H_2O + 6e^-$	-0.04
$SiO_3^{--} + 2OH^- = SeO_4^{--} + H_2O + 2e^-$	-0.05
$Pd + 2OH^- = Pd(OH)_2 + 2e^-$	-0.07
$2S_2O_3^{--} = S_4O_6^{--} + 2e^-$	-0.08
$Hg + 2OH^- = HgO(r) + H_2O + 2e^-$	-0.098
$2NH_4OH + 2OH^- = N_2H_4 + 4H_2O + 2e^-$	-0.1
$Ir + 6OH^- = Ir_2O_3 + 3H_2O + 6e^-$	-0.1
$Co(NH_3)_6^{++} = Co(NH_3)_6^{+++} + e^-$	-0.1
$Mn(OH)_2 = Mn(OH)_3 + e^-$	-0.1
$Pt + 2OH^- = Pt(OH)_2 + 2e^-$	-0.15
$Co(OH)_2 + OH^- = Co(OH)_3 + e^-$	-0.17

TABLE 85 (*Continued*)

OXIDATION-REDUCTION COUPLES IN BASIC SOLUTIONS

Couple	$E°$
$PbO(r) + 2OH^- = PbO_2 + H_2O + 2e^-$	-0.248
$I^- + 6OH^- = IO_3^- + 3H_2O + 6e^-$	-0.26
$PuO_2OH + OH^- = PuO_2(OH)_2 + e^-$	-0.26
$Ag + 2SO_3^{--} = Ag(SO_3)_2^{---} + e^-$	-0.30
$ClO_2^- + 2OH^- = ClO_3^- + H_2O + 2e^-$	-0.33
$2Ag + 2OH^- = Ag_2O + H_2O + 2e^-$	-0.344
$ClO_3^- + 2OH^- = ClO_4^- + H_2O + 2e^-$	-0.36
$Ag + 2NH_3 = Ag(NH_3)_2^+ + e^-$	-0.373
$TeO_3^{--} + 2OH^- = TeO_4^{--} + H_2O + 2e^-$	-0.4
$OH^- + HO_2^- = O_2^- + H_2O + e^-$	-0.4
$4OH^- = O_2 + 2H_2O + 4e^-$	-0.401
$2Ag + CO_3^{--} = Ag_2CO_3 + 2e^-$	-0.47
$Ni(OH)_2 + 2OH^- = NiO_2 + 2H_2O + 2e^-$	-0.49
$I^- + 2OH^- = IO^- + H_2O + 2e^-$	-0.49
$Ag_2O + 2OH^- = 2AgO + H_2O + 2e^-$	-0.57
$MnO_2 + 4OH^- = MnO_4^{--} + 2H_2O + 2e^-$	-0.60
$RuO_4^{--} = RuO_4^- + e^-$	-0.60
$Br^- + 6OH^- = BrO_3^- + 3H_2O + 6e^-$	-0.61
$ClO^- + 2OH^- = ClO_2^- + H_2O + 2e^-$	-0.66
$IO_3^- + 3OH^- = H_3IO_6^{--} + 2e^-$	-0.7
$N_2H_4 + 2OH^- = 2NH_2OH + 2e^-$	-0.73
$2AgO + 2OH^- = Ag_2O_3 + H_2O + 2e^-$	-0.74
$Br^- + 2OH^- = BrO^- + H_2O + 2e^-$	-0.76
$3OH^- = HO_2^- + H_2O + 2e^-$	-0.88
$Cl^- + 2OH^- = ClO^- + H_2O + 2e^-$	-0.89
$FeO_2^- + 4OH^- = FeO_4^{--} + 2H_2O + 3e^-$	-0.9
$ClO_2^- = ClO_2 + e^-$	-1.16
$O_2 + 2OH^- = O_3 + H_2O + 2e^-$	-1.24
$OH^- = OH + e^-$	-2.0

APPENDIX II

The Activity of Strong Electrolytes

The activity of a salt which ionizes according to the equation

$$X = \nu_+ X^+ + \nu_- X^-$$

is defined as:

$$a = a_+{}^{\nu+} a_-{}^{\nu-}.$$

The geometrical mean of the positive and negative ion activities is denoted as $a_\pm$:

$$a_\pm = a^{1/\nu},$$

where $\nu = \nu_+ + \nu_-$.

EXAMPLE

For barium chloride,

$$a = a_{Ba^{++}} \times a_{Cl^-}^2 = a_\pm^3.$$

If the molality is very low,

$$a_+ = \nu_+ m, \qquad a_- = \nu_- m,$$
$$a_\pm = [(\nu_+ m)^{\nu+} (\nu_- m)^{\nu-}]^{1/\nu} = m(\nu_+{}^{\nu+} \nu_-{}^{\nu-})^{1/\nu}.$$

EXAMPLE

For aluminum sulfate,

$$a_\pm = m(2^2 \times 3^3)^{1/5}.$$

If the mean molality is defined as

$$m_\pm = m(\nu_+{}^{\nu+} \nu_-{}^{\nu-})^{1/\nu}$$

it is then possible to define a mean activity coefficient γ. This co-efficient may be considered the thermodynamic degree of dissociation, and becomes equal to unity at infinite dilution for all types of salts:

$$\gamma = \frac{a_{\pm}}{m_{\pm}}.$$

This mean activity coefficient, which might have been written $\gamma_{\pm}$, becomes in terms of the activity coefficients of the individual ions:

$$\gamma = (\gamma_{+}{}^{\nu+}\gamma_{-}{}^{\nu-})^{1/\nu}.$$

The activity coefficients of a large number of salts at varying molalities have been summarized in the table at the end of this appendix, and a few examples of typical curves of γ against $m^{\frac{1}{2}}$ are given in Figure 4.

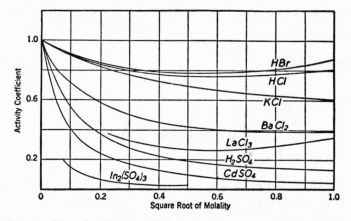

FIG. 4.   Plot of activity coefficients against square root of molality.

It was observed by G. N. Lewis as an empirical fact that, in a mixture of electrolytes, the activity coefficient of a salt is determined by the average ionic strength, μ, of the positive and negative ions, defined as

$$\mu = \frac{Z_{+}^{2}m_{+} + Z_{-}^{2}m_{-}}{2} \quad \text{or} \quad \mu = \tfrac{1}{2}\sum m_i Z_i^2,$$

where Z is the charge on an ion.

EXAMPLE

The ionic strength of $BaCl_2$ at a molality of m is

$$\mu = \frac{2^2m + 1^2(2m)}{2} = 3m.$$

The general principal may be stated: In dilute solutions, the activity coefficient of a given strong electrolyte is the same in all solu-

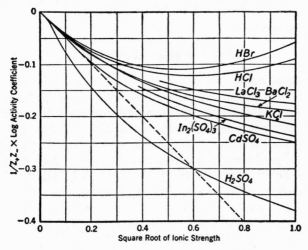

FIG. 5.   Plot of log γ/Z_+Z_- against $\mu^{1/2}$.

tions of the same ionic strength. The principal is to be looked upon as a limiting law, and large deviations occur at high concentrations.

The Debye and Hückel[1] theory has supplied the limiting laws for dilute solutions. Thus for a single ion,

$$\log \gamma_i = -0.505 Z_i^2 \mu^{1/2},$$

and for the mean activity of a salt,

$$\log \gamma = -0.505 Z_+ Z_- \mu^{1/2}.$$

The data in Figure 4 have been replotted in Figure 5 in terms of $\frac{1}{Z_+Z_-} \log \gamma$ against $\mu^{1/2}$. It will be observed that for dilute solutions

[1] P. Debye and E. Hückel, *Phys. Z.*, **24**, 185 (1923).

all the curves, except that for sulfuric acid, approach the limiting value (broken line). The behavior of the latter is to be accounted for by the weakness of the second dissociation step. If corrections are made for this, sulfuric acid also will fall upon one of the family of curves lying above the limiting line.

Randall and Vietti[1] have used the curves of Figure 5 in a graphical method of extrapolating potential measurements and equilibrium constants to zero ionic strength. As an example, we may discuss the application of the method by Bray and Hershey[2] to the ferrous-ferric electrode, that is, to the reaction

$$Fe^{+++} + \tfrac{1}{2}H_2 = Fe^{++} + H^+.$$

Experimental e.m.f. values for the reaction must be obtained at fairly high hydrogen ion concentration in order to prevent the hydrolysis of the ferric ion. For measurements in hydrochloric acid the potentials may be corrected to unit hydrogen ion activity from the known activity coefficients, and to equal concentrations of unhydrolyzed ferric and ferrous ions. This then gives the potential of Fe^{++}—Fe^{+++} couple in the hydrochloric acid solution. The E° value, however, refers to zero ionic strength and the extrapolation is a difficult problem.

The log γ-$\mu^{\frac{1}{2}}$ curve for a single ion approaches the limiting line whose slope is $0.505Z^2$. For the Fe^{++}—Fe^{+++} couple ΔZ^2 is 5 and the assumption is made that the curve for $\dfrac{E}{5 \times 0.05916}$ against $\mu^{\frac{1}{2}}$ will approach the limiting slope 0.505. A reproduction of the Bray and Hershey curve is given in Figure 6. The extrapolation to zero ionic strength is made by slipping the family of curves in Figure 4 over the experimental points until the best fit is secured. In this case it is a curve which lies just below that for HCl.

The problem of the extrapolation of this couple to zero ionic strength has been treated in a somewhat different manner by Schumb, Sherrill, and Sweetser.[3] These authors make use of an equation sug-

---

[1] M. Randall and W. A. V. Vietti, *J. Am. Chem. Soc.*, **50**, 1526 (1928). Unpublished calculations by Randall have also been available to the author.

[2] W. C. Bray and A. V. Hershey, *J. Am. Chem. Soc.*, **56**, 1889 (1934).

[3] W. C. Schumb, M. S. Sherrill, and S. B. Sweetser, *J. Am. Chem. Soc.*, **59**, 2360 (1937).

gested by Guggenheim and Schindler,[1]

$$\log \gamma = -0.505 Z^2 \frac{\mu^{\frac{1}{2}}}{1 + \mu^{\frac{1}{2}}},$$

which corresponds to about the average of the curves at low ionic strength. They calculate for each ionic strength a value

$$E' = E_{\text{observ.}} - 0.05916 \Delta Z^2 \times 0.505 \frac{\mu^{\frac{1}{2}}}{1 + \mu^{\frac{1}{2}}}.$$

E' is then plotted against μ and extrapolated to $\mu = 0$.

This method gives somewhat greater weight to the measurements at low ionic strength where the experimental errors are often quite

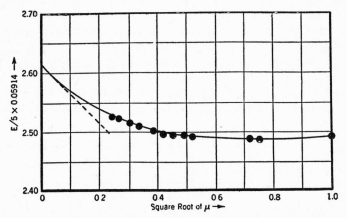

FIG. 6. $E/5 \times 0.05916$ for Fe^{++}—Fe^{+++} couple, plotted against square root of ionic strength.

large. The Randall method gives equal weight to all measurements throughout the concentration range but the assumption that the shape of the curve will always fit that of a curve for a single activity coefficient is open to some question.

---

[1] E. A. Guggenheim and T. O. Schindler, *J. Phys. Chem.*, **38**, 543 (1934).

TABLE 86

ACTIVITY COEFFICIENTS OF STRONG ELECTROLYTES

m	.001	.002	.005	.01	.02	.05	.1	.2	.5	1.0	2.0	3.0	4.0	Reference[1]
HCl	.966	.952	.928	.904	.875	.830	.796	.767	.758	0.809	1.01	1.32	1.76	(13)
HBr	.966		.929	.906	.879	.838	.805	.782	.790	0.871	1.17	1.67		(28), (50)
HNO$_3$	.965	.951	.927	.902	.871	.823	.785	.748	.715	0.720	0.783	0.876	0.982	(16), (1)
HClO$_4$										0.81	1.04	1.42	2.02	(14), (1)
HIO$_3$	.96	.94	.91	.86	.80	.69	.58	.46	.29	0.19	0.10	0.073	0.060	(15)
H$_2$SO$_4$	.830	.757	.639	.544	.453	.340	.265	.209	.154	0.130	0.124	0.141	0.171	(17)
NaOH								.73	.69	0.68	0.70	0.77	0.89	(36)
KOH			.92	.90	.86	.82	.80	.76	.73	0.76	0.89	1.08	1.35	(1), (28)
CsOH				.92	.88	.83	.80		.74	0.78				(7), (1)
Ba(OH)$_2$		.853	.773	.712	.627	.526	.443	.370						(49)
AgNO$_3$			.92	.90	.86	.79	.72	.64	.51	0.40	0.28			(1), (2)
Al(NO$_3$)$_3$							.20	.16	.14	0.19	0.45	1.0	1.2	(44), (1)
BaCl$_2$	.88		.77	.72		.56	.49	.44	.39	0.39	0.44 (1.8m)			(27), (45)
Ba(NO$_3$)$_2$	.88	.84	.77	.71	.63	.52	.43	.34						(36), (1)
Ba(IO$_3$)$_2$		.79	.71	.64	.55									(2)
CaCl$_2$	.89	.85	.785	.725	.66	.57	.515	.48	.52	0.71				(22)
Ca(NO$_3$)$_2$	.88	.84	.77	.71	.64	.54	.48	.42	.38	0.35	0.35	0.37	0.42	(19), (1)
CdCl$_2$	.76	.68	.57	.47	.38	.28	.21	.15	.09	0.06	0.018			(22)
CdI$_2$	.76	.65	.49	.38	.28	.17	.11	.068	.038	0.025				(25)
CdSO$_4$	.73	.64	.50	.40	.31	.21	.17	.11	.067	0.045	0.035	0.036		(3), (29)
CsF	.98	.97	.96	.95	.94	.91	.89	.87	.85	0.87				(8), (1)
CsCl			.92	.90	.86	.79	.75	.69	.60	0.54	0.49	0.48	0.47	(7), (1)
CsBr			.93	.90	.86	.79	.75	.69	.60	0.53	0.48	0.46	0.46	(7), (1)
CsI							.75	.69	.60	0.53	0.47	0.43		(4), (27), (1)
CsNO$_3$							.73	.65	.52	0.42				(27)

[1] Reference list will be found on pp. 357–358.

TABLE 86 (*Continued*)

ACTIVITY COEFFICIENTS OF STRONG ELECTROLYTES

m	.001	.002	.005	.01	.02	.05	.1	.2	.5	1.0	2.0	3.0	4.0	Reference[1]
CsAc							.79	.77	.76	0.80	0.95	1.15		(27)
$CuCl_2$	.89	.85	.78	.72	.66	.58	.52	.47	.42	0.43	0.51	0.59		(10), (1)
$CuSO_4$	.74		.53	.41	.31	.21	.16	.11	.068	0.047				(11), (1), (29), (2)
$FeCl_2$	.89	.86	.80	.75	.70	.62	.58	.55	.59	0.67				(12)
$In_2(SO_4)_3$				.142	.092	.054	.035	.022						(30)
KF		.96	.95	.93	.92	.88	.85	.81	.74	0.71	0.70			(8), (1)
KCl	.965	.952	.927	.901		.815	.769	.719	.651	0.606	0.576	0.571	0.579	(24), (18), (20)
KBr	.965	.952	.927	.903	.872	.822	.777	.728	.665	0.625	0.602	0.603	0.622	(18)
KI	.965	.951	.927	.905	.88	.84	.80	.76	.71	0.68	0.69	0.72	0.75	(46), (1)
$K_4Fe(CN)_6$						.19	.14	.11	.067					(27)
$KClO_3$	.967	.955	.932	.907	.875	.813	.755							(21)
K_2O_3	.89	.86	.81	.74	.68	.58	.50	.43	.36	0.33	0.33	0.39	0.49	(1)
$KClO_4$	.965	.951	.924	.895	.857	.788								(21)
K_2SO_4	.89		.78	.71	.64	.52	.43	.36	.27					(2), (47), (1)
$LaCl_3$				.57	.49	.38	.32	.28		0.36				(27)
$La(NO_3)_3$						.39	.33	.27	.27					(2)
LiCl	.963	.948	.921	.89	.86	.82	.78	.75	.73	0.76	0.91	1.18	1.46	(8), (1)
LiBr	.966	.954	.932	.909	.882	.842	.810	.784	.783	0.848	1.06	1.35		(18), (9)
LiI							.81	.80	.81	0.89	1.19	1.70		(20)
$LiNO_3$	.966	.953	.930	.904	.878	.834	.798	.765	.743	0.76	0.84	0.97		(21), (9)
$LiClO_3$	.967	.955	.933	.911	.884	.842	.810	.782	.77	0.81				(21)
$LiClO_4$	.967	.956	.935	.915	.890	.853	.825	.805	.82	0.91				(21)
$MgCl_2$							.56	.53	.52	0.62	1.05	2.1		(1), (19)
$Mg(NO_3)_2$	.88	.84	.77	.71	.64	.55	.51	.46	.44	0.50	0.69	0.93		(1), (32)
$MgSO_4$				.40	.32	.22	.18	.13	.088	0.064	0.055	0.064		(2), (29)
$MnSO_4$							.25	.17	.11	0.073	0.058	0.062	0.079	(29)

[1] Reference list will be found on pp. 357–358.

TABLE 86 (*Continued*)

ACTIVITY COEFFICIENTS OF STRONG ELECTROLYTES

m	.001	.002	.005	.01	.02	.05	.1	.2	.5	1.0	2.0	3.0	4.0	Reference[1]
NiSO$_4$							.18	.13	.075	0.051	0.041			(29)
NH$_4$Cl	.961	.944	.911	.88	.84	.79	.74	.69	.62	0.57				(33), (1)
NH$_4$Br	.964	.949	.901	.87	.83	.78	.73	.68	.62	0.57				(33), (1)
NH$_4$I	.962	.946	.917	.89	.86	.80	.76	.71	.65	0.60				(33), (1)
NH$_4$NO$_3$	.959	.942	.912	.88	.84	.78	.73	.66	.56	0.47				(33), (1)
(NH$_4$)$_2$SO$_4$	.874	.821	.726	.67	.59	.48	.40	.32	.22	0.16				(33), (1)
NaF			.93	.90	.87	.81	.75	.69	.62					(8), (1)
NaCl	.966	.953	.929	.904	.875	.823	.780	.730	.68	0.66	0.67	0.71	0.78	(34), (20), (18)
NaBr	.966	.955	.934	.914	.887	.844	.800	.740	.695	0.686	0.734	0.826	0.934	(18), (26)
NaI	.97	.96	.94	.91	.89	.86	.83	.81	.78	0.80	0.95			(8), (1), (9)
NaNO$_3$	.966	.953	.93	.90	.87	.82	.77	.70	.62	0.55	0.48	0.44	0.41	(35), (5)
Na$_2$SO$_4$	.887	.847	.778	.714	.641	.53	.45	.36	.27	0.20				(37), (38)
NaClO$_4$	.97	.95	.93	.90	.87	.82	.77	.72	.64	0.58				(21)
PbCl$_2$	.86	.80	.70	.61	.50									(22)
Pb(NO$_3$)$_2$	.88	.84	.76	.69	.60	.46	.37	.27	.17	0.11				(48)
RbCl				.90			.76	.71	.63	0.58	0.54	0.54	0.54	(27), (1)
RbBr							.76	.70	.63	0.58	0.53	0.52	0.51	(27), (1)
RbI							.76	.70	.63	0.57	0.53	0.52	0.51	(21), (1)
RbNO$_3$							.73	.65	.53	0.43	0.32	0.25	0.21	(27)
RbAc							.73	.65	.52	0.42				(27)
TlCl	.96	.95	.93	.90										(2), (39)
TlNO$_3$						.77	.70	.60	.53					(27)
TlClO$_4$						.79	.73	.65						(27)
TlAc						.80	.74	.68	.59	0.51	0.44	0.40	0.38	(27)
ZnCl$_2$	.88	.84	.77	.71	.64	.56	.50	.45	.38	0.33				(22)
ZnSO$_4$	.70	.61	.48	.39			.15	.11	.065	0.045	0.036	0.04		(41), (42), (29)

[1] Reference list will be found on pp. 357–358.

REFERENCES FOR ACTIVITY COEFFICIENTS OF STRONG ELECTROLYTES

(1) "Landolt-Bornstein," *Tabellen III*, p. 2147.

(2) Lewis, G. N., and Randall, M., *Thermodynamics*, New York: McGraw-Hill Book Company, Inc., 1923.

(3) La Mer, V. K., and Parks, W. G., *J. Am. Chem. Soc.*, **53**, 2040 (1931).

(4) Damköhler, G., and Weinzierl, J., *Z. physik. Chem.*, **A167**, 71 (1933).

(5) Robinson, R. A., *J. Am. Chem. Soc.*, **57**, 1161 (1935).

(6) Richards, T. W., and Rowe, A. W., *J. Am. Chem. Soc.*, **43**, 770 (1921).

(7) Harned, H. S., and Schupp, O. E., Jr., *J. Am. Chem. Soc.*, **52**, 3886 (1930).

(8) Karagunis, G., Hawkinson, A., and Damköhler, G., *Z. physik. Chem.*, **A151**, 433 (1930).

(9) Robinson, R. A., *J. Am. Chem. Soc.*, **57**, 1161 (1935).

(10) Partington, J. R., and Soper, W. E., *Phil. Mag.*, **7**, 209 (1929).

(11) Lange, E., Monheim, J., and Robinson, A. L., *J. Am. Chem. Soc.*, **55**, 4733 (1933).

(12) Randall, M., and Frandsen, M., *J. Am. Chem. Soc.*, **54**, 47 (1932).

(13) Harned, H. S., and Ehlers, R. W., *J. Am. Chem. Soc.*, **55**, 2179 (1933).

(14) Pearce, J. N., and Nelson, A. F., *J. Am. Chem. Soc.*, **55**, 3075 (1933).

(15) Abel, E., Redlich, O., and Hersch, P., *Z. physik. Chem.*, **A170**, 112 (1934).

(16) Hartmann, F., and Rosenfeld, P., *Z. physik. Chem.*, **A164**, 377 (1933).

(17) Harned, H. S., and Hamer, W. J., *J. Am. Chem. Soc.*, **57**, 27 (1935).

(18) Scatchard, G., and Prentiss, S. S., *J. Am. Chem. Soc.*, **55**, 4355 (1933).

(19) Lange, E., and Streeck, H., *Z. physik. Chem.*, **A152**, 1 (1931).

(20) Robinson, R. A., and Sinclair, D. A., *J. Am. Chem. Soc.*, **56**, 1830 (1934).

(21) Scatchard, G., Prentiss, S. S., and Jones, P. T., *J. Am. Chem. Soc.*, **56**, 805 (1934).

(22) Scatchard, G., and Tefft, R. F., *J. Am. Chem. Soc.*, **52**, 2272 (1930).

(23) Pearce, J. N., and Eckstrom, H. C., *J. Am. Chem. Soc.*, **59**, 2689 (1937).

(24) Harned, H. S., and Cook, M. A., *J. Am. Chem. Soc.*, **59**, 1292 (1937).

(25) Bates, R. G., and Vosburgh, W. C., *J. Am. Chem. Soc.*, **59**, 1584 (1937).

(26) Harned, H. S., and Crawford, C. C., *J. Am. Chem. Soc.*, **59**, 1904 (1937).

(27) Robinson, R. A., *J. Am. Chem. Soc.*, **59**, 84 (1937).

(28) Harned, H. S., Keston, A. S., and Donelson, J. G., *J. Am. Chem. Soc.*, **58**, 992 (1936).

(29) Robinson, R. A., and Jones, R. S., *J. Am. Chem. Soc.*, **58**, 961 (1936).

(30) Hattox, E. M., and De Vries, T., *J. Am. Chem. Soc.*, **58**, 2128 (1936).

(31) Hammerschmid, H., and Lange, E., *Z. physik. Chem.*, **A160**, 445 (1932).

(32) Ewing, W. W., Klinger, E., and Brandner, J. D., *J. Am. Chem. Soc.*, **56**, 1053 (1934).

(33) Scatchard, G., and Prentiss, S. S., *J. Am. Chem. Soc.*, **54**, 2696 (1932).

(34) Harned, H. S., and Nims, L. F., *J. Am. Chem. Soc.*, **54**, 423 (1932).
(35) Scatchard, G., Prentiss, S. S., and Jones, P. T., *J. Am. Chem. Soc.*, **54**, 2690 (1932).
(36) Harned, H. S., and Hecker, J. C., *J. Am. Chem. Soc.*, **55**, 4838 (1933).
(37) Harned, H. S., and Hecker, J. C., *J. Am. Chem. Soc.*, **56**, 650 (1934).
(38) Randall, M., and Scott, G. N., *J. Am. Chem. Soc.*, **49**, 647 (1927).
(39) Cowperthwaite, I. A., La Mer, V. K., and Barksdale, J., *J. Am. Chem. Soc.*, **56**, 544 (1934).
(40) Brüll, L., *Gazz. chim. ital.*, **64**, 261 (1934).
(41) Cowperthwaite, I. A., and La Mer, V. K., *J. Am. Chem. Soc.*, **53**, 4333 (1931).
(42) Masaki, K., and Ikkatai, T., *Bull. Chem. Soc. Japan*, **7**, 238 (1937).
(43) Naray-Szabo, S. v., and Szabo, Z., *Z. physik. Chem.*, **A 173**, 103 (1935).
(44) Pearce, J. N., and Blackman, L. E., *J. Am. Chem. Soc.*, **57**, 24 (1935).
(45) Tippetts, E. A., and Newton, R. F., *J. Am. Chem. Soc.*, **56**, 1675 (1934).
(46) Wüst, J., and Lange, E., *Z. physik. Chem.*, **116**, 161 (1925).
(47) Rümelin, G, *Z. physik. Chem.*, **58**, 449 (1907).
(48) Randall, M., and Vanselow, A. P., *J. Am. Chem. Soc.*, **46**, 2418 (1924).
(49) Harned, H. S., and Mason, C. M., *J. Am. Chem. Soc.*, **54**, 1439 (1932).
(50) Livingston, R. S., *J. Am. Chem. Soc.*, **48**, 45 (1926).

APPENDIX III

Methods for the Estimation of Entropy Values

A review of the various tables of thermodynamic data will show that experimental values exist for the entropies of most of the gaseous molecules, but that the values for salts, molecules, and ions in the aqueous solutions are far from complete. Since estimates have been made of the values in a large number of cases, it seems appropriate to discuss briefly the methods by which these estimates have been made.

Entropies of solid compounds. The entropy of a solid compound is a function of the masses of the constituent atoms and the forces acting between these atoms: the greater the mass and the lower the force, the larger is the entropy. For compounds whose specific heat has reached the Dulong and Petit value of 6 cal./gram atom, the mass is the principal factor, and in 1921 the author[1] gave an equation for the contribution of each element to the entropy of the compound.

$$S^{\circ}_{298} = \tfrac{3}{2}R \ln \text{at. wt.} - 0.94 \tag{1}$$

The dotted line in Figure 7 is determined by this expression. For simple salts, such as the alkali halides, the entropy may be estimated with fair accuracy as the sum of the entropies of the constituent elements as given by this equation. However, the forces in solid salts are largely ionic attractions, and the effect of the ionic radii upon the force constants and the vibrational frequencies is appreciable: in general the entropy of a large ion is increased and the entropy of a small ion is decreased from the values given by equation (1). Since there is a rough correlation between size and weight, the solid line in Figure 7 has been drawn to increase slightly the entropies of the heavier elements and decrease slightly the entropies of the lighter elements. The values taken

---

[1] W. M. Latimer, *J. Am. Chem. Soc.*, **43**, 818 (1921).

from this curve are summarized in Table 87, and by their use the entropies of solid salts may be estimated with somewhat greater accuracy than by the values from equation (1).

According to the argument just presented, it may be expected that the entropy of an ionic solid will also depend upon the magnitude of the ionic charges. To illustrate this effect, the apparent contribution of the chloride ion in combination with $+1$, $+2$, and $+3$ ions has been

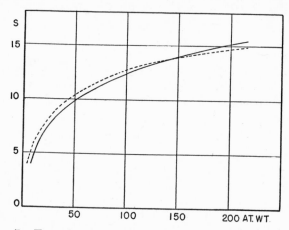

Fig. 7.   Entropies of elements in solid compounds as a function of atomic weight.

calculated (Table 88) by subtracting from the experimental entropy of the salt the entropy of the positive ion as given in Table 87. The agreement of the calculated Cl values for each type of salt is remarkably good, and the average values 10.0, 8.1, and 6.9 for the positive ions M^+, M^{+2}, and M^{+3} decrease with increasing positive charge as is to be expected.

The value for Cl from Table 87 is 8.8 and it may be seen from Table 88 that this is a fair approximation, but that much better agreement is obtained if the average values for the salt types MCl, MCl_2, and MCl_3 are employed. An examination of the data for a large number of negative ions shows that a similar charge effect exists in all cases.

It is proposed, then, to assign all the variation in charge arbitrarily to the negative ion and to prepare from the experimental entropies a table for the negative ions in which the value is modified by the charge on the positive ion. The entropy of any salt may then be estimated by

TABLE 87

ENTROPIES OF THE ELEMENTS IN SOLID COMPOUNDS AT 298° C.

(Values in cal./deg.)

Ag	12.8	Dy	14.4	Mn	10.3	Se	(11.6)
Al	8.0	Br	14.5	Mo	12.3	Si	8.1
As	11.45	Eu	14.1	N	5.8	Sm	14.1
Au	15.3	F	(6.9)	Na	7.5	Sn	13.1
B	4.9	Fe	10.4	Nd	13.9	Sr	12.0
Ba	13.7	Ga	11.2	Ni	10.5	Ta	14.9
Be	4.3	Gd	14.3	Os	15.1	Tb	14.3
Bi	15.6	Ge	11.3	Pb	15.5	Te	(13.4)
Br	(11.7)	Hf	14.8	Pd	12.7	Th	15.9
C	5.2	Hg	15.4	Pr	13.8	Ti	9.8
Ca	9.3	Ho	14.5	Pt	15.2	Tl	15.4
Cb	12.2	I	(13.4)	Ra	15.8	Tm	14.6
Cd	12.9	In	13.0	Rb	11.9	U	16.0
Ce	13.8	Ir	15.2	Re	15.0	V	10.1
Cl	(8.8)	K	9.2	Rh	12.5	W	15.0
Co	10.6	La	13.8	Ru	12.5	Y	12.0
Cr	10.2	Li	3.5	S	(8.5)	Yb	14.7
Cs	13.6	Lu	14.8	Sb	13.2	Zn	10.9
Cu	10.8	Mg	7.6	Sc	9.7	Zr	12.1

combining the values in this summary for negative ions, Table 90, with the values in Table 87 for the positive ions.

In addition to the simple negative ions, the summary includes values for the oxygen complex ions. As an example of the degree of consistency in the data employed, the calculations for sulfate are given in Table 89. The average values for type salts are: M_2SO_4, 22.0; MSO_4, 17.2; and $M_2(SO_4)_3$, 13.7. The variations in the individual values are somewhat greater than those for the chlorides given in Table 88, but the average deviation is only 1.3 cal./deg.

It is not possible to complete Table 89 from experimental data. For example, there are no data on fluorides of the types XF and XF_3. Where the trends appear fairly definite from similar compounds, estimates have been given (values in brackets). It will be noted that in some cases the values for the +4 ions are slightly larger than those for the +3 ions. There are sufficient data to establish this as a real effect, and it is doubtless due to the anion repulsion which exists with four large negative ions about a small positive ion. This repulsion tends to weaken the bond energies and increase the entropy.

The specific heats of oxides are considerably below the Dulong and

TABLE 88

CONTRIBUTION OF Cl TO THE ENTROPY OF MCl, MCl$_2$ AND MCl$_3$ COMPOUNDS.

(Calculated by subtracting entropy of positive ion, Table 87, from the entropy of the salt.)

Salt	Entropy of Salt	Entropy of Cl	Salt	Entropy of Salt	Entropy of Cl	Salt	Entropy of Salt	Entropy of Cl
NaCl	17.3	9.9	PbCl$_2$	32.6	8.5	CrCl$_3$	31.0	6.7
KCl	19.75	10.6	ZnCl$_2$	25.9	7.6	VCl$_3$	31.3	7.1
TlCl	24.8	9.3	CdCl$_2$	28.3	7.7	Aver.		6.9
AgCl	22.97	10.2	Hg$_2$Cl$_2$	46.8	8.0			
Aver.		10.0	NiCl$_2$	25.6	7.8			
			CoCl$_2$	25.4	7.5			
			FeCl$_2$	28.6	9.0			
			MnCl$_2$	28.0	8.8			
			CrCl$_2$	27.4	8.7			
			VCl$_2$	23.2	6.6			
			Aver.		8.1			

TABLE 89

CONTRIBUTION OF SULFATE TO THE ENTROPY OF M$_2$SO$_4$, MSO$_4$, AND M$_2$(SO$_4$)$_3$ TYPE OF COMPOUND

(Calculated by subtracting entropy of positive ion, Table 87, from the entropy of the salt.)

Salt	Entropy of Salt	Entropy of SO$_4$	Salt	Entropy of Salt	Entropy of SO$_4$	Salt	Entropy of Salt	Entropy of SO$_4$
Ag$_2$SO$_4$	47.8	22.2	CuSO$_4$	27.1	16.3	Al$_2$(SO$_4$)$_3$	57.2	13.7
K$_2$SO$_4$	42.0	23.6	MnSO$_4$	26.8	16.5	Aver.		13.7
Na$_2$SO$_4$	35.7	20.7	BaSO$_4$	31.6	17.8			
Aver.		22.0	CaSO$_4$	25.6	16.3			
			PbSO$_4$	35.2	19.7			
			ZnSO$_4$	29.8	18.9			
			CdSO$_4$	32.8	19.9			
			MgSO$_4$	21.9	14.4			
			FeSO$_4$	25.7	15.3			
			Hg$_2$SO$_4$	48.0	17.2			
			Aver.		17.2			

TABLE 90

SUMMARY OF ENTROPY CONTRIBUTION OF NEGATIVE IONS IN
SOLID COMPOUNDS AT 298° K.

(Values in cal./deg. per mole.)

Negative Ion	Charge on Positive Ion			
	+1	+2	+3	+4
F^-	(5.5)	4.7	(4.0)	5.0
Cl^-	10.0	8.1	6.9	8.1
Br^-	13.0	10.9	(9.)	(10.)
I^-	14.6	13.6	12.5	13.0
CN^-	7.2	(6.)		
OH^-	(5.0)	4.5	3.0	
ClO^-	(14.)	(10.)	(8.)	
ClO_2^-	19.2	(17.)	(14.)	
ClO_3^-	24.9	(20.)		
ClO_4^-	26.0	(22.)		
BrO_3^-	26.5	22.9	(19.)	
IO_3^-	25.5	(22.)		
$H_4IO_6^-$	33.9	(30.)		
NO_2^-	17.8	(15.)		
NO_3^-	21.7	17.7	(15.)	(14.)
VO_3^-	20.0	(18.)		
MnO_4^-	31.8	(28.)		
O^{--}	2.4	0.5	0.5	1.0
S^{--}	8.2	5.0	1.3	2.5
Se^{--}	(16.)	11.4	(8.)	
Te^{--}	(16.5)	12.1	(9.)	
CO_3^{--}	15.2	11.4	(8.)	
SO_3^{--}	(19.)	14.9	(11.)	
$C_2O_4^{--}$	(22.)	17.7	(14.)	
SO_4^{--}	22.	17.2	13.7	(12.)
CrO_4^{--}	26.2	(21.)		
SiO_4^{--}	(19.)	13.8	(9.)	7.9
SiO_3^{--}	16.8	10.5	(7.)	
PO_4^{---}	(24.)	17.0	(12.)	
HCO_3^-	17.4	(13.)	(10.)	
$H_2PO_4^-$	22.8	(18.)		
$H_2AsO_4^-$	25.1	(21.)		

Petit values, but consistent figures may be assigned for the contribution of the oxygen following the general scheme outlined above. The values given in the summary for oxygen in M_2O, MO, and M_2O_3 are based upon data for thirty-five oxides and the average deviation is 0.6 cal./deg. Values for oxygen in M_3O_4 and M_2O_5 have not been included in the summary, but the data are given in Table 91.

Likewise, values for carbide and nitride have not been included, since they have so many unusual valence types. Carbon in SiC and TiC has the values -4.2 and -4.1, respectively, and nitrogen in TiN and ZrN, the values -2.7 and -2.9.

TABLE 91

CONTRIBUTION OF OXYGEN TO THE ENTROPY OF M_3O_4
AND M_2O_5 TYPE OXIDES

(Calculated by subtracting entropy of positive ion, Table 87, from the entropy of the salt.)

Oxide	Entropy of Oxide	Entropy of O	Oxide	Entropy of Oxide	Entropy of O
Fe_3O_4	35.0	1.0	Ta_2O_5	34.2	0.9
Mn_3O_4	35.5	1.1	V_2O_5	31.3	2.1
Pb_3O_4	50.5	1.0	As_2O_5	25.0	0.4
	Aver.	1.0		Aver.	1.1

The entropies of hydrates may be estimated by assigning the value 9.4 cal./deg. to the contribution of a mole of hydrated water. The following calculation for $BaCl_2 \cdot 2H_2O$ is given as an example:

2Cl	16.2
$2H_2O$	18.8
Ba	13.7
Total	48.7 Experimental 48.6

If the water is strongly bound to the positive ion, the increase in size of the ion will weaken the charge effect. Thus for $Cr(H_2O)_6Cl_3$, the value used for chloride should be one or two units higher than the $+3$ value of 6.7 given in the summary.

There is a paucity of reliable data on hydroxides, but the values given in the summary are probably correct to about an entropy unit, and in general, better estimates are obtained by adding values for the metal ion and hydroxide than by considering the compound as the oxide plus water.

In complex salts, such as K_2PtCl_6, the best estimates result from using a value for the chloride corresponding to the average charge on the positive ions. For K_2PtCl_6, the average charge is $+2$, and we then calculate

2K	18.4
Pt	15.2
6Cl	48.6
Total	82.2 Experimental 79.8

The oxygen complex cations offer considerable difficulty. In an ion such as UO_2^{++}, the oxygen entropy appears to be around 3. Since the complex cation is large, and especially if it is hydrated, the $+1$ value of the ion should be used. Thus, for $UO_2(NO_3)_26H_2O$

2O	6.0
U	16.0
2NO$_3^-$	43.4
6H$_2$O	56.4
Total	121.8 Experimental 120.8

From the entropy of solid NH_4Cl, 23.6, and the value for Cl^-, 10.0, the value for NH_4^+ in solid salts is 13.6.

Table 90 includes all of the common negative ions, and the diversity of ion types is such that estimates may be made on less common ions by comparison with the value for a similar ion given in the table.

Entropies of monatomic aqueous ions. Powell and Latimer[1] have given the general equation for the entropies of the monatomic ions in water solution

$$S_{298.16}^{\circ} = \tfrac{3}{2}R \ln \text{ at. wt.} - \frac{270Z}{(r+x)^2} + 37$$

where Z is the numerical value of the charge, r is the crystal radius and x has the value 2.00 for positive ions and 1.00 for negative ions. A comparison of the experimental values with the equation is shown in Figure 8. The equation should include a term $R \ln Q$, where Q is the multiplicity of the ground state, but, since Q is zero for most ions and generally unknown for the others, this term has been omitted in the comparison. For ferrous ion the value of Q is 5 and $R \ln 5$ equals 3.2. The crystal radii are the values given by Pauling[2] and in certain cases,

---

[1] R. Powell and W. M. Latimer, *J. Chem. Phys.* **19**, 1139 (1951).
[2] L. Pauling. *Nature of the Chemical Bond*, Cornell University Press, 1939.

as for Ag^+, there is doubtless some covalent bonding. Thus, the silver radius, calculated from Ag_2O, would displace the point for Ag^+ to the other side of the curve.

In view of the large variation in the values for Z, r, and $S°$, the agreements are remarkable and the equation may be employed to es-

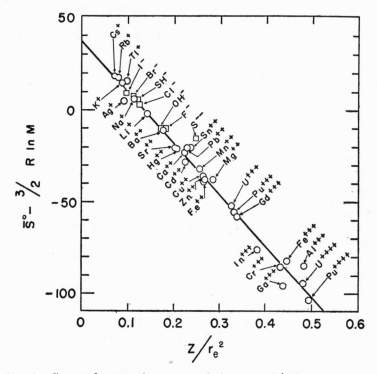

FIG. 8.   Corrected entropy in aqueous solution *versus* Z/r^2 for various ions.

timate unknown entropies with an accuracy which is comparable to most of the experimental values.

Entropies of unionized molecules in water.   The estimation of the entropy of a neutral molecule in aqueous solution is a difficult problem. From the work of Frank and Evans,[1] it may be concluded that the entropy of solution, i.e., the entropy of the molecule in $1M$ solution minus the entropy of the gas, is negative and roughly pro-

[1] H. S. Frank and M. W. Evans, *J. Chem. Phys.*, **13**, 507 (1945).

portional to the heat of solution. This relationship is illustrated in Table 92.

In many cases the heats of solution are not known, but from the boiling points listed in Table 92 it would appear that their values are equally useful in predicting the entropy of solution of such nonpolar

TABLE 92

ENTROPIES AND HEATS OF SOLUTION OF NONPOLAR
MOLECULES

	$-\Delta H$ (cal.)	$-\Delta S$ (cal./deg.)	Boiling Point ° K.
H_2	1280	18.	20.5
Ne	1880	20.8	27.3
N_2	2140	21.8	77.3
A	2730	22.2	87.3
O_2	2990	23.3	90.0
N_2O	4840	23.6	164.6
C_2H_6	4430	27.4	185.0
Cl_2	6000	25.5	238.3

compounds. The heats of solution are small in comparison to the heats for polar substances and the entropies of solution are surprisingly large.

Powell and Latimer[1] observed that the entropies of simple non-electrolytes in aqueous solution are represented by the equation

$$S^{-0} = \tfrac{3}{2}R \ln M + S^{int} + 10 - 0.22V_m.$$

Here M is the molecular weight, S^{int} is the molal internal entropy and V_m is the molecular volume in the pure liquid. A comparison of calculated and experimental values is given in their article.

As a means of estimating entropies by comparisons with similar substances, the partial molal entropies of a number of compounds are given in Table 93. It will be observed that most of the values lie between 25 and 40 entropy units and that the molecular weight or total number of heavy atoms is an important factor.

The entropies of weak acids may be estimated, if the entropy of the ion is known, from Pitzer's[2] rule that the entropy of the first ionization step is approximately 21 cal./deg. The entropy of a highly polar molecule, such as $CdCl_2$, is about 20 units less than the average for that

[1] R. E. Powell and W. M. Latimer, *J. Chem. Phys.*, **19**, 1139, (1951).
[2] K. S. Pitzer, *J. Am. Chem. Soc.*, **59**, 2365 (1937).

mass, but the entropy of a hydrogen bonding molecule such as HCN is even greater than that of CO with equal mass.

TABLE 93

PARTIAL MOLAL ENTROPIES, $\bar{S}°$, OF NONIONIZED MOLECULES IN AQUEOUS SOLUTION AT 25° C.

Substance	Entropy	Substance	Entropy	Substance	Entropy
HF	26.	HClO	31.	HCOOH	39.1
CO	25.5	I_2	32.	$HClO_2$	42.
NO	29.0	CH_3OH	31.6	H_2Se	39.9
				H_3PO_4	42.1
Cl_2	28.0	$CHCl_3$	35.1	H_2SeO_3	45.7
Br_2	30.0	H_3PO_4	37.6	$CO(NH_2)_2$	41.55
H_2S	29.4	H_3BO_3	38.2	H_2SO_3	44.
HCN	30.8	C_2H_5OH	38.4	$CdCl_2$	17.

Entropy of complex ions. The entropies of the more common negative ions are summarized in Table 94. From inspection of these values, it is obvious that the entropy increases with size and mass and decreases as the charge on the ion increases.

TABLE 94

ENTROPY OF OXYGEN COMPLEX IONS.
Values in cal./deg. at 20° C.

Ion	$\bar{S}°$	Ion	$\bar{S}°$	Ion	$\bar{S}°$	Ion	$\bar{S}°$
OH^-	-2.5	HCO_3^-	22.7	BeO_2^{--}	-27.	PO_4^{---}	-52.0
ClO^-	10.0	HSO_3^-	26.	CO_3^{--}	-12.7	AsO_4^{---}	-34.6
HCO_2^-	21.9	$HSeO_3^-$	30.4 (?)	SO_3^{--}	-7.		
ClO_2^-	24.1	$H_2BO_3^-$	7.3 (?)	SO_4^{--}	4.1		
NO_2^-	29.9	HSO_4^-	30.3	SeO_4^{--}	5.7		
NO_3^-	35.0	$HSeO_4^-$	22. (?)	$N_2O_2^{--}$	6.6		
ClO_3^-	39.0	$H_2AsO_4^-$	28.	$C_2O_4^{--}$	10.6		
BrO_3^-	38.5	$H_2PO_4^-$	21.3	$Cr_2O_7^{--}$	51.1		
IO_3^-	28.0	$HN_2O_4^-$	34.	HPO_4^{--}	-8.6		
ClO_4^-	43.2			$HAsO_4^{--}$	0.9		
MnO_4^-	45.4						

The entropies of the acid (H) ions are smaller than corresponding ions of the same charge which contain no hydrogen, e.g. HSO_3^-, 26; ClO_3^-, 39.0. This effect is doubtless the result of the polar character of such ions and because of it, there is an increase in the entropy of successive ionization steps.

$$\begin{array}{cccccc} & \Delta S & & \Delta S & & \Delta S \\ H_3PO_4 & -20.8 & H_2PO_4^- & -30.4 & HPO_4^{--} & -43.4 & PO_4^{---} \end{array}$$

At present there are not many data available on the entropies of the halogen or cyanide complex ions. The few known values are given in Table 95, as a rough guide in estimating values for similar ions. Many of these values are subject to large errors.

TABLE 95

ENTROPIES OF HALOGEN AND CYANIDE COMPLEX IONS

Ion	$\bar{S}^\circ$	Ion	$\bar{S}^\circ$
HF_2^-	0.5	$FeBr^{++}$	$-28.$ (?)
BF_4^-	40.	$AuBr_4^-$	75. (?)
SiF_6^{--}	$-12.$	$HgBr_4^{--}$	84. (?)
$FeCl^{++}$	$-22.$	I_3^-	41.5
$CuCl_2^-$	49.2	HgI_4^{--}	90. (?)
$AuCl_4^-$	61.	$Ag(CN)_2^-$	49.
$PdCl_4^{--}$	36.	$Au(CN)_2^-$	29.5 (?)
$PtCl_4^{--}$	42.	$Ni(CN)_4^{--}$	33.
$PtCl_6^{--}$	52.6		

APPENDIX IV

Study Problems

1. Metal A is soft and low-melting; metal B is hard and high-melting. Both form $+1$ ions of the same size and both have ionization potentials which are about equal. Which metal is the more electropositive?

2. The ionization potential and the heat of sublimation of Li are greater than those of Na. Explain why, in spite of these facts, Li is a better reducing agent than Na.

3. Radii of $W > X > Y > Z$. Arrange the following in order of increasing strength as acids: H_3Z, HW, HX and H_2Y.

4. Calculate the formal charge on the central atom of the following: $HAtO_2$, H_3BO_3, $HBrO$, H_4SiO_4, $HReO_4$. Predict which acid is (a) the strongest, (b) the weakest.

5.

	Element X	Element Y
Energy of sublimation	20 kcal.	80 kcal.
Energy of ionization.............	120 kcal.	100 kcal.
Energy of hydration of $+1$ ion....	-90 kcal.	-120 kcal.

Which element is the more electropositive? Explain. Calculate $\Delta F°$ and $E°$ for the reaction $X + Y^+ = Y + X^+$, assuming $\Delta S°$ is 0.

6. Calculate E for the couple

$$H_2 \quad (0.01 \text{ atm.}) = 2H^+ \ (10^{-4}M) + 2e^-.$$

Make the same calculation for

$$\tfrac{1}{2}H_2 \quad (0.01 \text{ atm.}) = H^+ \ (10^{-4}M) + e^-.$$

7. Complete the following electron group structures:

$$
\begin{array}{llll}
\text{Ca} & 1s^2, & 2s^2, & 2p^6 \\
\text{La} & 1s^2, & 2s^2, & 2p^6
\end{array}
$$

8. Write the elements (give symbols) from Rb (37) to La (57).

9. Give electron formulas of the following: CH_4, ICl, NH_4OH, Cl_2O, SO_3^{--}, H_3PO_2, S_2^{--}, N_2O, NO_3^-, and P_2O_5.

10. $M + 2H^+ = M^{++} + H_2$, $\Delta H^\circ = -3000$ cal. at 25° C. Entropy values: $M = 10.0$, $M^{++} = -20.0$, and $H_2 = 31.2$. Calculate the free energy of formation of M^{++} and E° for the couple $M = M^{++} + 2e^-$.

Ans. $\Delta F^\circ = -3.37$ kcal.; $E^\circ = 0.073$ volt.

11. The ΔH° of formation of RO_2 is $-46,000$ cal. The entropies are $RO_2 = 26$, $R = 16$, and $O_2 = 49.0$ cal./deg. Calculate the free energy of formation of RO_2 and E° for $R + 2H_2O = RO_2 + 4H^+ + 4e^-$. Calculate K for the reaction $R + 2Br_2 + 2H_2O = RO_2 + 4H^+ + 4Br^-$.

Ans. $\Delta F^\circ = 34.4$ kcal.; $E^\circ = -0.856$; $K = 1.2 \times 10^{14}$.

12. If the reaction $X(s) + Y^+ = X^+ + Y(s)$ is to be quantitative to 1 part in 1000, how much difference must there be in the E° values for the two couples?

Ans. 0.177 volt.

For the reactions $M(s) + R^{++} = M^{++} + R(s)$?

Ans. 0.089 volt.

13. What must be the value of the solubility product for (a) ZOH and (b) $Y(OH)_2$ if the concentrations of Z^+ and Y^{++} are $1M$ in equilibrium with the solid hydroxide and $1M$ H^+?

Ans. 10^{-14}; 10^{-28}.

14. Calculate E for the $Mn^{++} - MnO_4^-$ couple under conditions of the ordinary "endpoint" in $KMnO_4$ titration, say $(Mn^{++}) = 0.01M$, $(MnO_4^-) = 10^{-5}M$, and $H^+ = 0.2M$.

15. (a) $M = M^{+++} + 3e^-$, $E^\circ = -0.705$;

$M + 3OH^- = M(OH)_3 + 3e^-$, $E^\circ = -0.104$.

Calculate the solubility product of $M(OH)_3$. (b) The entropy (cal./deg.) of M^{+3} is -40; OH^-, -2; and $M(OH)_3$, 30. Calculate ΔH for $M(OH)_3 = M^{+3} + 3OH^-$.

Ans. $K = 3.16 \times 10^{-31}$; $\Delta H^\circ = 18.9$ kcal.

16. Given the following tabulation of E° values ($1M$ H^+) connecting the various oxidation states:

$$Z^- \xrightarrow{+0.8} Z \xrightarrow{-0.5} Z^+ \xrightarrow{-0.1} Z^{++} \xrightarrow{-0.1} Z^{+++} \xrightarrow{-0.8}$$

$$ZO_2 \xrightarrow{-1.7} ZO_3^- \xrightarrow{-1.6} ZO^{--} \xrightarrow{-1.4} ZO_4^- \xrightarrow{-2.3} ZO_4,$$

predict which of the various oxidation states will be stable in water and $1M$ H^+ and write equations for the reactions which would occur for the unstable states.

17. $X \xrightarrow{-0.2} X^{+++} \xrightarrow{0.6} X^{+++} \xrightarrow{-1.0} XO_2$. Predict what would happen if

(a) XCl_2 (soluble) were treated with H_2O, (b) X (metal) were treated with Fe^{+++} solution, (c) X were treated with MnO_4^- in $0.1M$ H^+, (d) XO_2 in $1M$ H^+ were treated with I^-. Calculate K for the following: $X + X^{+++} = 2X^{++}$ and $XO_2 = X + O_2$. Calculate $E°$ for

(a) $X = X^{+++} + 3e^-$,
(b) $X + 2OH^- = X(OH)_2 + 2e^-$ [sol. prod. for $X(OH)_2$ is 10^{-18}],
(c) $X + 4OH^- = XO_2 + 4H_2O + 4e^-$,
(d) $X(OH)_2 + OH^- = X(OH)_3 + e^-$ [K for $X(OH)_3$ is 10^{-36}].

18.

	$E°$		$E°$
$X = X^{++} + 2e^-$,	$+2.0$.	$Y = Y^+ + e^-$,	-0.5.
$X^{++} = X^{+++} + e^-$,	$+1.0$.	$Y^+ = Y^{++} + e^-$,	-1.0.
$X^{+++} = X^{+4} + e^-$,	-0.5.	$Y^{++} = Y^{+++} + e^-$,	-1.9.

Predict what, if anything, would occur in the following experiments: (a) X is added to water, (b) X^{++} is added to water, (c) Y is added to $1M$ H^+, (d) Y^{+++} is added to hot water, (e) $1M$ Y^+ in $10^{-3}M$ H^+ is treated with O_2 at 1 atm., (f) Y^{+++} is added to Y^+, (g) 1 mole of X^{+++} is added to a liter of $1M$ Y^+, (h) Y is added (in excess) to $1M$ X^{+++}.

19. Write equations for the following:
   (a) An excess of Cl_2 is added to a $1M$ HBr solution.
   (b) NaClO is added in excess to a solution containing Br^- (small amount) in excess $1M$ H_2SO_4.
   (c) A small amount of H_5IO_6 is added to excess HI solution.
   (d) A small amount of HI is added to excess H_5IO_6 solution.
   (e) Ozone is passed (in excess) into a solution of a small amount of I^- in excess $HClO_4$ solution.

20. Write equations for the following:
   (a) Np is dissolved in excess H^+.
   (b) Np is dissolved in excess Cl_2 solution.
   (c) NpO_2^{++} is added to excess HI. NOTE. All neptunium iodides are soluble.

21. For the following ions indicate whether the complex with CN^- is linear (L), tetrahedral (T), square planar (S), or octahedral (O). (a) Ag^+, (b) Au^{+3}, (c) Ni^{+2}, (d) Fe^{++}, (e) Zn^{++}.

22. Use dots to indicate the distribution of electrons in the various orbits of the ruthenium atom in $Ru(CN)_6^{-3}$.

4d	5s	5p
( ) ( ) ( ) ( ) ( )	( )	( ) ( ) ( )

23. Solubility of H_2S at 1 atm. is $0.1M$. Use equilibrium constants and calculate concentration of S^{--} in saturated H_2S in (a) $1M H^+$, (b) $0.3M H^+$, (c) $10^{-4}M$ H^+. Calculate S^{--} in (a) $1M$ Na_2S, (b) $1M$ $(NH_4)_2S$.

24. Use solubility product and calculate maximum concentrations of Zn^{++} in (a) $10^{-2}M$ H^+, (b) $10^{-4}M$ H^+, when solution is saturated with H_2S.

25. Calculate concentrations of Hg^{++} in equilibrium with HgS in a solution saturated with H_2S at $1M$ H^+.

26. Calculate (H^+) in a $10^{-6}M$ solution of H_3AO_3. $K_1 = 3 \times 10^{-5}$.

27. Calculate (H^+) in a $1M$ $NaHCO_3$ solution.

28. A cell has a silver cathode dipping into an electrolyte containing Ag^+, Fe^{+++}, Sn^{+4}, NO_3^- and $H^+(10^{-3}M)$. Write half reactions for all possible reductions. From the $E°$ values and a knowledge of the reaction rates, predict which reaction would occur when the electrode operates as a cathode.

29. A cell has a silver anode dipping into an electrolyte containing Fe^{++}, Zn^{++}, Ni^{++}, Sn^{++}, $H^+(10^{-3}M)$, Cl^-, I^- and SO_4^{--}. Write half-reactions for all possible oxidations. From the $E°$ values and a knowledge of reaction rates, predict which reaction would occur when the electrode operates as an anode.

30. A solution containing Cr^{+++}, Eu^{+++}, Fe^{++}, V^{+++}, H^+ ($1M$) and Cl^- is electrolyzed at low-current density with platinum electrodes. Write equations for the reactions at (a) anode, (b) cathode.

31.

$$Zn = Zn^{++} + 2e^-, \qquad E° = 0.763;$$
$$Zn + 4X^- = ZnX_4^{--} + 2e^-, \qquad E° = 1.118.$$

The free energy of X^- is -10.0 kcal. Calculate the free energy of ZnX_4^{--} and K for the reaction $ZnX_4^{--} = Zn^{++} + 4X^-$.

32. In any cell what is the sign of the anode (a) with respect to the internal circuit, (b) the external circuit?

33. A solution containing $H_2AlO_3^-$, $Sn(OH)_6^{--}$, SO_4^{--}, OH^- ($1M$), and Na^+ is electrolyzed with silver electrodes. Write equations for the reactions at the anode and cathode.

34. Complete and balance:
   (a) $Pt + O_2 + OH^- =$
   (b) $MnO_4^{--} + H^+ =$
   (c) $CrCl_2 + H^+ =$
   (d) $H_2MoO_4 + Zn$ (acid solution) $=$
   (e) $PH_3 + Cr_2O_7^{--}$ (excess) $+ H^+ =$
   (f) $Sb + Bi_2O_4$ (excess) $+ H^+ =$
   (g) Fe (excess) $+ H_3AsO_4 + H^+ =$
   (h) $O_3 + Ag^+ + H^+ =$
   (i) $AuS + Cl_2$ (excess) $+ Cl^- =$
   (j) $I_3^- + S_2O_3^{--} =$

35. Classify the following oxides by using the appropriate abbreviation: *SA* strong acid, *WA* weak acid, *SB* strong base, *WB* weak base, *AA* amphoteric acid side, *AB* amphoteric basic side, *AN* amphoteric neutral.

1. B_2O_3.	7. SnO.	13. Cs_2O.	19. MnO_2.
2. La_2O_3.	8. MgO.	14. CeO_2.	20. CO_2.
3. HfO_2.	9. RaO.	15. As_2O_3.	21. Mo_2O_3.
4. OsO_4.	10. Ac_2O_3.	16. MoO_3.	22. Ga_2O_3.
5. I_2O_5.	11. Al_2O_3.	17. Ta_2O_5.	23. UO_3.
6. SnO_2.	12. Ag_2O.	18. PtO_2.	24. Te_2O.
		25. V_2O_5.	

36. In each group select the substance having the property indicated to the weakest or least degree and the substance having the property to the strongest or greatest degree.

Acid	B_2O_3	CO_2	Cl_2O_7	P_2O_5	SO_2
Acid	H_3P	HBr	HF	H_2Te	NH_3
Acid	H_3AlO_3	$HClO_3$	H_3AsO_3	H_3BO_3	H_2SO_3
Base	$Al(OH)_3$	$La(OH)_3$	$Lu(OH)_3$	$Sc(OH)_3$	$B(OH)_3$
Base	$Ca(OH)_2$	$Pt(OH)_2$	$Mg(OH)_2$	$Ba(OH)_2$	$Fe(OH)_2$
Base	Cl_2O	Tl_2O	Ag_2O	Cu_2O	Hg_2O
Acid	HgS	SnS	SnS_2	CuS	Ag_2S
Base	ZnS	FeS	CuS	SnS	CaS
Hydrolyzed . . .	S^{--}	NO_3^-	SO_4^{--}	HPO_4^{--}	SO_3^{--}
Hydrolyzed . . .	Cu^{++}	Tl^+	Fe^{+++}	Hf^{++++}	UO_2^{++}

Oxidizing Agent:

in $1M$ H^+ . . .	HNO_3	Cl_2	Fe^{+++}	Br_2	O_2
in $1M$ H^+ . . .	MnO_4^-	$Cr_2O_7^{--}$	Ag^{++}	$S_2O_8^{--}$	O_3
in $1M$ H^+ . . .	I_3^-	Cu^{++}	Sn^{++}	Fe^{++}	Ni^{++}
in $1M$ H^+ . . .	Ca^{++}	Al^{+++}	Mg^{++}	Co^{++}	Ti^{++++}
in $1M$ H^+ . . .	MoO_3	PtO_2	NiO_2	TiO_2	Ta_2O_3
in $1M$ OH^- . . .	ClO^-	$Fe(OH)_3$	O_2	CrO_4^{--}	NO_3^-

Reducing Agent:

in $1M$ H^+ . . .	H_2	Sn^{++}	Fe^{++}	Cr^{++}	Mo^{+++}
in $1M$ H^+ . . .	Cu^+	Hg_2^{++}	Fe^{++}	Tl^+	Br^-
in $1M$ H^+ . . .	H_2S	NH_4^+	HF	H_2Se	I^-
in $1M$ HCl . . .	Ag	Pt	$PbCl_2$	H_2	Sn^{++}
in $1M$ OH^- . . .	Zn	Na	Li	S^{--}	Cu

Oxidizing Agent:

in $10^{-7}M$ H^+ . .	Ag_2S	AgI	$AgCl$	Ag_2CO_3	Ag_2SO_4

37. The elements listed below were treated with hot concentrated HNO_3 + HCl and the solution diluted with water to approximately $1M$ H^+. Give the formula of the ion or molecule resulting from the oxidation of the element.

1. I_2.	2. S.	3. Te.	4. P.
5. As.	6. Sb.	7. Bi.	8. Sn.
9. Pb.	10. Ga.	11. Zn.	12. Cd.
13. Hg.	14. Cu.	15. Ag.	16. Ni.
17. Pt.	18. Co.	19. Fe.	20. Ru.
21. Os.	22. Mn.	23. Re.	24. Cr.
25. Mo.	26. U.	27. V.	28. Hf.
29. La	30. Ra.		

38. The following substances in dilute HCl solution are treated with excess of metallic Zn. Give the formula of the reduction product. If there is no reduction, mark it $N.R.$

1. BrO_3^-.	2. H_6IO_6.	3. H_2SeO_3.	4. $S_2O_8^{--}$.
5. H_3PO_4.	6. H_3AsO_3.	7. Sn^{+4}.	8. Cu^{++}.
9. $PdCl_4^{--}$.	10. Fe^{++}.	11. Mn^{++}.	12. $H_2O(MoO_3)$.
13. TiO^{++}.	14. ZrO^{++}.	15. H_3BO_3.	16. Al^{+++}.
17. Eu^{+++}.	18. Mg^{++}.	19. Cs^+.	20. NO_3^-.

39. In the following compounds mark with the letter (A) compounds *readily* soluble in dilute HNO_3 and the letter (B) those *readily* soluble in dilute NaOH. In some cases both (A) and (B) should be given. If inert, enter (I).

1. $Mg(OH)_2$	2. $HAlO_2$.	3. $La(OH)_3$.	4. SiO_2.
5. UO_3.	6. $Cr(OH)_3$.	7. Ta_2O_5.	8. $Pt(OH)_2$.
9. MnS.	10. Ag_2S.	11. $Zn(OH)_2$.	12. HgO.
13. $Sn(OH)_2$.	14. I_2O_5.	15. PH_3.	

40. For each of the conditions specified in the table below, give the formula of the predominant species for elements in the oxidation states indicated.

Element	Oxidation State	$1M$ HClO$_4$	$1M$ NaOH	$1M$ HF	$1M$ (NH$_4$)$_2$S
Ag	1				
Ta	5				
Sn	4				
Zr	4				
Be	2				

Author Index

Subject Index